Stanley Woodworking Tools

The Finest Years

Research and Type Studies of the Tools

Adapted from *The Chronicle* of the
Early American Industries Association

Walter Jacob

Covers
Front A selection of Stanley tools from the Jacob Collection.
Back Walter Jacob with a spice chest that he built using Stanley hand tools The chest is 23 inches high, 15 inches wide, and 11 inches deep and includes hand-cut dovetails throughout. Walt made it for his loving wife, Suzanne, in 1988. Sue stores cloves, bay leaves, cinnamon, and lavender in the various drawers.

Credits All photos (unless noted): Walter Jacob. Tools and ephemera from the Jacob Collection

Editor Patty MacLeish, Editor, *The Chronicle* of the Early American Industries Association, Newport, Rhode Island

Copy Editing Elizabeth Kemper French, South Dartmouth, Massachusetts

Cover Design Wesley B. Tanner, Passim Editions, Ann Arbor, Michigan

Technical Assistance Gary Roberts, Toolemera Press, www.toolemera.com

Published by The Early American Industries Association, P.O. Box 524, 402 South Main St., Hebron, MD 21830
Executive Director John Verrill
Founded in 1933, the Early American Industries Association, Inc., preserves and presents historic trades, crafts, and tools, and interprets their impact on our lives. Membership in the EAIA is open to any person or organization sharing its interests and purposes. For membership information, visit www.EAIAinfo.org or e-mail: execdirector@EAIAinfo.org.

ISBN 978-0-943196-00-8 ©2011 Walter Jacob & the Early American Industries Association

Editor's Note

All of the articles in this collection originally appeared in *The Chronicle* of the Early American Industries Association. The articles were organized and updated by the author and do not match the original text. Errors in the original were corrected, and information was updated by the author. Multiple-part articles were edited to read smoothly as a single piece; figures and footnotes were renumbered to accommodate changes from the original.

This book would not have been possible without the cooperation of Walter Jacob and Suzanne Fellman Jacob. Gary Roberts of Toolemera Press provided important technical assistance with the publication of the book. Elizabeth Kemper French read the various drafts with an exquisite attention to detail.

Patty MacLeish, Editor

Table of Contents

Foreword

The interests of the Early American Industries Association are very broad. They are driven by the predilections of our many members—thousands during the past seventy-eight years—who have shown a variety of interests. We were established because a group of enthusiasts interested in traditional trades and industries and the tools with which they were carried on realized that many of those trades were dying out, as were the artisans who worked in them, taking with them the knowledge without which the physical remains are nothing but curiosities. The first significant undertaking was to establish publication of a quarterly journal devoted to tools, trades, and related matters. *The Chronicle* provided a vehicle for members to record in a permanent form the information they were so eagerly gathering. That effort has been going on ever since, and until the advent of the World Wide Web, it was unrivalled as a source of information on the material that engages our interest. Our purpose has remained constant for almost eight decades and is simply expressed in our mission statement: The Early American Industries Association preserves and presents historic trades, crafts, and tools and interprets their impact on our lives.

From time to time the EAIA has issued a variety of occasional publications, almost fifty in number, including reprints of early treatises and manufacturer's catalogs as well as original material. The first was *Conestoga Wagon 1750-1850* by George Shumway, Edward Durell, and Howard C. Frey in 1964. The occasions for these publications were probably as varied as the subject matter itself. But the common factor was that they were seen to advance the mission of the EAIA and provide sufficient useful information or pleasure to our constituents. Thus the publication program of the EAIA has always tried to follow the interests of the membership at the time each title came out.

Not long after I became executive director of the EAIA, I met Walter and Suzanne Jacob. It was probably at one of the Mercer Museum's "Tool Discovery Days," a then annual event with a variety of programs aimed at generating interest in tools. The EAIA Library was located at the Mercer, which attracted me. The Jacobs lived not far away and were attracted to anything having to do with tools. I became aware that Walt had a remarkably extensive collection of Stanley tools and was one of the leading authorities on the subject. As I maintained constant vigilance for potential contributors to *The Chronicle*, I spoke to Walt about the possibility of his contributing a regular feature on Stanley tools. I thought it would be a nice complement to "Plane Chatter," the series that Jack Whelan was then writing on wooden planes. Walt did not need me to point out the great interest there is in Stanley or the fact that the subject was not receiving much coverage in *The Chronicle*. He readily agreed, and has in the intervening years produced a total of forty-eight articles with, I hope, no end in sight. In 2002, Walt was honored with the J. D. Hatch Award for his outstanding contributions to knowledge.

This book comprises the complete set of articles to date, arranged in a more logical sequence than as originally published and enhanced with an index. It is intended both as a useful reference for those interested in tools of the last century and a half, especially Stanley enthusiasts, and as a gesture of thanks to Walter Jacob for his great service in collecting this information, organizing it, and sharing it with all of us.

Elton W. Hall
Past Executive Director,
Early American Industries Association

Introduction

From the middle of the nineteenth through the third quarter of the twentieth century, tools for the woodworking trades made by the Stanley Rule & Level Company were the first choice of both the professional woodworker and the home craftsman. Stanley offered the broadest product line and the highest quality tools for every category of user. Professionals were often ranked by the quality of the tools they used; home craftsmen earned bragging rights with the tools they showed to friends. Stanley tools were their obvious choice.

Stanley became the top producer of quality woodworking tools for both the national and international markets. Stanley's success in the international markets added to the United States' reputation for being an exporter of high quality products.

 The Stanley Rule & Level Company built its company by buying existing companies that had a successful product. The company acquired the patents, machinery, personnel, and sometimes even the factory building used in the manufacturing process. Stanley wanted the experience and skill along with the company. Stanley's acquisition of Seymour & Churchill, Seth Savage, and E. A. Stearns & Company, gave it the machinery, tools, and experienced personnel it needed to manufacture boxwood and ivory rules. Its merger with Hall & Knapp brought Stanley additional capital and expertise in squares, bevels, and levels. Its acquisition of Bailey, Chaney & Company, and the exclusive rights to use Bailey's patents, made it possible for Stanley to manufacture and sell Bailey's adjustable metallic planes, which had already earned an excellent reputation. Hiring Bailey to supervise the manufacturing of his planes gave them access to his inventive genius. Buying Charles Miller's patent for a combination plow, filletster, and matching plane gave Stanley a state-of-the-art and aesthetically pleasing, metallic plow plane to add to the tools it made. These acquisitions were the beginning of Stanley producing all types of metallic planes: bench, plow, beading, matching, chamfer, and combination. Stanley was in the early stages of becoming a supplier of a complete range of tools for the woodworking trades. In 1902, Stanley purchased three small bit brace companies, and in 1905 it acquired a well-known bit brace maker, the John S. Fray Company. Over the years, Stanley acquired many more companies to expand its line of products. A few examples include: Hurley & Wood, for the Hurley screwdriver; the Atha Tool Company, for hammers and other impact tools; the Eagle Square Company, for framing squares; a license to manufacture the Zig-Zag folding rule; the Farrand Rule Company, for the steel tape rule; and the North Brothers Manufacturing Company, for "Yankee" ratchet bit braces, hand drills, and screwdrivers. In a short period of time, Stanley had assumed a major role in making every type of woodworking tool, with the exception of the saw, which was in Henry Disston's domain.

Stanley attracted, nurtured, and rewarded its most talented inventors, managers, and marketers. Justus Traut, Leonard Bailey, Charles L. Mead, Charles Miller, Edmund A. Schade, Henry Clark, and many others. They all made their own contributions according to their particular talents. It is to Stanley's credit that the company was able to get all of these different personalities to work together. Stanley also knew how to market the products of creative people using its own efficient and successful sales organization.

Several years ago, I had the privilege of visiting Walter and Suzanne Jacob and Charles Jacob, Walter's brother, at Walter and Sue's home in Pennsylvania. I was blown away by what I saw. In the tiny study, the wall immediately behind Walter's desk was covered with a row of steel, four-drawer filing cabinets. I soon learned the filing cabinets were filled with almost every consumer, pocket, and dealer catalog that Stanley published. The small, multi-drawer cabinets on the end wall were crammed with hundreds of Stanley tape measures. Walter proudly called my attention to a very special, limited-edition, master, steel tape rule that Stanley made to an astonishing level of accuracy. These rules were reserved for very special customers.

After seeing a small fraction of the Jacob Collection of Stanley and early Bailey planes, we descended to the inner sanctum—the basement. Stanley bit braces were hung between parallel rows of wood joists that supported the floor above. Other Stanley tools of every description were neatly stored on closely spaced shelves. Examples of several variations of each Stanley tool were arranged in chronological order, awaiting the research and study that would eventually lead to an article on that tool. It was obvious that Walter Jacob had the resources required to do the research, and the skills and dedication to document, in writing and photography, the invention, evolution, and refinement of the tools that Stanley made.

Stanley tools are collected by almost two-thirds of all tool collectors. There are more papers and studies written about them than about any other maker's tools. Stanley's line of tools was so diverse and comprehensive, that only a small percentage of what can be discovered has been documented. A great deal has been written about Stanley planes, but more research and documentation is needed on all of the other tools that Stanley made. Walter Jacob's book *Stanley Woodworking Tools* is a wonderful start at doing that. He has the rare talent to lead the reader through the labyrinth of history and unveil the fascinating story of Stanley's finest years in tools. I hope this book is the first of others to come. It offers the reader the rare opportunity to see the world of Stanley through the eyes of a true expert and enthusiast.

John G. Wells

My Life with Walter

Walter W. Jacob, the author of the various articles in this book, began collecting Stanley tools in the late 1950s. A Stanley catalog offer found in the back of *Popular Mechanics* started Walt and his twin brother, Charles, on a lifetime adventure of using, collecting, and researching Stanley tools and sharing their knowledge with others.

By the time he was in his teens, Walt knew he had a talent for woodworking, which required the use of numerous hand tools, which in turn added to the need to fill his growing tool bin. Any extra money he made or saved from his allowance was spent at a Coatesville, Pennsylvania, hardware store that sold Stanley tools. But it was that no. 34, 1958 catalog advertised in *Popular Mechanics* that started it all. The catalog included all the Stanley planes available at that time. The brothers were determined to have one of each of the types. But as they scoured flea markets, they discovered variations on the planes, which required more research, which meant obtaining more planes. And the cycle began.

Walt graduated from West Virginia University with a B. S. in wood industries from the College of Forestry—a perfect complement to his talent for woodworking and his collecting passion. After college, Walt and Charles began their business, Jacob Brothers, which became known for antique repair and restoration work, using original hand tools. Every Saturday and Sunday morning, they would travel to flea markets and farm auctions, where they could purchase many Stanley tools for a song. At the time—the 1960s and 1970s—most people were interested only in "American Colonial" tools such as wooden planes and goose-wing axes, but not Stanley tools. Many a Sunday the brothers would fill their decrepit old station wagon with dozens of Stanley tools purchased at bargain basement prices. People snickered behind Walt's back for many years. Stanley Tools were just not a good investment.

They visited many old hardware stores in a three-state area. These were the days when there were phone booths and phone books in those booths. The Jacobs would pull into a town and check the Yellow Pages of the local directory under "hardware." If a hardware store was listed at 11 Main Street or 2 Front Street, they would make a visit under the assumption that the store had to have been located in the center or earliest part of the town for years. Seldom was that assumption incorrect. Upon entering the store, they would find Stanley boxes piled on the top shelf. They would be full of dust and dirt because they were old, unwanted items, and usually, the "old, unwanted items" took a ride in that station wagon to join the Jacob collection.

Some of the stories of how specific tools were obtained are laugh-out-loud funny. Two of the nicest Miller patent plow planes in the collection were purchased at a farm auction. A. M. Beidler, a well known and popular tool collector and dealer from Philadelphia, was also at that auction. Beidler made it known that he was going to bid on the Miller patent planes, and Walt knew Beidler had very deep pockets. But minutes before the planes were to be placed on the auction block, a Pennsylvania state trooper entered the grounds and announced that anyone parked on the road would be ticketed. Beidler had to hurry back to his car and moved it. By the time he returned, the planes had been hammered down and had become part of the Jacob collection. Beidler, after grinding his teeth for a while, was gracious in his congratulations to Walt and his brother.

And the collection grew from planes to screwdrivers to miter boxes, to drills, braces, saws, Zig-Zag rules, measuring tapes, levels, and hammers. And each time some new type of tool was added research was required. The research required old Stanley catalogs and ephemera, and more items were added to the collection. Along the way, as the years passed, other people began collecting Stanley tools. It was a small, tightly-knit fraternity that other tool collectors tolerated. Walt and his brother became experts, and other tool collectors began going to them with questions. In 1996, John Walters published the reference, *Stanley Tools Identity and Value*. The value of Stanley tools was rising, and over the years there were many exciting tales of purchases missed or obtained as others discovered all things Stanley. The story of an early Stanley plane that made it into the Jacob collection is one of many. At a Saturday farm auction on early February day that was bitterly cold with a nasty wind blowing, Walt arrived with sandwiches and a thermos of hot chocolate and found a good parking spot. He reconnoitered the sale then returned to the car, opened his Walters book, and identified the plane type that he wanted to bid on. Walt figured the tool would be sold early in the auction because of its position on the auctioneer's block. When the tool came up for sale, the auctioneer opened the bid at $3. Walt waited until the plane was almost sold before he jumped in with a bid. It hovered at a low, reasonable price of about $80. Walt almost had it for his own, when a fellow tool collector turned to see who was going to get this dirty, ugly, rusty plane. When he did, the bidding began anew. Walt would eventually walk out with the plane (the Bailey no. 9 block plane that Walt discusses in this book), but only after paying a four-figure price that left the auctioneer in shock. After the gavel rapped out sold, the auctioneer turned to one of the auction runners and said into an open mike "What the hell was that?"

By the time I met Walt in 1986 (we "dug each other up" at an archaeology convention in Delaware), the Jacob collection had its own "tool room" in the Jacob family home. It was there in October 1987 on our second date that I was reverently introduced to the collection. I had never met anyone as passionate about inanimate items and the story behind each one as Walt was about the planes he showed me that night. He commenced at the top of four shelves, each of which was about twelve feet long. And down the line we went. He'd say "This is the best" or "This is really unique" as he took each plane off the shelf. Walt took the planes apart and showed me blades, adjustments parts, and casting differences. By the end of row two, my eyes had glazed over, my feet ached from standing, my cheeks hurt from smiling for so long, my neck needed an aspirin from nodding in total (mis-)understanding at everything Walt said, and my lower back throbbed from peering at the planes because at that point in our relationship, I wasn't allowed to touch them since Walt didn't know how much natural grease my hands produced. Walt could handle tools without any fingerprints showing, while I might leave a trail that police investigators would love. Frankly, every damn one of those planes looked alike to me except for their sizes. If we hadn't had to be at an event by a certain time that night, he would have spent another couple of hours and finished the entire wall of tools. When you're dating, you want to act interested and enthralled in every thing the other person says. I did wonder that night if he ever would act as excited about me as he did about his tools.

Twenty-three years later, Walt still gets animated about the slight variation in anything Stanley. In writing the articles for *The Chronicle* over the past decade, Walt has discovered important information that has added to our knowledge of Stanley tools and the history of the company. The articles in this book will add to the Stanley scholarship published by John Walters, Al Sellens, John Wells, Dr. Paul VanPernis, Roger Smith, and others.

I now touch the tools as Walt hands them to me, but I'll often put on gloves first. And I have my own favorites, as does Walt. And yes, he is still excited about me and the Stanley tools—in that order, I might add.

Suzanne Fellman Jacob

Stanley Woodworking Tools

The Finest Years

Research and Type Studies of the Tools

The Stanley Rule & Level Company–
Its Historic Beginning

The history and products of the Stanley Rule & Level Company, later known as the Stanley Works, has been of great interest to tool collectors and industrial historians. The Stanley Rule & Level Co. and the Stanley Works were two companies formed by different branches of the same family. The companies merged in 1920. (The tools division of the company was historically known as the Stanley Works. Since 2010, following its merger with Black and Decker, the company is known as Stanley Black and Decker. "The Stanley Works" no longer exists as an entity in the United States. It appears that the Stanley Works does exist, in some form, in the international divisions.) Within the history of the present-day Stanley Works, one can track the development of the industrialization of America from the mid-nineteenth century to the present, so how the Stanley Rule & Level Company began is of interest to historians.

There have been several accounts of Stanley's early beginnings, but new research has uncovered heretofore unknown discoveries. The story begins with the town of New Britain, Connecticut. To understand the business of the town, the reader must realize that New Britain was unique in that any individual in town who had money to invest did so within the town rather than elsewhere. Their philosophy was that, "If I invest in the town, it will make the town prosper." They were not wrong in that assumption.

A. Stanley & Company, a manufacturer of boxwood and ivory rules (Figure 1), was formed by a partnership of Augustus Stanley; his brother, Timothy W. Stanley; cousin, Gad Stanley; and Thomas A. Conklin, Augustus Stanley's father-in-law.[1] Warren in *The Stanley Families of America*, gives 1850 as the date the partnership commenced.[2] *The New Britain Record*, however, published a history of the Stanley Rule & Level Company on May 18, 1866, claiming that A. Stanley commenced in October, 1854.[3]

A. Stanley & Company purchased the firm of Seth Savage of Middletown, Connecticut, in February 1855, and employed all of Savage's rulemakers (Figure 2).[4] This acquisition enabled A. Stanley to improve the quality of its rules with better machinery.

Hall & Knapp

But we must pause here and discuss Hall & Knapp before proceeding with the story of Stanley, for the two stories are intertwined. Thomas S. Hall and Frederick Knapp began the manufacture of plumbs, levels, and tri-squares in

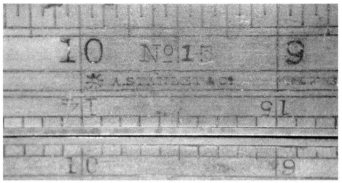

Figure 1 (above). A two-fold Stanley no. 15 rule marked "A. STANLEY. & C⁰" 1850 [?]-1857. A. Stanley & Co. would become Stanley Rule & Level Company.

Figure 2 (below). The mark of Seth Savage on a rule made before 1855. A. Stanley & Co. purchased Savage's company in 1855.

1853 (Figure 3). Early in 1854, a joint stock company with a capital of $15,000 was established. On March 25, 1854, the following Articles of Association were agreed upon.[5]

Article of Association of the Manufacturing Company Known by the Name of Hall & Knapp

Be it known that we the subscribers do hereby associate ourselves as a body politic and corporate to the provisions of the Statute Law of the State of Connecticut relating to Joint Stock Corporations—and the following are the articles of our agreement and association:

1. Said Corporation shall be known by the name of Hall & Knapp.
2. Capital stock of the said corporation shall be fifteen thousand dollars divided into six hundred shares of twenty-five dollars each.
3. The purposes for which the said corporation is established are the following, to wit: The combin[in]g and manufacture of materials and wood, finishing and converting the same goods into goods for sale such as plumbs and levels, try-squares, bevels and gauges and various other articles of hardware, and to sell and deal in the same; also buying, selling and dealing in all kinds of goods, wares, and merchandise necessary

for the prosecution of said business and general[ly] to do all things necessary and convenient for the management of the same.

4. The Statute Law of the State of Connecticut herein before referred to relating to Joint Stock Corporations is hereby referred to and made part of these articles, and the corporation hereby established and organized under and pursuant to the same shall have all the powers enumerated therein and proceeded according to the relations set fourth and specified in said law.

5. Each subscriber to these articles agrees to take the number of shares affixed to his name of the capital stock of said corporation, each share to be twenty-five dollars, as aforesaid, and to be paid for by installments as the directors of said corporation shall call in the same.

6. The said corporation is established and located in the town of New Britain, in the County of Hartford, and the State of Connecticut.

New Britain, March 25, 1854 [signed]

T. S. Hall	180 shares	$4,500
F. Knapp	100 shares	$2,500
Henry Walter	40 shares	$1,000
A. Stanley & Co.	40 shares	$1,000
William A. Churchill	40 shares	$1,000
James Stanley	40 shares	$1,000
Oliver Stanley	20 shares	$500
Charles M. Lewis	20 shares	$500
George M. Landers	20 shares	$500
Henry E. Russell	20 shares	$500
C.B. Erwin	20 shares	$500
Gerardus Knapp	20 shares	$500
William H. Smith	20 shares	$500
Henry Stanley	20 shares	$500
	600 shares	$15,000

Published by order of the President and Board of Directors

New Britain, March 25, 1854 F. Knapp, Secretary.

On September 29, 1854, a special meeting was held to amend Article 6 as follows:

Offices shall not have more than five directors, President, Secretary, Treasurer and agent appointed by ballot at each regular annual meeting. Up to February, 1869, annual meetings to be held in [the] boro of New Britain last Wednesday of February of each year at the office of the company.[6]

The first board of directors of Hall & Knapp was comprised of Thomas S. Hall, Frederick Knapp, Henry Walter, Gad Stanley, and James Stanley.

The Hall & Knapp/Stanley Connection

Returning to the origins of A. Stanley & Company, the reader will note that the shareholders for Hall & Knapp of March 25, 1854, included 40 shares owned by A. Stanley & Company, worth $1,000. This proves that A. Stanley & Company was in business before the October

1854 date mentioned in the *New Britain Record*. In my opinion, the acquisition of Seymour & Churchill in October 1854 has misled many historians into believing that A. Stanley & Company started on that date. We now have a primary source and one secondary source that proves otherwise.

The Hall & Knapp board of directors held its first meeting on March 28, 1854, with the full board present, and by a motion to ballot of the officers, Henry Walter became president, Frederick Knapp , secretary; Thomas S. Hall, treasurer; and Frederick Knapp, agent.[7]

The new Hall & Knapp Company was using a building on Elm Street, New Britain, on land owned by Henry Stanley. At the board meeting of April 6, 1854, James Stanley was appointed to confer with Henry Stanley to close the purchase of this land, not to exceed $1,300. It was also voted to call in (collect) 50 percent on the capital stock, payable May 1, 1854. At the directors' meeting of April 8, 1854, the board voted to accept the inventory of machining tools and fixtures and goods wrought and unwrought, and to obtain shafting with iron pulleys. Also, the agent (F. Knapp) was instructed to obtain plans for a 30-x-50-foot, one-story, wooden building above the basement, with an attic, and to secure estimates for the stocks of both.

On April 13, 1854, James Stanley reported that the said land on Elm Street was purchased for $1,300 from Henry Stanley.

At the next Hall & Knapp directors' meeting, estimates were received from three builders. They voted to accept the bid from Sylander Ellis for a two-story, wooden building above a basement, with an attic.[8]

At the June 24, 1854, directors' meeting it was voted to call in the second installment on the capital stock of 25 percent. At the August 1854 meeting, the last installment of 25 percent was called.

On October 5, 1854, the Hall & Knapp directors met and discussed the refusal of Henry Stanley to give a clear deed to the land purchased by James Stanley and now occupied by the Hall & Knapp Corporation. The agent, F. Knapp was directed to pursue legal action.

At the annual stockholder meeting of Hall & Knapp, on February 7, 1855, President Henry Walter was absent. The meeting was organized by the appointment of Gad Stanley as chairman. Election of officers took place on February 15, 1855, with James Stanley elected president; Thomas L. Hall, secretary, treasurer, and agent. Three and a half weeks later, Gad Stanley resigned as chairman. A directors' meeting was called on March 13, 1855, and Augustus Stanley was voted in to fill his cousin's position as director.

At the directors' meeting on June 4, 1855, the board sold at auction 100 shares of stock in the name of Frederick Knapp and 20 shares from Geraldine Knapp. All 120 shares were purchased by Augustus Stanley.

At the annual shareholders' meeting of Hall & Knapp on February 6, 1856, the president was absent, and Augustus Stanley was appointed chairman. Something was happening within the company. Since not all board members were present, the meeting was adjourned to the next day when Henry Stanley was voted president; Thomas S. Hall secretary, treasurer and agent; and Henry Stanley, auditor.

A special meeting was held on March 14, 1856, where a motion was made and voted to increase the capital stock of the company by $5,000. It was also voted that Theodore A. Stanley be allowed to subscribe for the increase amount of stock ($5,000). On April 12, 1856, T. [Theodore] A. Stanley agreed to take 200 shares. At the same meeting, Thomas L. Hall resigned as secretary-treasurer and agent, and T. A. Stanley was voted in to fill the vacancy.

The directors' *Minute Book* for the annual meeting of February 4, 1857, states that:

> The President voted to proceed to ballot for Directors for the ensuing year. Chosen for the year were Augustus Stanley, Thomas A. Hall, Henry Stanley, William Hubbard, and Theodore A. Stanley. A statement of the affairs of the Company was read and accepted. Henry Stanley was voted

President, Theodore A. Stanley, Secretary and Treasurer, Thomas A. Hall, Agent, and Henry Stanley Auditor.

At a special meeting held July 1, 1857, the firm of A. Stanley & Company became part of Hall & Knapp.

> The president being in the chair, it was voted that in consideration of the management of A. Stanley & Co. agreeing to write their business of rule making with this company, that the capital stock of the company [Hall & Knapp] be increased thirty thousand dollars and the members of the firm of A. Stanley & Co. have the privilege of subscribing for the same. It was then voted to adjourn *sine die*, T.A. Stanley, Sec.

At this meeting the following document was prepared and signed:

> We the subscribers hereby agree to take the number of shares affixed to our names of the increased capital stock on the corporation of Hall & Knapp.
> Voted July 1, 1858 and pay for the same as called by the directors.

Augustus Stanley	240	$6,000
Gad Stanley	240	$6,000
Thomas A. Conklin	240	$6,000
Timothy W. Stanley	260	$7,000
Henry E. Russell	80	$2,000
Cornelius B. Erwin	80	$2,000
Theodore A. Stanley	40	$1,000
		$30,000[9]

So, on July 1, 1857, the groundwork was started for the formation of a combined company of A. Stanley & Company and Hall & Knapp (Figures 4 and 5). At the February 3, 1858, Hall & Knapp directors' meeting, the Stanley family held the major chairs, with Henry Stanley, president; T. A. Stanley, secretary and treasurer; Gad Stanley, agent; and Oliver Stanley, auditor.

A special meeting was held on August 14, 1858, to fill the vacancy on the board of directors due to the death of Gad Stanley. Timothy W. Stanley was appointed director to serve in the position for the remainder of the year.

A special directors' meeting was held on October 11,

Figures 4 (above). A Stanley no. 45 machinist's level.

Figure 5 (left). The level is marked "STANLEY RULE & LEVEL COMPANY /NEW BRITAIN/CONN" on the body of the level and "HALL & KNAPP, NEW BRITAIN, CT "on the spirit level.

1858. All the directors and officers were present and the following was unanimously adopted:

> Whereas the title of corporation heretofore known under the name of Hall & Knapp having been changed by an act of the legislature at the May Session AD 1858 to the "Stanley Rule & Level Co." It is therefore voted that the certificates of capital stock outstanding under the name of Hall & Knapp be called in and new certificates given in exchange for them in the name of Stanley Rule & Level Co.
>
> It was voted to adjourn. T. A. Stanley Sec.[10]

A. Stanley & Company became Stanley Rule & Level Company by certificate of organization filed with the Connecticut secretary of state on September 27, 1858.[11]

These transactions officially joined the two companies—Hall & Knapp and A. Stanley & Company, both of which had common shareholders—into one name, the Stanley Rule & Level Company. Although 1858 is when all the legal work was completed, the original voted agreements were decided on July 1, 1857.

Thus ends the story of the beginning.

Charles L. Mead and the Acquisition of E.A. Stearns

The newly formed Stanley Rule & Level Company was well organized by February 1859. Stanley now had a warehouse located in New York City at 52 Beekman Street, the heart of the wholesale merchant district. Ninety-two different boxwood and ivory rules were being manufactured by Stanley. This was an increase of six rules from the time of the 1858 merger. Stanley added two sizes of boxwood chess sets, in addition to twenty-six styles of carpenter and machinist's levels, two types of squares (making eighteen sizes), and ten models of marking gauges.[12]

The new company was on a roll. The management set up a marketing system that would prove to be one of Stanley's greatest assets in later years. At the February 2, 1859, board of directors meeting. Henry Stanley was elected to continue as president; Timothy W. Stanley, secretary-treasurer; Oliver Stanley, auditor; and Thomas A. Conklin, agent. These men were reelected to their positions at the 1860, 1861, and 1862 annual meetings.[13]

At the board meeting of February 12, 1862, a vote was taken to "Authorize to purchase a certain [tract] of land [in New Britain] of Frederick H. North bounded on the north on [the] line of the Hartford Providence and Fishkill Railroad, east and south by Thomas Griswold and T.H. North; west by Elm Street." This became the main, or Elm Street, factory.

In addition, "It was also voted that Henry Stanley, Thomas A. Conklin be appointed a committee to negotiate with Charles L. Mead of Brattleboro, Vt., and if thought expedient to purchase his entire rule business...."[14]

On July 22, 1862, Stanley Rule & Level Company paid its first dividend of 6 percent on capital stock from surplus earnings.[15] The company was doing well.

The rule business mentioned in the Stanley minute books, E.A. Stearns & Company of Brattleboro, Vermont, was owned by Charles Levi Mead. E.A. Stearns was started in about 1838, when Edward A. Stearns purchased the remaining rule stock, machinery, and factory operated by S. Morton Clark of Brattleboro. According to a history of Brattleboro:

> In 1833; S. Morton Clark started manufacturing boxwood and ivory rules. Business increased rapidly and in 1836 and in 1835, they removed to a factory built for their use on Birge Street, where the old wooden mill stood, and where they employed from twenty-one to thirty hands in the manufacture of boxwood and ivory rules. In 1837, the "hard times" put a stop to their operations.[16]

E.A. Stearns made boxwood and ivory rules of very high quality and Stearns had the reputation of producing the Cadillac of American folding rules (Figures 6 and 7). Mr. Stearns died on July 29, 1856. Charles L. Mead acquired the business upon Stearns's death.[17]

Charles L. Mead was born in Chesterfield, New Hampshire, on January 21, 1833 (Figure 8). Chesterfield was located four miles northeast of Brattleboro. Mead's father was a successful banker and lawyer in Brattleboro and saw that his son, Charles, was well educated. When Charles's education was completed, he was engaged in an unknown type of business in Providence, Rhode Island. Mead was later

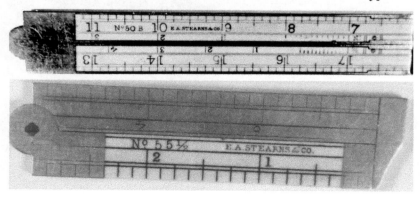

Figure 6 (left, top). An E. A. Stearns & Company no. 50B 2-foot, four-fold, ivory rule.

Figure 7 (left, bottom). An E. A. Stearns no. 55½ ivory rule.

employed by G. & C. Merriam, publishers of *Webster's Dictionary*, in Springfield, Massachusetts. In 1854, Charles Mead accepted a part-time appointment on the staff of the adjutant-general of Vermont, a position he retained to the end of the Civil War.

According to an article in *Iron Age*, Mead left Merriam in 1856 and went into the business of "manufacturing of levels and pocket rules in Brattleboro, having bought the business of E.A. Stearns & Co. of that place."[18] The article also noted that "When the Civil War began he [Mead] sold the business to the Stanley Rule & Level Company of New Britain, Connecticut."[19]

The April 1, 1863, "Price List of Boxwood and Ivory Rules Manufactured by The Stanley Company" states:

> We have this day purchased of Mr. Chas. L. Mead, (successor to E.A. Stearns & Co.) his entire interest in the Rule business, including the "Stearns Rule," with the stock manufactured and in the process of manufacture. Having retained the full corps of rule-makers long time employed in the establishment, every assurance can be given that the Rules will preserve their distinctive merits, and we trust that in connection with our other varieties of Goods, we may be able to serve all old and new customers with these Rules, promptly and acceptably. The Rules will continue to bear the original stamp E.A. Stearns & Co. Makers, Brattleboro, VT., where the goods will still be manufactured. Orders to be directed to the Stanley Rule & Level Co., at New Britain, Conn.[20]

At the director's meeting of November 1865, it was voted to increase facilities at the Elm Street factory and to purchase another 40-horsepower steam engine.

After the Civil War, the company's minutes note, "Stanley Rule & Level Co. secured [Mead's] services, one of the inducements held out by the then president (Henry Stanley) of the company being that [Mead] could spend two or three hours a day at the factory and employ the balance of the time as best suited him, a condition Mr. Mead often facetiously remarked he had been looking for ever since."[21]

At the 1867 annual meeting, "...on the motion of C. B. Erwin, it was voted to amend article 1 of the by-laws, to read as follows:"

> Viz. The officers of this company [Stanley Rule & Level Company], shall consist of not less than five nor more than seven directors. A president, secretary, treasurer and agent shall be appointed by ballot of each regular annual meeting of the company.

> Voted that the Board of Directors shall consist of 7

Figure 8 (left). Charles L. Mead. Figure 9 (right). Henry Stanley.
BOTH COURTESY OF THE STANLEY WORKS.

members for the ensuing years and further ordered by the stock holders. It was voted to proceed to ballot for directors to the ensuing year. The following directors were chosen: Henry Stanley, Augustus Stanley, Thomas A. Conklin, Timothy W. Stanley, C.B. Erwin, Charles L. Mead, and T. E. Gaynor. [22]

About 1871, Mead moved to New York to direct the Stanley business there. Henry Stanley continued as president of the company until his death in 1884.[24] Charles L. Mead then became president and served until his death in Norfolk, Connecticut, on August 19, 1899, of a heart problem.[25]

Notes

1. Thomas A. Conklin was apprenticed to Seymour & Churchill of Bristol, Connecticut. They were rule manufacturers.
2. Israel P. Warren, *The Stanley Families of American as Descended from John, Timothy, and Thomas Stanley of Hartford, Connecticut, 1636*, reprint (Bowie, Maryland, 1990), 145.
3. *New Britain Record*, May 1866.
4. Ibid.
5. Board of directors of Hall & Knapp, *Minute Book*, March 25, 1854.
6. Ibid., September 39, 1854.
7. Ibid., March 38, 1854.
8. The date has been omitted from the *Minute Book*. The meeting occurred between April 13, 1854, and June 24, 1854.
9. *Minute Book* February 4, 1857
10. *Minute Book*, October, 11, 1858.
11. Kenneth D. Roberts, "Introduction to Rule Collection," *Fundamentals of Rule Collecting* (Kenneth D. Roberts Publishing, 1982).
12. "Stanley Rule & Level Co. Price List" (Hartford, Connecticut, 1859).
13. The board of directors Hall & Knapp and Stanley Rule & Level Co., *Minute Book*, February 2, 1859, February 1, 1860, February 6, 1861, and February 5, 1863.
14. The board of directors of Stanley Rule & Level Co. *Minute Book*, February 12, 1862.
15. The board of directors of Stanley Rule & Level Co. *Minute Book*, July 27, 1862.
16. Mary R. Cabot, *Annals of Brattleboro 1681-1895* (Brattleboro, Vermont: E. L. Hildrith, 1921), 414–415.
17. Philip E. Stanley, *Boxwood and Ivory Stanley Traditional Rules, 1855-1975* (Westborough, Vermont, 1864), 2.
18. *Iron Age* (August 24, 1899): 40.
19. Ibid.
20. "Stanley Rule & Level Co. Price List & Circular" (April 1, 1862).
21. Stanley Rule & Level Co., Minutes, November 30, 1865.
22. Stanley Rule & Level Co., Minutes, February 6, 1867.
23. *Iron Age*, loc. cit.
24. Warren, 191.
25. *Iron Age*, loc. cit.

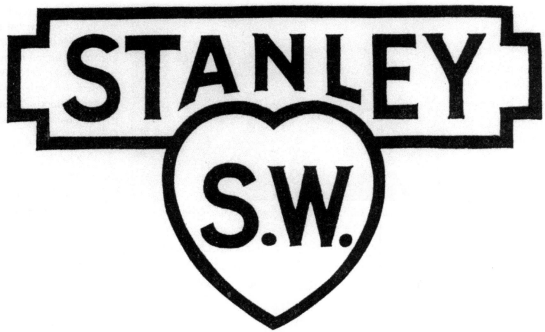

The Man Who Turned
The Stanley Works Around:
The Story of William H. Hart

Among the most sought-after Stanley tools are the ones marked with the well-known Stanley "Sweetheart" trademark (Figure 1). Most collectors know that the trademark was used in several variations on Stanley-made products from 1921 to 1934, and that the "S W" stands for the Stanley Works. But what is the significance of the heart? That is the topic of this article.

The Stanley Works began as a joint stock company established in New Britain, Connecticut, in 1852 as a manufacturer of wrought-iron hinges. Frederick T. Stanley was elected president of the new company and, for all intents and purposes, was the founder. Years earlier, in 1843, Stanley had begun manufacturing door bolts and handles. In 1857, he sold that business to his other business venture, Stanley Works. The machinery was part of the sale and included a small-burden steam engine, which was the first steam engine in New Britain, Connecticut.

Meanwhile, living in the New Britain area was a sixteen-year-old by the name of William H. Hart (Figure 2). While still attending high school in New Britain, Hart obtained a job, in 1850, as a clerk with the newly formed Hartford, Providence & Fishkill Railway. In this capacity, Hart sold the first tickets for passenger train service to New Britain.

William H. Hart was born in New Britain on July 23, 1834, and, by all accounts, was the kind of man who would reach into your heart and listen to what you had to say. It has been said that he would place his hand on your shoulder and look you in the eyes, giving you a sense of trustworthiness that helped lead you forward. He was a man of honor, and many individuals in and around New Britain knew it. Hart did a great job checking waybills and operating the rail office. The experience gave him a firm knowledge of the transportation industry—a knowledge that would prove invaluable in the years ahead.

On March 4, 1854, Frederick T. Stanley, president of the Stanley Works, and C. B. Erwin, director of the Stanley Works, approached William Hart—now age nineteen—about working for the Stanley Works. The Stanley Works needed someone who had a first-hand

Figure 1 (top of page). Stanley Works's well-known "Sweetheart" logo.

knowledge of transportation, and Stanley and Erwin saw qualities in young Hart that would help the fledgling company. Many of the Stanley Works's competitors were located on major waterways, which made for a competitive edge in shipping costs.

Hearing the offer, William Hart resigned from the Hartford, Providence & Fishkill Rail Company and began a lifetime career with the Stanley Works. Frederick T. Stanley and C. B. Erwin were so impressed with Hart's performance that on May 16, 1854, two months after he joined the company, Hart was elected by the board of directors to serve as secretary and treasurer of the Stanley Works. At this time, the company employed twenty-five people and had a capital of $30,000.

The growth of the Stanley Works was slow at first, but in 1861, the demand for material for the Civil War gave the company a financial boost. Hart was valuable during this time not only as

Figure 2 (above). William H. Hart.

Figure 3 (below). The telescope or double box (circa 1880), a design created by Hart shown with hinges and screws. With this new concept in packaging, Stanley shipped hinges and the necessary bolts together, the way that the two parts would eventually be sold.

secretary and treasurer, but also a man with a great management ability. He is quoted in *Hardware Age* as having reduced labor costs of hinge manufacture in the first four years of his employment from a $10.00 base to a $4.00 base.[1] He also stated in that article that "Perfect harmony can be maintained only when the shortening of operation carries with it mutual advantages to the workmen and the producers."[2]

Hart was very inventive. Labor-saving ideas were always on his mind, as he recognized their importance as an edge in competing with the opposition. He noticed, for example, that when a person needing a pair of hinges went into a hardware store to purchase them, the merchant would pull hinges wrapped in paper off the shelf. The merchant would have to unwrap the hinges so the customer could see if the hinge was the proper size. If the hinge was the type the customer desired, the merchant would then go to another place in the store to fit screws to the hinges and then wrap the hinges and the screws for the customer. This was time consuming for both merchant and customer. To simplify the sale of hinges and screws, Hart invented the first telescoping, or double, box in 1869 (Figure 3). The box consisted of three parts, a lid and a double box on the bottom. The interior size of the box bottom could be changed to

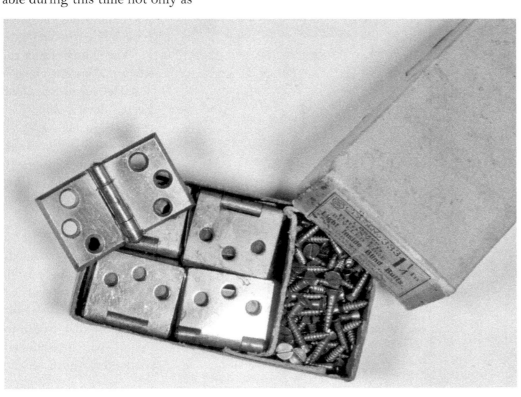

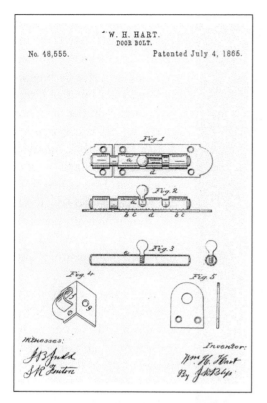

W. H. HART.
DOOR BOLT.

No. 48,555.   Patented July 4, 1865.

Fig. 1
Fig. 2
Fig. 3
Fig. 4   Fig. 5

Witnesses: Inventor:

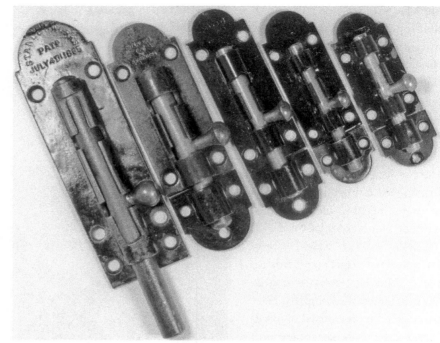

Figures 4 (above) and 5 (above, right). William Hart invented the barrel bolt in 1865. The original patent is shown at left (Figure 4). Figure 5 shows examples of the bolt, including one on the left dating from circa 1865–1875; the other four bolts are from the 1920s.

Figures 6 and 7 (below). Hart continued to improve on his invention with additional patents granted in 1865 (below, left) and 1870 (below, right).

accommodate the contents. Stanley was able to pack the hinges or bolts together with the proper screws. He never patented the idea and said "…it was too useful of a thing to the merchants of the world to be retarded by patents."[3]

Later, Hart went on to design print labels for the telescopic boxes with class numbers and descriptions large enough to be read from a reasonable distance in a hardware store. Two years after the introduction of the telescoping box, the Stanley Works had half the butt-hinge business in the United States.

The ubiquitous barrel bolt was also a Hart invention. He received a patent for the device on July 4, 1865 (Figures 4 and 5). He subsequently received, on September 26, 1865 (Figure 6), and May 31, 1870 (Figure 7), additional patents for barrel bolts.

Stanley had been manufacturing its hardware from wrought iron, but in 1870, Hart learned of a new method—cold-rolling Swedish iron into strips—which produced a smoother finish on the

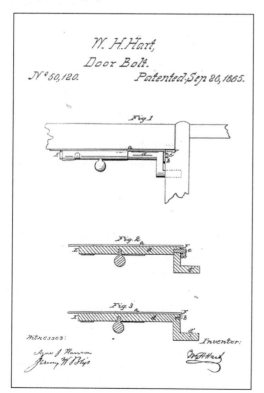

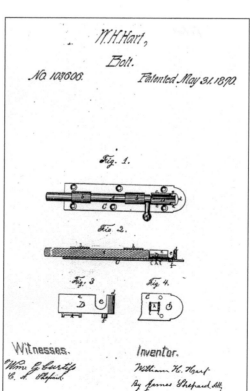

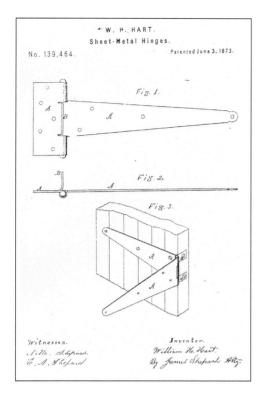

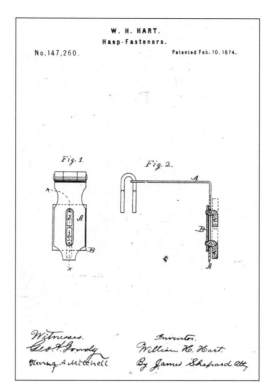

Figure 8 (far left). William H. Hart's June 3, 1873, patent for sheet-metal hinges.

Figure 9 (left). Hart's patent for a hinge hasp.

Figure 10 (below). An example of a Hart hinge hasp, circa 1870-1880s.

end product. Wrought iron was manually hammered out to the thickness desired. Cold-rolled iron was pressed through rollers, making the strip of iron that was more uniform and smoother. He purchased a Boston copper mill for the purpose of cold-rolling Swedish iron-making the Stanley Works the first company in the United States to manufacture hardware using the process.

In 1873, William Hart patented large, sheet-metal hinges (Figure 8) with right-angle leafs, which was a unique twist to a standard piece of hardware. The right-angle, rigid-arm support behind one leaf supported the hinge when the door was open preventing these larger hinge leaves from twisting. A year later, on February 10, 1874, Hart patented another commonplace piece of hardware, the hasp fastener (Figures 9 and 10).

The first reinforced hinge was patented by Hart on June 10, 1879 (Figure 11). On August 12, 1897, he received a patent for another reinforced hinge (Figure 12), an example of which is illustrated in Figure 13. Also, on May 27, 1879, a wire-lifting handle was patented by Hart. The lifting handle could be used on a trunk or cane and would lie flat when not in use. Hart's handle used a base-plate formed into two parts (Figure 14).

Between 1880 and 1890, with the success of cold-rolling Swedish iron firmly established, Hart had the idea that it might be possible to cold-roll steel. He experimented until he found a steel that was ductile enough for rolling into strips. Stanley, in 1890, became the first American company to produce cold-rolled steel hinges. This technique left a smoother surface finish and overcame many of the difficult problems common with hinges and butts up to that time. This process remained a company secret for at least six years before competitors became aware of

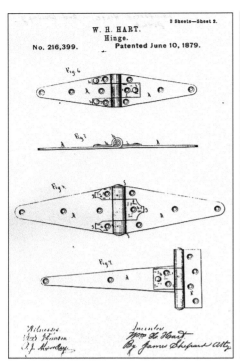

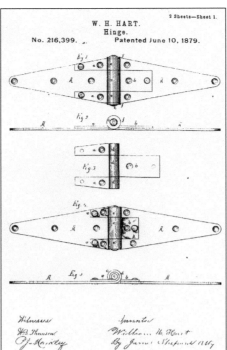

Figures 11a and 11b. Hart's patent for a reinforced hinge.

the use by the Stanley Works of cold-rolled steel.

On January 31, 1888, William Hart and Thomas Corscaden patented an improvement in sheet-metal hinges, the corrugated hinge (Figures 15 and 16).

William H. Hart was elected president and treasurer of the Stanley Works in May 1884, a position he held until May 16, 1904. From 1904 until 1915, he held only the position of president. For the next three years (1915–1918), he served as chairman of the board, retiring from the Stanley Works in 1918 at the age of eighty-four.

For sixty-three consecutive years, William H. Hart gave active service to the Stanley Works. His devotion was unparalleled and many have called him the "Dean of Hardware Manufacturers." He nursed the company through good times and bad and built a company with $30,000 in capital and twenty-five workers into one of the largest hardware manufacturing facilities in the world with between three to four thousand employees.

In June 1893, the Stanley Works began using a new trademark, a heart—a play on Hart's name—with the

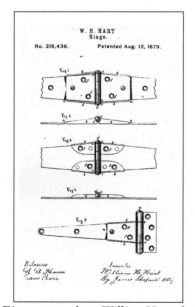

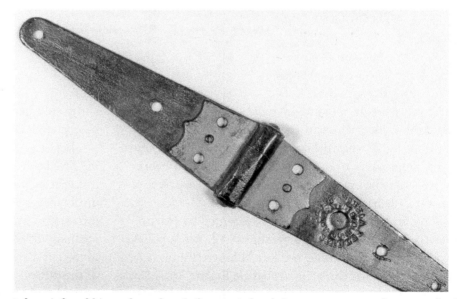

Figures 12 and 13. William Hart also invented a reinforced hinge; shown here is the patent, dated August 12, 1879, and an example of the hinge (above, right) as manufactured. This hinge is a no. 945, 6-inch strap hinge.

letters S W inside (Figure 17) in appreciation and honor of an employee and company officer who had given his entire working life to the company. When Hart retired, on February 5, 1918, from the board of directors, the company's shareholders prepared the following public statement:

> The career of William H. Hart with The Stanley Works is unique for its length—he having served as Secretary for eighteen years, as Treasurer for fifty years, as President for thirty years—a total of more than sixty-three years' continuous service—remarkable in many ways.
>
> Always of an optimistic and creative disposition, his courage, aggressiveness and determination enabled him in the early days to overcome what to others would have been insurmountable obstacles.
>
> His complete grasp of the manufacturing, selling, purchasing, shipping—in fact every department of the business—for many years, even to the minutest detail, gave to the concern its early impetus and to Mr. Hart that ripe business judgement which during later years has so prominently contributed to the successful growth and expansion of the business.
>
> His energy, devotion and enthusiasm, his cordial support and encouragement of and staunch belief in young men, his constant thoughtfulness of others, have been a continual source of inspiration to all employees and largely responsible for the spirit of loyalty and fine esprit de corps that pervades the entire organization.
>
> Few men have been honored by so long a service; and none would withdraw from active work more loved and esteemed by all who came in contact with him than Mr. Hart.
>
> (signed) E. W. Christ
H. D. Humphrey
E. W. Eddy
A Committee of Stockholders[+]

William H. Hart died on December 13, 1919. From June 1893 to May 1920, the trademark "sweetheart/hart" was used on Stanley Hardware products (Figure 17). On May 1, 1920, the Stanley Rule & Level Co. and the Stanley Works (two separate companies started by two branches of the same fam-

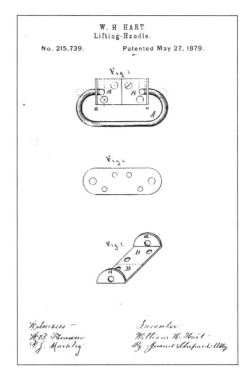

Figure 14 (above). William Hart's patent for a wire-lifting handle.

Figures 15 and 16 (below). William Hart's and Thomas Corscaden's patent for a corrugated hinge and an example of the hinge described in the patent.

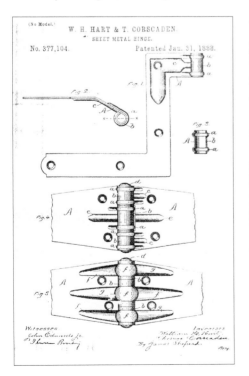

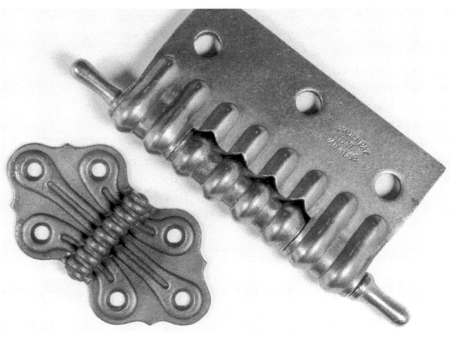

Figure 17 (left). Two examples of the 1893 Stanley Sweatheart trademark—on a hinge and next to a listing on trademark from The Official Patent Gazette. *The note from* Patent Gazette *reads, "The representation of a heart shaped figure accompanied by the initials 'S.W.' Used since June, 1893."*

Figure 18 (below). An advertisement announcing the new Stanley logo. The advertisement appeared in the March 5, 1921 issue of The Literary Digest.

ily) announced the merger of the two companies. With the merger came the challenge of creating a new logo to symbolize the union. The board of directors decided to hold a contest for employees, with the winner to receive a cash prize.

Employees E. C. Hartman and W. L. Hagen had almost identical ideas and both won. The resulting logo is the well-known Stanley sweetheart logo, which incorporated the 1893 trademark of the Stanley Works that honored William Hart, and the Stanley Rule & Level Company notched rectangle (Figures 1 and 18). Fused together, the two icons symbolized the creation of the world's largest hardware and tool company of the day. The trademarked symbol remained Stanley's logo until 1934.

The heritage of William H. Hart lives on in legacy products of Stanley—hinges, bolts, and hasps among other hardware items. Unfortunately, his telescopic boxes have been replaced by blister packs and vacuum-sealed tools. But Hart's contributions to the company enabled Stanley to pay stock dividends throughout the Great Depression. Stanley remains the oldest company on the New York Stock Exchange to pay continuous dividends from 1877. William H. Hart left the Stanley Works, the town of New Britain, Connecticut, the hardware and tool world, and American industrial history a wonderful heritage.

Notes

1. "William H. Hart," *Hardware Age* 101, no. 9 (1918): 51.
2. "Hart," 51.
3. "Hart," 52.
4. "Hart," 52-53.

Our new trade mark!

STANLEY
S.W.

A Guaranteed Purchase

THE next time you visit your hardware merchant for

Wrought Steel Hardware or Carpenters' Tools

you may be assured of a satisfactory purchase if you mention the name STANLEY.

For the repair work around the house, that inclination to pound a nail, or to see the shavings curl up and fall on the floor, STANLEY Tools will give you hours of real service and pleasure.

Get ready to replace the old screen hardware with new. Don't hesitate about building the new garage; build it and swing the doors on STANLEY Ball Bearing Garage Hinges.

All of the products illustrated bear the guarantee of a three-quarter century reputation of dependable manufacture.

Our advertising department will send a separate catalog of each, or one of both lines, of our products; ask for B31

THE STANLEY WORKS
Main offices and plant:
NEW BRITAIN, CONN.
Branch offices: New York Chicago San Francisco
Los Angeles Seattle Atlanta

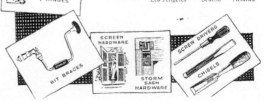

Stanley Diversifies into the Handle Business

The Stanley Rule & Level Co. was formed by the merger of A. Stanley & Co. and Hall & Knapp in 1857. The product line of the new company included rules, levels, and marking gauges. Stanley acquired the rule business of E. A. Stearns of Brattleboro, Vermont, on April 1, 1863. This acquisition added a very well-made line of rules to Stanley's product line.

Besides these products, which have all been well documented, Stanley, in 1865, began offering wooden products such as handles, mallets, hand screws, bench screws, chalk lines, door stops, handsaw and plane handles, and stocking lasts. Most of these products, except for the hand screws, did not have the Stanley name marked on them. Identifying them is done by matching items with catalog illustrations and dimensions. Some have also been identified by finding original boxed items. This article will consider Stanley's handle business.

Early in the nineteenth century, axe, pick, adze, and hatchet handles were roughed out on a rocking-beam copy lathe (Figure 1). This lathe had a horizontal beam, which had a pattern handle mounted on the left side of the rocking beam and a handle blank on the right side (Figure 2). The pattern handle rode on a metal sliding rest. As the pattern side rotated up and down, following the pattern handle, the blank was slowly turned. A rotary cutter (Figure 3) would duplicate the irregular shape of the pattern onto the blank. As the beam moved up and down, it also would move sideways thus following the pattern down its length and duplicating the shape of the pattern handle onto the blank (Figures 4 and 5). As the beam moved horizontally, the flat belt would track sidewise on the long cylinder pulley. A stop on the machine would prevent the horizontal beam from moving when the handle was finished and ready for a final polishing. This style of copy lathe was patented by Thomas Blanchard in 1819 for the mass production of rifle stocks at the Springfield Armory. The patent was basically for the sliding rest.

Blanchard went on to patent an improved lathe in 1843 (U.S. patent no. 3008, March 21, 1843). Any lathe with a sliding rest was known as a Blanchard lathe. Any owners of a lathe with this sliding rest had to pay royalties to Blanchard. Assignees of Blanchard's lathe were required to pay a ½ cent to 1½ cents royalty on every handle produced.

Figure 1 (top). A rocking-beam copy lathe.

Figure 2 (above). The rocking-beam copy lathe showing the horizontal beam with the pattern on left and the copy on right.

Figure 3 (right). The rotary cutter on the lathe.

Figure 4 (above). The view from the end showing the long cylinder pulley with the flat belt and beam-moving spool in the center. As the large pulley turns, a gear mechanism turns the center spool with a flat rope that pulls the horizontal beam.

Figure 5 (left). The view from the opposite end showing the flat rope around it to pull the beam.

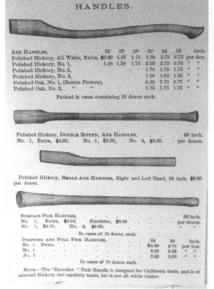

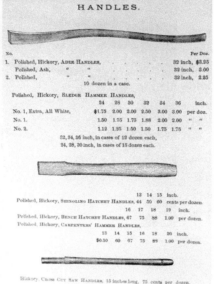

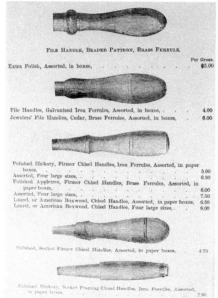

Figure 6 (above, left). A page from the 1866 Stanley catalog showing axe handles.

Figure 7 (above, right). An illustration from the same catalog showing adze, hammer, and shingling-hatchet handles.

Figure 8 (left). The page showing chisel and file handles.

Figure 9 (below). An example of a Stanley socket-framing chisel handle, circa 1870.

Blanchard's 1843 lathe patent expired in 1863 and may be the reason Stanley did not enter the handle business until 1865, thus avoiding paying royalties. It is the author's assumption that Stanley used a Blanchard copy lathe and Blanchard patent polishing machines for Stanley's handle production due to these machines making a superior quality product at a higher production rate.

In 1866 and 1867, Stanley manufactured hickory and white oak handles for single-bit axes, ranging from 22 to 36 inches in length (Figure 6). The most expensive were made of white wood (sapwood) hickory because these handles were more elastic and stronger than heartwood.

Double-bitted ax handles were also part of the line being made in whitewood only. Left- and right-hand polished broad axe handles in 26-inch lengths were produced.

Surface, drifting, and poll pick handles made of hickory, both in whitewood (extra) and heartwood, were produced in 34- and 36-inch lengths. Polished hickory and ash adze handles in 32-inch lengths were manufactured in three grades (Figure 7). All of these handles were manufactured and offered by Stanley from 1865 through 1870. Sledge, shingling, and bench hatchet handles and hammer handles were also produced beginning in 1865 and continuing through until 1872.

Handles for files and chisels (Figure 8) were pro-

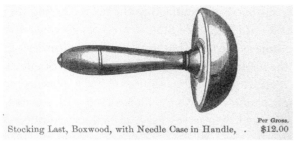

Stocking Last, Boxwood, with Needle Case in Handle, . $12.00 Per Gross.

Figure 10 (left). A stocking last illustrated in the Stanley catalog for 1867.

Figure 11 (left, below). An example of a stocking last with a rosewood handle.

Figure 12 (below). The stocking last opened, showing the needle case.

duced in assorted sizes of hickory, applewood, American boxwood, and laurel. Handles for firmer chisels and framing chisels were turned from hickory, which would withstand heavier work, and had galvanized iron ferrules. Figure 9 shows a Stanley socket framing-chisel handle made of hickory with a total length of 7 inches. The boxwood handles were for tanged chisels and carving tools. Chisel handles remained in the Stanley line of products until about 1878.

Stocking lasts made of boxwood (Figure 10) with rosewood handles were produced from 1867 through August 1871 (Figure 11). The diameter of the last portion is 2¼ inches, and the rosewood handle, which was nicely turned with a bead at its base, is 3⅛ inches in length. The handle threads into the last head and is hollow, providing a needle case inside (Figure 12).

Pegging-awl handles and sewing-awl hafts (Figure 13) were other products offered by Stanley beginning in 1865. The Stanley no. 6 pegging-awl handle is 3⅞ inches long and has a leather top and a steel chuck and was sold with a wrench used to tighten the chuck (Figure 14). These handles did not include the polished, cast-steel pegging awls, which were sold separately in sizes 00 through 6 (see Figures 13 and Figure 15). Stan-

Figure 13 (above, left). The Stanley catalog for 1866-1867 showing illustrating sewing-awl hafts and peg awls.

Figure 14 (above, right). Stanley's no. 6 peg-awl hafts with the box. The haft came with a wrench to tighten the chuck.

Figure 15 (below). Various sizes of Stanley cast steel.

Figure 16 (at right). Stanley's no. 6½ sewing-awl hafts.

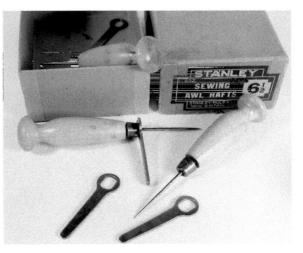

SAW HANDLES.

All full sizes, SPEAR & JACKSON's pattern, of perfect timber, well seasoned, and every way superior and reliable goods.

No.					Per Gross.
1.	Extra, Full size, Mahogany, Polished Edges,				$36.00
1.	Full size, Cherry, Polished Edges,				20.00
2.	" Beech, " "				17.50
3.	" " Plain "				15.00
4.	Small panel, " Polished " for 16 to 20 inch Saws,				17.50
5.	Meat Saws, " " "				17.50
6.	Compass Saw " " "				17.50
7.	Back Saw " " "				17.50

Packed two gross in a case.

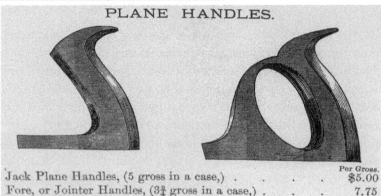

PLANE HANDLES.

	Per Gross.
Jack Plane Handles, (5 gross in a case,)	$5.00
Fore, or Jointer Handles, (3¾ gross in a case,)	7.75

8

Figure 17 (left). A page from the 1867 Stanley catalog illustrating saw handles.

Figure 18 (below, top). A page from the same catalog showing plane handles.

Figure 19 (below, middle). Examples of Stanley's no. 10 jack plane handles.

Figure 20 (below, bottom). Stanley no. 12 fore and jointer plane handles with box.

ley continued to manufacture the no. 6 pegging-awl handle until 1942. The Stanley no. 5 pegging awl was the same as the no. 6, but it did not have a leather top on the handle; it was discontinued in 1929. Stanley's no. 6½ sewing-awl hafts (Figure 16) had applewood or maple handles and were 4 inches long with a 2-inch sewing awl. These sewing-awl hafts were offered from 1867 through 1942. The no. 7 sewing-awl hafts were meant for heavier work in leather and canvas. These hafts were the same as a no. 6 ½ except the handle was 4 ½ inches long; Stanley discontinued the haft in 1909.

Saw handles were another product that commenced in 1865. Stanley made eight different saw handles in the Spear & Jackson pattern (Figure 17). The no. 1 Extra was made of polished mahogany. The no. 2 was polished cherry wood with all other types in beechwood. Saw handles were offered until 1902.

Plane handles (Figure 18) for wood planes were made in two configurations beginning in 1865. They were discontinued in 1902.

The no. 10 (Figure 19) was for jack planes and was made out of beech or maple. The no. 12 plane handle (Figure 20) was for fore or jointer planes. They were also made of beech or maple. They were sold to hardware merchants in boxes of twelve.

Outside of pegging-awl handles, sewing-awl hafts, and saw and plane handles, most of Stanley's wooden handles were discontinued in 1872. The awl handles and hafts remained in the Stanley product line until 1942.

Notes

1. The photographs in Figures 1 through 5 are of an original rocking-beam copy lathe with Blanchard's sliding rest. This lathe is located at Joanna Furnace, near Morgantown, Pennsylvania. Joanna Furnace is owned and operated by the Hay Creek Valley Historical Association, which operates the lathe during its annual Fall Festival in September and Apple Festival in October. The author thanks Hay Creek for permitting photography of the lathe.
2. More information on Blanchard's machinery may be found in *Shaping Invention: Thomas Blanchard's Machinery and Patent Management in Nineteenth-Century America*, by Carolyn C. Cooper (New York: Columbia University Press, 1991).

Stanley Hollow-Handle Tool Sets

The story of Stanley hollow-handle tool sets starts with an inventor by the name of Nathan S. Clement, who resided in Worcester, Massachusetts. On April 21, 1857, Clement patented a hollow awl handle (Figure 1) that contained a hollow handle or cavity in which awls or tools could be contained.[1] Clement's invention was such that an awl could be removed from the hollow handle and inserted into a split-threaded screw end. The end was machined to take a square bit, making a collet, and then held by a bur-nut, which when screwed in place, tightened the collet onto the awl bit.

Nathan Clement, ten years later and now a resident of New Britain, Connecticut, improved the awl handle with another patent (Figure 2).[2] With the new patent, the collet was closed by tightening the cap to the hollow cavity. The difference on this patent was that the cavity to hold the tool bits was in the rear or handle end of the tool, whereas in his first patent the cavity had been in the front or nose end of the tool.

The 1867 patent does not state that it was assigned to Stanley, but the tool appears in Stanley's January 1, 1867, catalog as a "Patent Excelsior Tool Handle" (Fig-ure 3). Did Stanley hire Nathan Clement or did Stanley just buy his patent rights? I feel that since Clement moved to New Britain and the patent was granted on March 19, 1867, and the catalog was issued on January 1, 1867, that Clement was probably in the employ of Stanley.

Pictured in Figures 3 and 4 is the two-page 1867 catalog description of the Clement patent awl handle with an illustration of the twenty tool bits offered with the handle. The catalog illustration follows the patent drawing very closely.

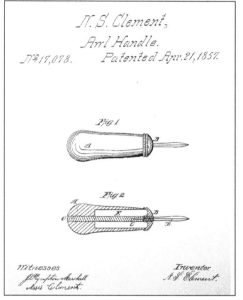
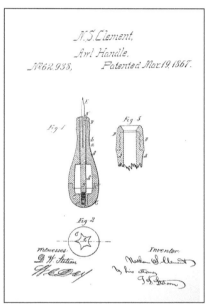

Figure 1 (above, left). Nathan S. Clement patent of April 21, 1857, for an awl handle.

Figure 2 (above, right). Nathan S. Clement patent of March 19, 1867, for an awl handle.

Figure 3 (left). Stanley's 1867 catalog, page 40, showing the Clement patent awl handle.

Figure 4 (below). Stanley's 1867 catalog, page 41, showing the tool bits supplied with Clement's patent tool handle.

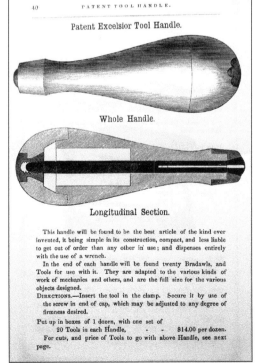

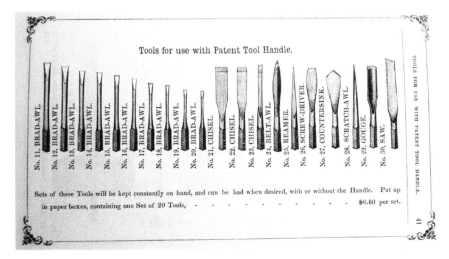

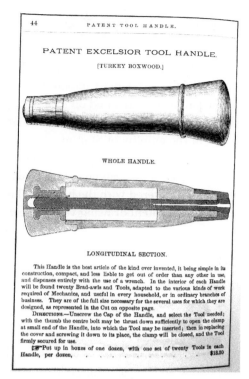

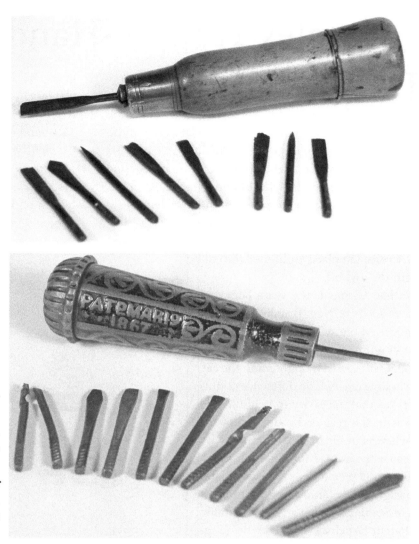

Figure 5 (above). Page 44 of Stanley's 1870 catalog showing the revised version of Clement's tool handle.

Figure 6 (right, top). An example of Clement's "Excelsior" tool handle with some bits; Stanley eventually assigned it the model number 1.

Figure 7 (right). Stanley made cast-iron versions of the Excelsior. This example is a model no. 3, with some of its twenty bits. Model no. 2 was similar, but had only twelve bits.

In Stanley's January 1870 catalog, Clement's tool handle is shown in a new, revised form (Figure 5). The basic, internal mechanism of the tool is the same, but the outside had been redesigned in 1869. An example of the revised handle made of Turkish boxwood is shown in Figure 6. The bolster was pewter and was marked "Clement's Pat'd March 19, 1867."

At first, Stanley did not assign a model or product number on these tool sets. By 1877, however, the title of "Number 1" was assigned to Clement's Patent Excelsior Tool Handle, and a new, cast-iron version was introduced. The cast-iron model was cast with a fancy floral design with the background black japanned and was marked with the patent date of March 19, 1867. Assigned the number 2, the cast-iron version had twelve tool bits. A no. 3 cast-iron tool handle was also introduced and was the same as the no. 2 except it contained twenty tool bits instead of twelve (Figure 7).

The no. 1 tool handle remained in the Stanley line from 1869 to 1902. The no. 2 and no. 3 cast-iron models were offered from 1877 to 1902. Beginning in 1879, Stanley offered the no. 2 and no. 3 Excelsior tool handles in a new model with a nickel-plated body, numbering them 22 and 23 respectively. The nickel-plated bodies were offered with the no. 2 and no. 3 models until 1902, when all the Excelsior tool handles were discontinued.

John S. Fray Hollow-Handle Tool Sets

John S. Fray had invented and had filed a patent application on his hollow-handle tool on April 23, 1883, which was granted on August 7, 1883 (Figure 8).[3] Once the patent was received, Fray added the hollow-handle tool sets to his company's bit brace line. Figure 9 shows Fray's early "Pat'd Apl'd for" tool with applewood handle that contained ten bits.

Stanley, in its quest to return to the bit brace business, acquired the John S. Fray Company of Bridgeport, Connecticut, in April 1909.[4] With that acquisition, Stanley also acquired Fray's line of hollow-handle tool sets, which it continued to sell from its John S. Fray division in Bridgeport, Connecticut.

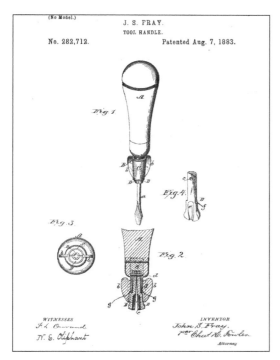

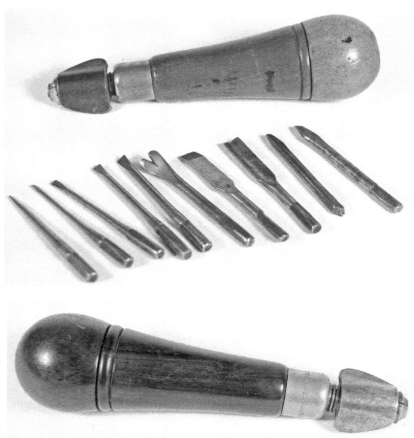

Figure 8 (above, left). John S. Fray patent of August 7, 1883, for a tool handle.

Figure 9 (right, top). An example of the Fray model no. 1 with applewood handle marked "Pat'd Apl'd for."

Figure 10 (right, bottom). The Fray model no. 1 with co-cobolo handle and the inscription "Fray's Pat. Aug. 7, 83."

By the time of the company's acquisition by Stanley, Fray had ten different hollow-handle tool sets available. Fray's model no. 1 hollow-handle set was like that shown in Figure 9, except that it had a cocobolo handle and was inscribed "Fray's Pat. Aug. 7, 83" on the bolster (Figure 10). A model no. 1C was also available. It was the same as the model no. 1, except the no. 1C had a knurled chuck shell to close the collet instead of the wing nut. Fray's no. 1 and no. 2 were the same except the no. 2 was larger. The no. 2C was the larger version of the no. 1C, with the knurled collet chuck. Set no. 3 was the same as the models no. 1 and no. 2 except that it was a little larger than no. 2 and had only three screwdriver bits. Fray's no. 4 and no. 5 were sets similar to the no. 1 but with maple handles.

Fray's no. 6 is identical to the original "Pat'd Apl'd for" model shown in Figure 9, except there was no inscription and it had an applewood handle. Fray's no. 7 with a coco-bolo handle and no. 8 with a maple handle were smaller models, which will be described briefly later.

Stanley's Fray-Style Tool Kits

By 1911, Stanley was offering seven models of hollow-handle tool sets. All used Fray's patent, and all the models were numbered using three digits beginning with the number 3. Model no. 300 (Figure 11) was Stanley's

largest hollow-handle tool set with an overall length of 7⅝ inches. It was made of cocobolo and had a knurled chuck, and inside the handle there were ten tools (a file, a saw, a gimlet, a chisel, a gouge, a reamer, a scratch awl, a brad awl, and two screwdrivers). The handle cap was fitted with a steel strike plate. This tool handle was the most expensive of Stanley's line of tool handles, and it remained in the line until 1941.

Figure 11 (above). Stanley no. 300 hollow-handle tool.

Figure 12 (below). Stanley no. 302 hollow-handle tool with two bits.

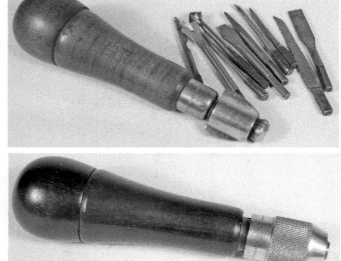

Figure 13 (above, left). A Stanley no. 303 cocobolo hollow-handle tool set with tool bits, a gimlet, a gouge, a chisel, a scratch awl, a screw driver, a tack puller, and four brad awls.

Figure 14 (right, top). Stanley no. 304 was the same as the 303 except the handle was maple.

Figure 15 (right, bottom). Stanley no. 303 cocobolo hollow-handle tool set with knurled chuck. In 1923, Stanley changed the no. 303 replacing the wing-nut chuck with a knurled chuck.

Stanley's no. 301 and no. 302 (Figure 12) were similar in size (7⅝ inches) to the no. 300, except they did not contain a steel strike plate and were furnished with only eight tools with no scratch or brad awls. The no. 301 had a cocobolo handle, and the no. 302 handle was maple. Both models had the knurled chuck. The no. 301 was discontinued in 1939. No. 302 was made until 1923.

The next two models were numbers 303 and 304. The no. 303 (Figure 13) was the same as Fray's no. 1 and had a cocobolo handle, a wing-nut chuck collet, and

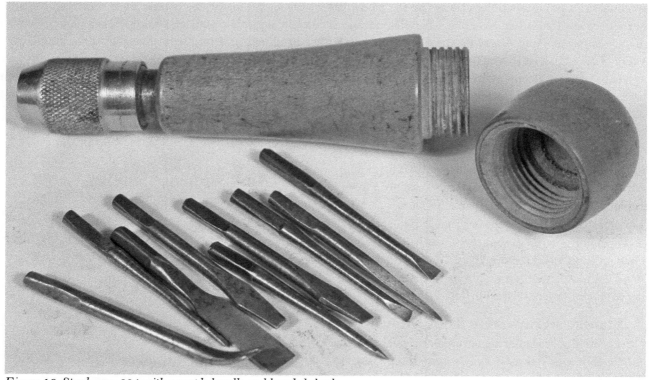

Figure 16. Stanley no. 304 with a maple handle and knurled chuck.

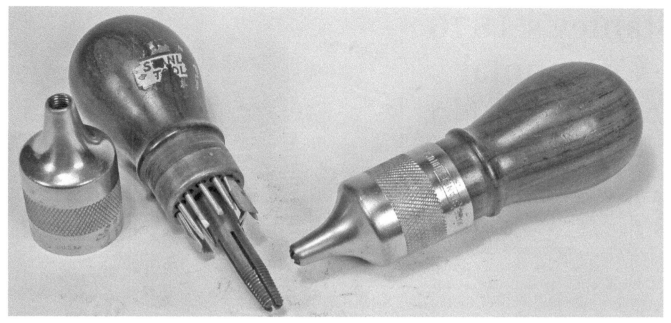

Figure 17 (above). Two examples of Stanley's no. 305 cocobolo hollow-handle tool sets known as combination hafts. The chuck shell has been removed on the one on the left to show bit storage.

ten tools. Measuring 5¾ inches in length, it contained a gimlet, a gouge, a chisel, a scratch awl, a screw driver, a tack puller, and four brad awls. No. 304 (Figure 14) was similar to the model no. 303 but had a maple handle. The model 304 was also purchased by the U. S. government for use in its Ordnance Department in World War I.

Nos. 303 and 304 were made from 1911 to 1922 with the wing-nut chuck. In 1923, the chuck on model no. 303 (Figure 15) had changed to a knurled chuck; no. 303 was manufactured until 1941. In 1923, the chuck of model no. 304 (Figure 16) was also changed to a knurled two-jaw design. This model was discontinued from the line in 1933.

The last two Stanley models were actually renumbered models—nos. 7 and 8—from the Fray line of hollow-handle tool sets. These were called combination hafts and were hollow-tool handles with a collet chuck with a knurled shell. Inside were twelve tools. Shown in Figure 17 are two no. 305 cocobolo-handle combination hafts. One has the chuck shell removed to expose the tools. The no. 305 was manufactured from 1911 to 1941.

Stanley's no. 306 was the same as the no. 305 but with a maple handle. This model was discontinued in 1937.

In 1941, Stanley discontinued model nos. 300, 303, and 305, the Fray-style, hollow-handle tool kits. Thus ended a period of almost seventy-five years of Stanley's manufacture of a unique, compact tool kit.

Notes

1. U.S. patent no. 17,078.
2. U.S. patent no. 62,938, dated March 19, 1867.
3. U.S. patent no. 282,712, dated April 23, 1883.
4. Walter W. Jacob, "Brace Up For a Bit of Stanley History, Part II, 1909-1916," *The Chronicle* 53, no. 1 (2000): 9-12.

Stanley's 1876 Centennial Exposition No. 9 Level

The Stanley Rule & Level Co. of New Britain, Connecticut, began manufacturing levels in 1857 following the merger of A. Stanley and Co. and Hall and Knapp, both of New Britain, Connecticut. Throughout the 1860s, levels and rules were Stanley's main product lines. By 1870, carpenter's woodworking planes added a third major product group.

As the nation's one-hundredth anniversary approached, many companies purchased exposition space at the 1876 Centennial Exposition in Philadelphia, in hopes that it would provide a grand international show of the world's best products. Stanley was no exception. Figure 1 shows part of Stanley's display at the exposition. The case in the photo illustrates the various boxwood and ivory rules and woodworking planes, including the ornate Miller's patent plow plane. The display was such that it was a walk-around exhibit. The sides not shown in this photo displayed the full line of levels, marking gauges, mallets, tool handles, and screwdrivers in Stanley's product line.

Stanley wanted to impress the world, so visitors to the exposition saw not only the company's high-volume sales products but also unique and high-grade tools. Most tool companies at this time made tools in various quality levels from inexpensive to top-of-the-line with embellishment.

Why did tool companies offer all the various models when any of the tools would, basically, do the same thing? It boiled down to how a person or craftsman was judged at that period of time. A high-quality, top-of-the-line

CONTINUED PAGE 24

795—RULES AND LEVELS

Figure 1. One of the cases that displayed Stanley's products at the Centennial Exposition in Philadelphia. A close inspection reveals, in the far left, end-facing case, Miller's patent plow planes (see close-up, left) and circular planes. In the left side of the case are log and board rules, boxwood two-fold and four-fold rules, and, vertically, three Internal Revenue gauges. The second part of the case displays ivory and boxwood rules and spokeshaves. The third part of the case (far right) exhibits bench planes. If we could walk around to the other side of this impressive case, would we see a special version of Stanley's no. 9 level made especially for the Exposition?

Photo: Free Library Company of Philadelphia, Philadelphia, Pennsylvania.

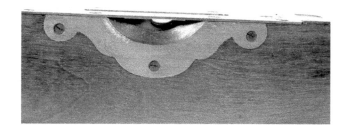

Figure 2 (left). Stanley's no. 9 carpenter's level made of quartered Cuban mahogany with both adjustable plumb and level vials. The no. 9 has side lips and brass plates with smooth faces.

Figure 3 (below). A no. 9 with vial covers and side lips cast in gunmetal with an ornate design in them.

Figures 4, 5, and 6. Details of the no. 9 level.

Figure 4 (left, top). The top plate on the no. 9. Note the green paper beneath the level vial. Later levels did not have a paper under the vial.

Figure 5 (left, middle). Detail showing the intricately designed cast-gunmetal side lips.

Figure 6 (left, bottom). The adjustment plate to the plumb level was also cast in gunmetal.

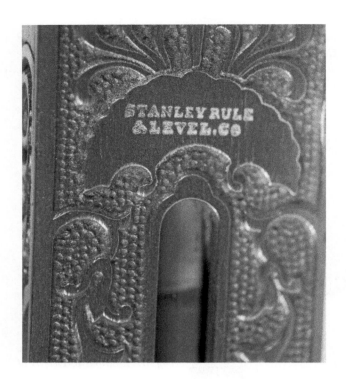

able plumb and level vials. These vial covers and side lips were brass plates with smooth faces (Figure 2).

The no. 9 level shown in Figure 3 is an exception. In the no. 9, the vial covers and side lips of this example are ornately decorated and cast in gunmetal, similar to a Miller's patent plow plane. Figure 4 shows a close-up of the top plate, illustrating the level vial with green paper beneath it. (Later levels—from the late 1870s or early 1880s—did not have a paper.) The ornamental side lips (Figure 5) were cast in gunmetal in the same floral motif as the vial cover. The adjustment plate to the plumb level was also cast in gunmetal and decorated (Figure 6).

This no. 9 level has Stanley's patent adjustment mechanism, utilizing its patents of September 10, 1867; October 6, 1868; and July 2, 1872. The name "Stanley Rule & Level Co" is stamped on the level top plate (Figure 7) and is the same style stamp used on its Miller's patent adjustable plow planes (Figure 8). The level has split-cast bronze end tips, as shown in Figure 9. Beginning in 1877, Stanley's high-grade level had solid end tips.

All the indicators about this unusual example of a no. 9 level point to an 1875-1876 manufacture. The adjustment mechanism and shape of the plates were first illustrated in Stanley's 1874 catalog, but the description of the patent mechanism showed up in the July 1876 pocket catalog. The ends of the "normal" no. 9 levels illustrated in the 1877 catalog were solid tipped instead of half tipped, as in this level.

All these facts suggest that this level was probably manufactured for exhibition at the 1876 Centennial Exposition in Philadelphia, Pennsylvania. Positive proof will only be known when a photo of the reverse side of Stanley's 1876 Centennial display appears.

tool gave the impression that a workman had an expertise above the normal. In other words, the quality of his work was judged not only in his performance but also by the quality of the tools he had in his tool kit.

Stanley manufactured a full line of carpenter's levels, both adjustable and non-adjustable. Adjustable levels permitted the craftsman to make a correction if the level was "out of true."

Stanley's adjustable carpenter's levels were numbered from the lowest grade (no. 1) to the highest grade (no. 11). The no. 9 was normally in Stanley's upper-class range. Made of quartered Cuban mahogany, the no. 9 had adjust-

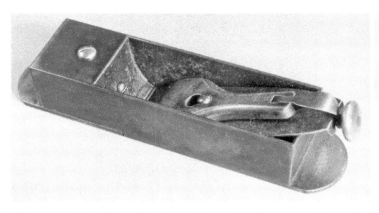
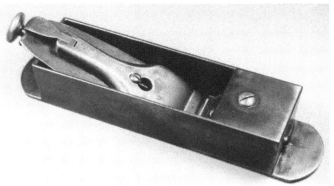

Figures 1 and 2. The earliest known Leonard Bailey no. 9 cabinetmaker's block plane.

Leonard Bailey's Cabinetmaker's Block Plane

Industrial historians regard Leonard Bailey of Boston, Massachusetts, as one of the pioneers of change in the Industrial Revolution of woodworking plane development. Mr. Bailey was a very colorful person, and the many variations of his tools show a continuing refinement of a design that, ultimately, became the bench plane as we know it today. From the bench plane, a smaller version, known as the block plane, evolved. Early in the 1860s, an adjustable-iron block plane, similar to the English miter planes, was developed by Leonard Bailey.

The plane shown in Figures 1 and 2 is the earliest known Leonard Bailey no. 9 cabinetmaker's block plane that has appeared to date. It is 10 inches long and 2¼ inches wide and has a 2-inch iron. The cutter, made by William Ash & Co., has its upper end reheated and bent into a right angle to engage the adjusting screw (Figures

3 and 4). Figure 5 shows the strike on the lever cap. This plane was produced by Leonard Bailey in Boston probably before 1867, and predated Bailey's December 14, 1867, thin-cutter, patented no. 9 planes that were produced later. The adjustment mechanism was changed from a direct screw to a horizontal screw (patented on August 6, 1867) to accommodate his patented thin iron.

The front throat plate has three screws holding it in place instead of two as found in most no. 9s (Figure 6). The top screw is bronze and is the main lock screw. The adjustment of the throat is accomplished by loosening all three screws and moving the throat either front or back. Then all the screws are tightened, but not so snugly as to crack the frame. The adjustment screw located in the throat of the plane is only found on early models. Figure 7 shows a top view of this plane with the lever cap and iron

Figures 3 (above, left). The cutter of the plane. The upper end was reheated and bent to engage the adjusting screw.
Figure 4 (above, right) The adjusting screw.

Figures 5. The strike on level cap reads "Bailey's Patent Aug. 31 1858" referring to the patent date of the lever cap.

removed, revealing the blade-adjustment screw, which has a knurled brass knob, and the steel screw leading through a cast-brass nut device riveted to the cast-iron frame.

The plane was purchased by the author at a New Jersey farm auction. The no. 9 was rusty, but fully intact and all original. It was well used—the cutter iron had been sharpened and resharpened—and consequently there is only a tempered blade remaining.

With continuing analysis of early examples of Leon-

ard Bailey's planes, historians will someday be able to piece together a chronological development of the products of one of the nineteenth-century's great inventors.

Notes

For further information about Leonard Bailey and his connection, see Roger K. Smith's *Patented Transitional and Metallic Planes in America*, volumes I and II (Athol, Massachusetts, 1981 and 1992).

Figures 6 (above). The three screws holding the front throat plate in place.

Figure 7 (right). The top view of the plane with the lever cap and iron removed.

Justus Traut's Improved Miter Box

On June 8, 1875, Justus Traut filed a patent for an improved miter box, which launched the Stanley Rule & Level Co. into the miter-box manufacturing business that continued for the next one hundred-plus years. Justus Traut was one of Stanley's inventors and contractors. His patent was granted on June 19, 1877 (Figure 1). This miter box was designed to be an improvement to miter boxes that were available at the time by other manufacturers.

Traut's miter box featured a cast-iron frame and facing board of one-piece construction (Figure 2). This design guaranteed that the frame and the facing board would remain perpendicular and square to one another at all times. Most miter boxes of the era apparently had the facing board and frame of two or more separate parts, which could allow the right angle to become untrue.

The facing board on Traut's miter box had, in the center, a V-sided slot through which a saw could pass. Below the frame was a rotating cast-iron swing beam that accepted on each end vertical saw guides that could be rotated and adjusted to hold saw blades of different thickness. These saws could be a normal carpenter's saw or a backsaw. The rotating swing beam pivoted on the miter box frame directly below the V-sided slot in the facing board, so that with the saw in place, stock could be

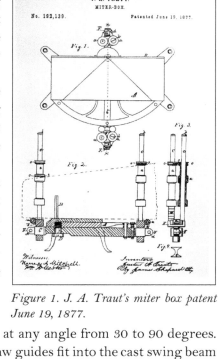

Figure 1. J. A. Traut's miter box patent June 19, 1877.

sawed at any angle from 30 to 90 degrees. The saw guides fit into the cast swing beam vertically and supported the saw when in use in a vertical manner over the miter box frame. Also, the saw supports were fitted with lead rollers so that when the saw was down, it would not cut into the frame.

Cast into the miter box frame or bed was a circular index plate that had holes that accepted a spring-catch pin fitted to the swing arm. This index plate had cast numbers indicating how many sides could be cut at that setting, i.e. square, hexagonal, octagonal, etc. The saw supports could also be raised or lowered so that the lead rollers, which support the saw edge, could be adjusted, so that the saw didn't cut into the bed board.

The first models of this miter box were painted green and had bronze feet (Figure 3). The spring pin lever was cast in brass with a checkered design (Figure 4).

When the miter boxes were first introduced on October 1, 1875, Stanley did not have a designated number for them. They were offered without a saw or with a 20-inch Disston backsaw at an additional

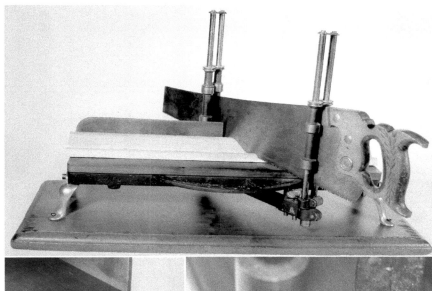

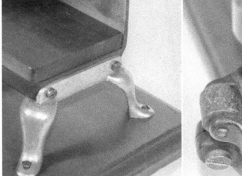

Figure 2 (top). The first model of Traut's miter box with bronze feet.
Figure 3 (bottom, left). Detail of the bronze feet.
Figure 4 (bottom, right). Brass spring pin on Traut's miter box. Pushing down on the pin would retract it out of the index hole.

Figure 5 (above). The second model no. 50 miter box with cast-iron feet.

arm to be used with Richards's patent (Figure 7). The 240 had the same feet as the nos. 50 and 60. My guess is it was a cost-cutting measure to standardize some parts. (Figure 8 shows a no. 50 miter box in the new style, illustrating Richards's index precisionizer, which was easier to use and adjust.) With this new style, the paint color was changed to red with an aluminum-color facing board.

Justus Traut filed a patent on April 24, 1903, for a new-style saw guide for a miter box. He received patent approval March 15, 1904 (Figure 9). This was applied to the nos. 50 and 60 miter boxes by changing the old saw guides to the new style. The change resulted in two new miter box models, no. 50½ and no. 60½ (Figure 10). Both miter boxes were the same, but model no. 50½ was not supplied with a saw.

$3.00. (The miter box cost $7.00; the additional cost of the backsaw would bring the total to $10.00.)

Within the first year or two, the bronze feet were replaced with cast-iron feet (Figure 5). The second model also had no assigned Stanley number until 1887 or 1888, when the miter box with no saw was designated as no. 50. With a saw, the miter box was no. 60. Outside of the addition of the saw, the miter boxes were the same. The no. 50 and the no. 60 miter boxes were unchanged in appearance until 1908.

The no. 50 and no. 60 frame and feet were changed in late 1908 to reflect Francis Richards's August 2, 1904, patent (Figure 6) for a "precisionizer for index pins." Richards's patent was also used beginning in 1904, for a new line of Stanley miter boxes with number designations beginning at 240. The new line incorporated Justus Traut's patent of September 27, 1904, for a swing

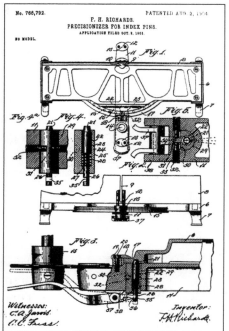

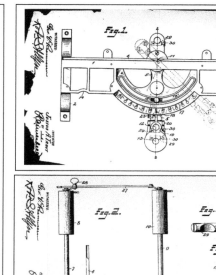

Figure 6 (above, left). Francis Richards's patent, August 2, 1904, for a precisionizer for index pins for a miter box.

Figures 7a & b (above, right). Justus Traut's September 27, 1904, patent for a miter box.

Figure 8 (right). The new-style no. 50 miter box. Note that although it is a new-style miter box, it has the old-style saw support guides.

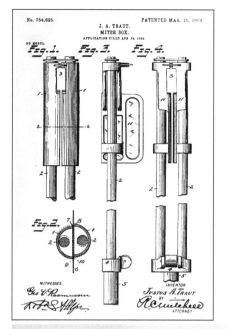

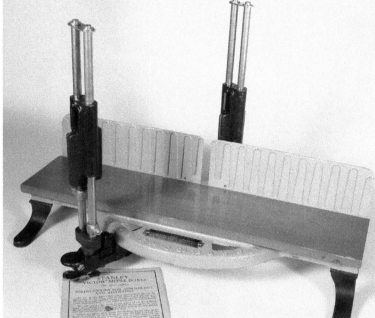

Figure 9 (above, left). Justus Traut's patent March 15, 1904, for a new style of saw guides.

Figure 10 (above, right). A Stanley no. 60½ miter box with saw.

Figure 11 (left). A Stanley no. 50½ miter box made in the late 1930s.

Figure 12 (below). A Stanley improved no. 60 miter box introduced in 1955.

Around 1923, Stanley discontinued the no. 50 and no. 60 miter boxes, but the nos. 50½ and 60½, with Traut's improved saw guides, remained. By the mid-1930s, the miter boxes were being painted a light aluminum color on the frame and facing board, with blue feet and blue saw guides with an orange wooden bed board (Figure 11). The nos. 50½ and 60½ were discontinued around 1955.

A new, completely reworked, no. 60 miter box (with a saw) was introduced in 1955 (Figure 12) and remained in the Stanley line into the 1980s, as the no. 60MB.

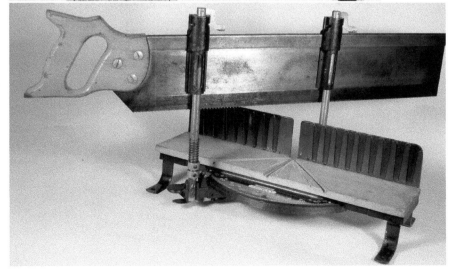

Stanley's Open-Front Miter Box, No. 150

Luman W. Jacobs resided in the little town of Warren in south central Massachusetts. But there was nothing small town about the patent that he filed on February 21, 1889 (Figures 1a and 1b). Jacobs's patent for a miter box made significant new and useful improvements over what was then on the market.

Jacobs's miter box was designed to support the saw vertically while having the front open. The box was adaptable, and it could be used with most of the saws that carpenters would commonly have in their tool boxes. The uniqueness of this patent, which was granted on November 5, 1889 (patent no. 414,544), was that not only did the carpenter have at his disposal a miter box that would saw miters at any angle from 90 degrees to 45 degrees, but he could also use a common handsaw or a backsaw in the miter box (Figure 2). He could saw boards with wider widths because of the open front. When using the miter box with a backsaw—a saw with a stiff, rolled-metal bar across the top of the saw—the carpenter could control or gauge the depth of cut, for example when making dado cuts or halving, by simply adjusting the saw yoke (Figure 3). Another innovation of Jacobs's miter box was the small wooden roller located on the yoke arm at the rear of the slot, which prevented the saw from cutting into the table (Figure 4).

Jacobs had designed the box so that the saw yoke could also be reversed, that is turned upside down, thereby making the miter box a convenient saw vise for filing or sharpening a saw. This feature, however, was apparently not too efficient, perhaps due to the rigidness of the saw yoke, and was dropped early in production, eliminating the need to mill one surface on the yoke to make the reversal possible.

Luman Jacobs relocated thirty-two miles south, to the village of West Willington, Connecticut, to set up the manufacture of miter boxes under the name of Jacobs Mitre Box Works (Figure 5). His miter box is known in at least two sizes: the 4-inch (Figure 2), which had a 14-inch long cast back rest, and the 5-inch (Figure 6),

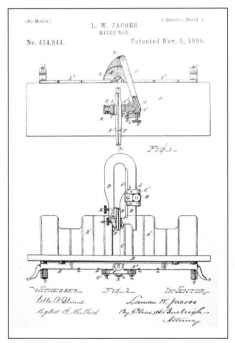
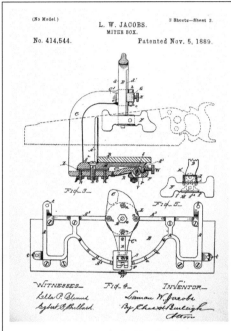

Figures 1a and 1 b (above). Luman W. Jacobs's November 5, 1889, patent for a miter box.

Figure 2 (below). A Luman W. Jacobs no. 4 miter box, circa 1890.

Figure 3 (above). Detail of Jacobs's no. 4 miter box showing how the depth of the cut is controlled by this backsaw sliding against the top of the saw supports.

Figure 4 (above, right). Detail of the miter box showing the wooden rear roller that prevented the saw from cutting too deep into the table.

Figure 5 (right). The underside of the no. 4 miter box table with "L.W. JACOBS. W. WIL." cast into it, identifying the maker and where it was made, West Willington, Connecticut.

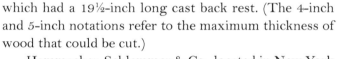

Figure 6 (above). The L.W. Jacobs no. 5 miter box.

Figure 7 (below, left). The first model of the Stanley no. 150 miter box (1), which is identical to the Jacobs no. 4 model.

Figure 8 (below, right). The underside of the Stanley 1 miter box. Compare it to the underside of the Jacobs model in Figure 5, above.

which had a 19½-inch long cast back rest. (The 4-inch and 5-inch notations refer to the maximum thickness of wood that could be cut.)

Hammacher, Schlemmer & Co., located in New York City, sold Jacobs's miter boxes in 1891, and listed them in its catalog for that year (September 1, 1891). The catalog touted the miter box, noting that "It could be instantly adjusted in the most perfect manner to any saw, keeping it perfectly straight and allowing it to move freely, unencumbered [sic] by weight or spring; is readily adjusted to saw at any required angle or for an undercut or draft on pattern work."[1] These miter boxes were also sold by William P. Walters & Sons, located in Philadelphia, Pennsylvania, and are shown in the Walters and Sons 1910 (no. 20) catalog.

I have found no references about the operations of the Jacobs Mitre Box Works, after 1910, but curiously

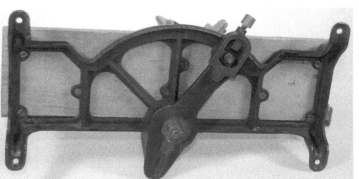

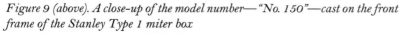

Figure 9 (above). A close-up of the model number— "No. 150"—cast on the front frame of the Stanley Type 1 miter box

Figure 10 (above, right). "MADE IN USA" cast on the rear yoke of the Stanley no. 150.

Figure 11 (right). A detail showing the length stop on the right corner of the table of the Stanley no. 150.

Figure 12 (bottom). Stanley's no. 150 Type 3 miter box with a Disston Keystone saw.

enough, Stanley introduced its no. 150 miter box (Type 1) in 1923 (Figure 7), which is without question the same design as the 4-inch-size Jacobs patented miter box. The no 150's frame casting is different, but essentially the same design remains, with minor changes. (Figure 8 shows the underside that can be compared with Figure 5.) There were other differences as well. Stanley cast the model number—"No. 150"—on the front frame (Figure 9) and cast "MADE IN USA," on the rear side of the saw yoke (Figure 10). The angle adjustment latch spring was changed from a leaf spring to a coil spring, and an adjustable length stop was added to the right side (Figure 11). The frame board was painted orange. I have found no records, however, describing the circumstances of how Luman W. Jacobs's miter box became part of Stanley's line.

With the next model 150 Stanley produced, 2, the

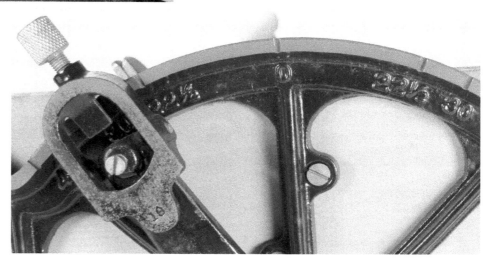

Figure 13 (left). A close-up of the top side of the no. 150 Type 4 showing the degree markings. Note the 22½.

Figure 14 (right). The underside of the front frame showing the degree markings.

company cast "STANLEY," in orange paint on the front side of the saw yoke and "MADE IN U.S.A." on the rest of the saw yoke. This model was kept in production until 1950, when Stanley again made changes. The 1950 version (Type 3) of Stanley's no. 150 miter box had both the model number and the company name cast on the top of the saw yoke; the "STANLEY," however was highlighted in orange (Figure 12). Where the "No. 150" had previously been cast on the frame, there were on the 3 a series of marks on both the top and bottom: "0" for 90 degrees, "22½" for eight sides, "30" for six sides, and "45" for four sides. Type 3 remained in production until 1962, at which time Stanley introduced 4 (Figures 13, 14, and 15), which had a new color scheme—blue japanning with yellow trim, instead of black japanning and a natural-finish frame board rather than the orange. The no. 150 series miter boxes were sold without a saw, but many are seen with a Disston Keystone K1 backsaw in the 3-x-12-inch length size (see Figure 12).

Figure 15. A detail of the Stanley no. 150 Type 4 showing the casting of the company name and model on the top of the yoke.

Stanley discontinued the no. 150 miter box in 1969.

Notes

1. Hammacher, Schlemmer & Co. Catalog, (September 1, 1891): 24.

Stanley's Adjustable Cabinetmaker's Rabbet Planes

The Stanley Rule & Level Company by 1897 was moving ahead and expanding its plane line with new models for special purposes, including a line of cabinetmaker's rabbet planes. Developed by Stanley in the late 1890s, the planes were designated nos. 90, 92, 93, and 94 and were meant for use by craftsmen where extreme accuracy in rabbet cuts was desired. These planes utilized Justus A. Traut's August 3, 1897, design patent for the "Hand-y" feature on the side of the plane (Figure 1) and his patent for a cutter adjustment mechanism (Figure 2). Although the application of the cutter adjustment patent was filed on December 10, 1897, the patent was not granted until March 13, 1900. It was used by Stanley on a variety of planes as well as its rabbet planes series.

The first of the cabinetmaker's rabbet plane series to be advertised to the trade, in 1898, was the no. 90, a bull-nose variety (Figure 3). With its stubby shape, the plane could be worked close in tight spots. One inch wide and 4 inches long, it was completely adjustable and had an adjustable throat to control the thickness of the shaving. The adjustment of the throat was achieved by making the top portion of the plane, including the "pony tail," a separate casting. This casting had an adjustment screw hidden on its underside to control the throat opening by seating against the screw, which held the casting to the plane body (Figure 4). By removing the top casting, the plane could also be used as a chisel plane. The first models have "8-3-1897," a reference to the "Hand-y" feature design patent, and "3-13-1900," the date of Traut's

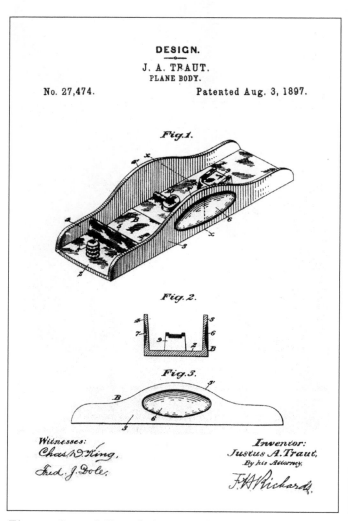

Figure 1. Justus A. Traut design patent for the "Hand-y" feature.

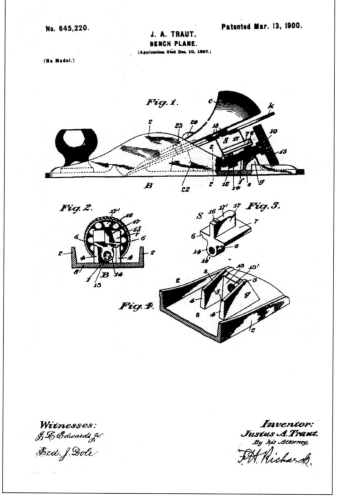

Figure 2. Justus A. Traut's patent for blade adjustment.

Figure 3 (left). The first model of the Stanley no. 90.

Figure 4 (below). The top portion of the Stanley no. 90, including the "pony tail," was a separate casting, with an adjustment screw hidden on the underside of the casting to control the throat opening. With the top casting removed, the plane could be used as a chisel.

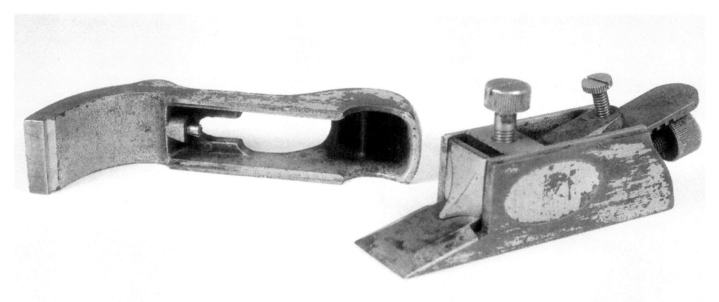

blade adjustment patent, marked on the blade. The planes were nickel-plated with "STANLEY" stamped on the rear cutter adjustment screw in a circle.

In 1902, Stanley added three more cabinetmaker's rabbet planes to the line. These were the no. 92, with a ¾-inch cutter width; the no. 93, with a 1-inch cutter width; and the no. 94, with a 1¼-inch width (Figure 5). These three planes were longer than the no. 90, at 5½ inches, 6½ inches, and 7½ inches respectively. All were manufactured with the sides and bottom square with each other, and they could be used right or left. They were nickel-plated and had the "Hand-y" feature on the sides. The model numbers were cast in the front top facing the rear of the plane.

The first models of the nos. 92, 93, and 94 planes were marked with the two patent dates on the cutter and had an adjustment screw with "Stanley" cast into it (Figure 6) or were similar to the first model no. 90—which had the company name stamped into the adjustment screws.

Figure 5 (above). Examples of Stanley's cabinetmaker's rabbet planes, nos. 92, 93, and 94 (bottom to top). The 92 and 93 are the early models, which were introduced in 1902. The no. 94 is a later model.

Figure 6 (right). The nos. 92, 93, and 94 models had cast adjustment wheels marked "STANLEY."

Figure 7 (above). On the front nose of the early nos. 92, 93, and 94 models, there was a ¼-inch cast plate pinned to the top casting. Stanley discontinued the use of the pin when it changed to a cored casting in 1910.

Figure 8 (right). When Stanley changed to a cored casting, a steel disc was used to cover the cored nose casting. The disc was stamped with the Stanley "V" logo, which was in use from 1910–1920.

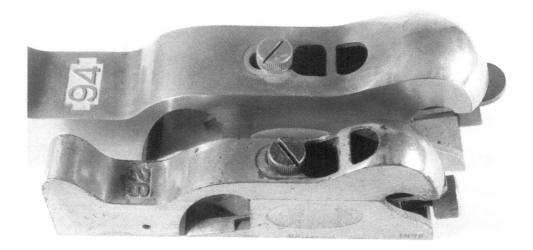

Figure 9 (right). In 1910, a bar was added to the top of the casting.

Figure 10 (above). In 1910, the cutter adjustment wheel had a knurled side and a smooth, unmarked face.

To reduce weight, the early versions of the nos. 92, 93, and 94 had top castings with a cavity or hollow front nose with no sole. A ¼-inch cast sole plate was fitted to the nose and pinned to the sides (Figure 7). The hollow nose also stabilized the casting, making it remain flat, which was essential to the proper operation of the plane.

Apparently, placing a sole by way of a separate operation onto the hollow front end was time consuming and/or expensive. In 1910, Stanley changed to a cored casting, which was cheaper to manufacture and worked just as well. With a cored casting—in this case, a sand core or mold— a hollow cavity was created. After the casting was cool, the sand was poured out of the hole in the front of the plane. This hole was subsequently hidden by the plug, a steel disc. This disc was stamped with the Stanley logo of the early 1900s, a triangular-shaped mark known as the "V" trademark (Figure 8). The "V" trademark was used from 1910 to 1920.

At the same time, all of the nos. 92, 93, and 94 planes had an additional cast bar added to the top casting (Figure

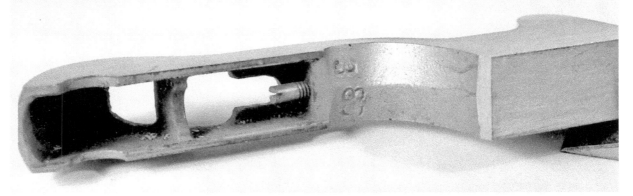

Figure 11. A casting number was placed on the underside of the top casting.

9). Some models made after 1910 exist with the cast model number on an orange painted background. (An example of the painted background is shown in Figure 18.) Starting in 1910, the cutter adjustment wheel was changed to a smooth face with knurled sides instead of cast sides (Figure 10). In 1920, Stanley began placing a casting number on the top casting under the neck on the top (Figure 11). Also, in 1920, the Stanley Rule & Level Company and Stanley Works, two separate companies started by two branches of the same family, merged. With the merger, the logo on the stamped disc on the front was changed to the Stanley Sweetheart (Figure 12). That logo was used on the planes until 1936 when it was changed to Stanley's cut label (Figure 13). All other features on the planes remained the same until 1942.

In 1937, Stanley introduced two medium-priced, cabinetmaker's bull-nose rabbet planes with nonadjustable throats and a one-piece body. These were numbered 90J and 90A.

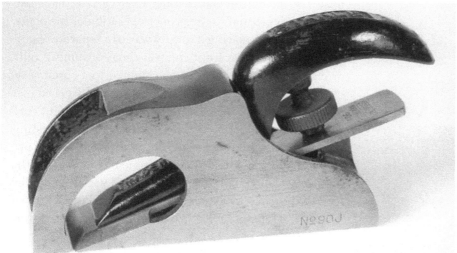

Figure 12 (above, left). The Stanley Sweetheart logo was used on the steel disc covering the cast hole beginning in 1920.

Figure 13 (above, right). In 1936, Stanley's logo, known as the cut label or rectangular notched logo, was stamped on the disc.

Figure 14 (above). An early form of the model no. 90J.

Figure 15 (right). The second form of the no. 90J is ¼-inch smaller than the earlier form. Although both this plane and that shown in Figure 14 were discontinued in 1943, this one was manufactured in England until recently.

Figure 16 (left). The no. 90A adjustable blade model cabinetmaker's bull-nose rabbet plane with its original box.

Figure 17 (right). The versions of Stanley nos. 90 and 92 cabinetmaker's rabbet planes produced during World War II. During the war, the finish on models 90, 92, and 93 was either a dull, aluminum-looking plate finish with copper-plated screws and cutter holder, as seen in the example of the no. 92 on the left, or a copper-plated model, such as the no. 90 example on the right.

Figure 18 (left). The Stanley no. 94 cabinetmaker's rabbet plane. The background framing the model number ("94") is painted orange.

The no. 90J (Figure 14) was a black japanned plane with polished sides and bottom made square to each other so that it could be used on its side. It had a 1⅛-inch cutter and existed in two side profiles. The earliest version is illustrated in Figure 14. It had a cyma curve, sloped on the rear, and was 4¼ inches in length. The second profile no. 90J is 4 inches in length, and it had the form shown in Figure 15. These planes were marked with "Stanley" and "Made in USA" cast into the "pony tail." They were discontinued in 1943, although the second profile type of the no. 90J was made in England until recently.

The other rabbet plane, the no. 90A, (Figure 16) was a nickel-plated, adjustable cutter version of the 90J. It was introduced in 1937 and manufactured with both of the no.

Figure 19 (left). The nos. 90 and 93 post-World War II planes.

Figure 20 (below). The British version of the no. 92 cabinetmaker's rabbet plane with its box.

90J side profiles. Likewise, this plane was discontinued in 1943. All the dimensions were the same as the no. 90J, including the 1¹/₈-inch cutter. The bull-nose design allowed these planes to plane close into corners. The 90J and the 90A with "Made in USA" cast into the "pony tails" are among the rarest of the Stanley planes.

During World War II, nickel was needed for the war effort, and Stanley changed the finish on model nos. 90, 92, and 93 to either one that was copper-plated or one that had a dull aluminum-looking plate finish with copper-plated screws and cutter holder (Figure 17). During the war, the largest size of the cabinetmaker's rabbet planes (the no. 94) was permanently discontinued (Figure 18).

After World War II, production of nos. 90, 92, and 93 continued but with two changes to the castings. The model number cast in the front top of the planes was reversed (readable looking at the front of the plane instead of from the rear), and the top casting looked like the pre-1910 models, with no bar in the "pony tail" (Figure 19). Manufacture of the no. 93 in the United States was discontinued in 1964, and U.S. manufacture of model nos. 90 and 92 stopped in 1975. The model nos. 90, 92, and 93 are now manufactured in Stanley's Sheffield, England, facility and are stamped on the cutter "Made in England" (Figure 20).

Stanley's cabinetmaker's rabbet planes remain, as they have in the past, the rabbet plane of choice by woodworkers. Stanley's adjustable cabinetmaker's rabbet planes were and are renowned for accuracy of cut and easy adjustment. They added depth to the Stanley line of fine woodworking tools.

Stanley's Odd-Jobs:
A Tool of Many Uses

George F. Hall, of Long Beach, Monmouth County, New Jersey, invented an attachment for the common 1-inch wide, four-fold, 2-foot carpenter's rule that enabled the user to do multiple tasks. The application he filed for his invention with the United States Patent Office on May 7, 1886, was titled "T-Square and Gage Attachment for Rules."

A few months later, *Iron Age Magazine* (October 7, 1886) described Hall's new invention as an "adjustable rule attachment" and went on to say that "this is designed for use of the carpenter, cabinet-maker, coach and car builder as well as for other mechanics who have occasion to draw lines and construct angles."[1] The article also noted that the firm of Herring & Sweasy of 70-72 Reade Street, New York, was placing it on the market. Apparently, Hall was marketing his invention before he had received the patent. Eight months after filing, Hall received

his patent on January 25, 1877, which was assigned number 356,533 (Figure 1). The description of his patent stated that:

> The object of my invention is to provide an attachment for rules of that class used by carpenters and other workmen, whereby a miter or angle of forty-five degrees can be conveniently obtained or formed; to provide means whereby a try square is obtained, and which shall obviate the employment of a separate or independent square of the usual well known class, and which shall admit of the adjustment of the rule to different lengths, and to provide the attachment with an adjustable gage.
>
> A further object of my present invention is to provide an improved attachment for rules which can be very compactly folded, so that it can be very conveniently and readily carried by the workman in his pocket or packed for storage, and which shall furthermore be simple and durable in construction, thoroughly designed, and cheap and inexpensive of manufacture.

Figures 2 and 3 show the front and back side of Hall's rule attachment, which is stamped

Figure 1 (above). George R. Hall's patent (no. 356,533, January 25, 1877) for a "T-Square and Gage Attachment for Rules."

Figures 2 and 3 (right). Examples of the patent. Figure 2 (near right), the front; Figure 3 (far right), the back, which is imprinted "PAT AP'D FOR.".

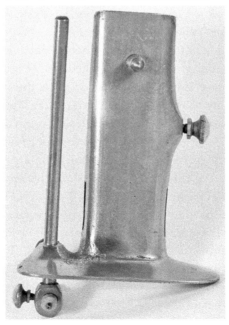

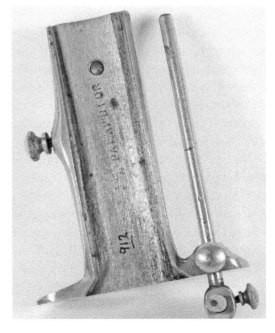

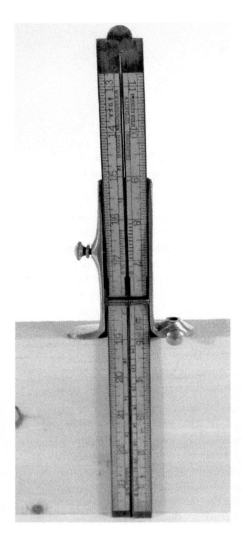

Figure 4 (left). The Odd-Jobs tool set up as a try-square.

Figure 5 (right). The Odd-Jobs tool set up as a miter square.

Figure 6 (below). The miter square set up.

"Pat AP'd For" in the rear channel. (I refer to this tool as Type 1.) When attached to a boxwood rule (Figure 4), it could be used as a try square or a marking gauge, which could be set by the rule end. Either a pencil or the supplied point was used in the sliding holder. When the holder was removed and a rule fold inserted, a miter square was produced (Figure 5). When the holder was extended and the point was screwed into the face side, circles could be scribed from seven to fourteen inches in diameter (Figure 6). Type 1 tools were manufactured from May 1886 to mid-1887.[2]

In late 1887 or early 1888, Hall moved to Newark, New Jersey. It is not clear who first manufactured this early model, but it is the author's opinion that Herring & Sweasy were hardware merchants and that the Stanley Rule & Level Co. appreciated the novelty of Hall's innovation and worked out a deal with Hall to manufacture the tool. This arrangement only lasted for a short time because Hall apparently became employed by Stanley, and together with Justus A. Traut, he redesigned the rule attachment and Stanley named it "Odd-Jobs No. 1" (Type 2).

Stanley applied for a patent for the redesigned Odd-Jobs invention on April 26, 1888. Within five months, the invention was approved and a patent was granted on September 18, 1888, as no. 389,647 (Figure 7).

The first redesigned model Odd-Jobs had a miter square incorporated into the top of the casting, similar to a pitched roof (Figure 8). The face side had a stippled decoration with the words "Stanley Odd-Jobs" cast in raised letters and "Pat. Jan 28, 87." Another new feature of the redesign was a level. The level vial contained what appeared to be a green colored liquid, but the color actually came from a green paper beneath the vial. With this redesign, the multi-use tool was made even more practical. This model had the patent date of January 25, 1887, on the face, but Stanley probably had been manufacturing it before the patent for the redesigned joint was granted. Type 2 was manufactured only in mid-1887. In Figure 9, a Stanley advertisement shows the various uses of the Type 2.

The main casting of the Odd-Jobs Type 3, which was manufactured from mid-1887 through 1895, was similar

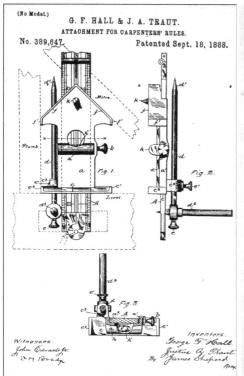

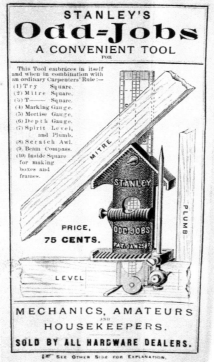

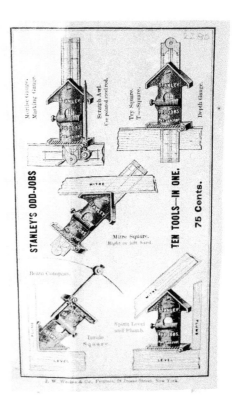

to the Type 2 model except that "No. 1" was added above "Stanley" on the face side (Figure 10.)

Up to this point, all Odd-Jobs models were not sold with a rule. A 2-foot, four-fold, 1-inch boxwood rule could be purchased as an attachment to the tool. In 1896, Stanley began including a maple, 12-inch rule to fit the Odd-Jobs (Type 4). The rule became part of the tool, expanding what could be done with the Odd-Jobs tool (Figure 11). The rule had vertical numbering with a scriber point set in it with a slotted, knurled capstan screw threaded into the scriber point (Figure 12) at the 12-inch mark. It did not have the Stanley name on the rule. The main casting, on the back side in the rule groove, had an "S" and "Pat Sept 18, 88" cast into the groove, beneath where the rule would fit (Figure 13).[3] The Odd-Jobs Type 4 was manufactured for only a short time because the way the scriber point on the rule was secured did not allow the point to be adjusted up or down.

Because of this deficiency, in 1897 or 1898 Stanley redesigned how the scriber point was fastened to the tool (Figure 14). In the new design (Type 5), the capstan screw

Figure 7 (above, left). Justus Traut and George Hall's patent no. 389,647 of September 18, 1888.

Figure 8 (above, center). A Stanley advertisement for the Type 2 Odd-Jobs tool.

Figure 9 (above, right). A Stanley advertisement for the Odd-Jobs tool ad showing the various uses of the tool.

Figure 10 (right). The Stanley Odd-Jobs (Type 3), front side. The tool is shown with a ruler, but it was not sold with one.

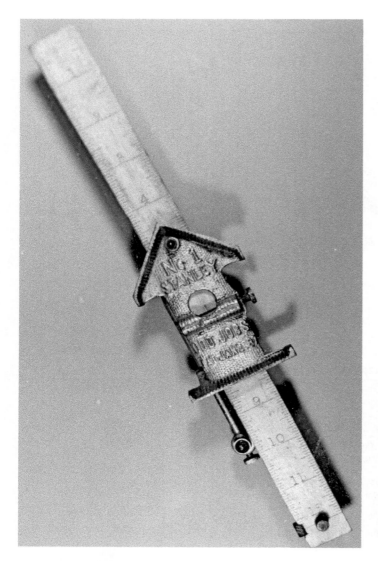

Figure 11 (left). The Stanley Odd-Jobs tool (Type 4). This version of the tool was sold with a ruler.

Figure 12 (above). A detail of the ruler end. Note the vertical numbering and the scriber point.

Figure 13 (below). The back of the Odd-Jobs tool in Figure 11. Note the patent date and the "S" mark and "Pat Sept 18, 88."

was no longer threaded into the scriber point but rather into the wooden ruler, which then could be seated onto the side of the scriber point. At this time, Stanley also redesigned the main casting (Figure 15). The nickel-plated main body had raised letters saying "Stanley No. 1 Odd-Jobs" above the level and "Pat'd Jan 25, 87" and "Sept 18, 88" below the level. The level vial still had the green-colored paper beneath it.

The scriber point, now shorter, did not have the pencil holder but a scriber point and a screwdriver. The screwdriver was for adjusting the scriber point at the top of the main casting (Figure 16). The rule was still graduated vertically, but Stanley's name was not marked on it.

In 1899, Stanley began manufacturing Odd-Jobs Type 6. They were manufactured with the "B" cast mark shown above the scriber point (Figure 17). With Type 6, the colored paper beneath the level vial was gone, and the liquid appeared clear. Also, the Type 6 screws were not slotted. Stanley also found that the arrangement of the scriber on the wood ruler was inadequate. Due to

tightening the screw against the scribe point, the wood rule would split. To solve this problem, Stanley engineers eliminated the capstan screw and simply placed a saw kerf (Figure 18) length-wise down the center of the rule one inch. This created a friction hold onto the scriber point, which could then be adjusted.

Later, in 1899, Stanley's Odd-Jobs Type 7 (Figure 19) changed the numbers and graduations on the 12-inch rule to a horizontal read. The "B" casting was eliminated, but trace marks showed where the "B" mark had been located (Figure 20). The level vial in the Type 7 had a line etched in the center of the vial.

In 1903 Stanley began placing its three-line logo on the Odd-Jobs rule (Figure 21), and it remained on the Type 8 rule through 1920 (Figure 22).

In 1920, with the merger of the Stanley Rule & Level Co. and the Stanley Works, the logo on the Odd-Jobs (Type 9) was changed to the "Sweetheart" logo on the maple rule end (Figures 23 and 24).

CONTINUED PAGE 46

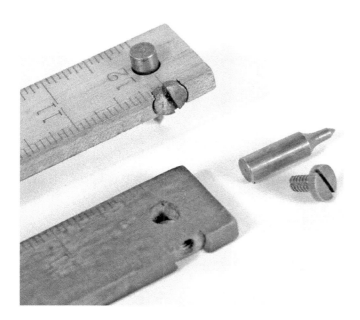

Figure 14 (above). Two examples of the redesigned rule end of the Type 5 Odd-Jobs tool showing the new scriber point attachment work.

Figure 15 (right). The Stanley Type 5 Odd-Jobs with its original box.

Figure 16 (left). The rear side of the Type 5 with the ruler removed.

Figure 17 (right). The back side of the Stanley Odd-Jobs Type 6 revealing the "B" mark.

Figure 18 (below). A close-up of the Type 6 rule end. Note the kerf and scriber point.

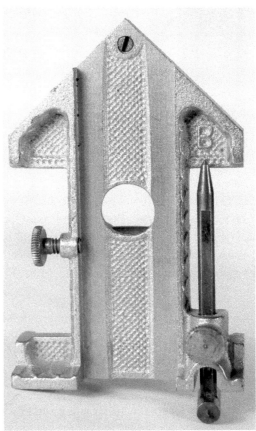

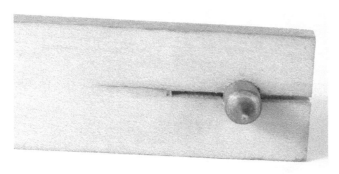

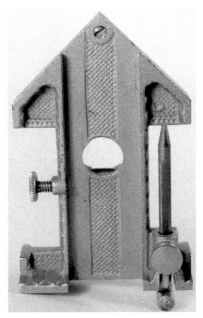

Figure 19 (left). Stanley Odd-Jobs Type 7.

Figure 20 (above). The rear side of the Type 7. Note the trace marks where the "B" mark had been.

Figure 21 (right, top). The three-line Stanley logo on the Odd-Jobs Type 8 rule.

Figure 22 (near right). The Odd-Jobs Type 8.

Figure 23 (far right). The Odd-Jobs Type 9.

Figure 24 (right, bottom). The Sweetheart logo on the Type 9.

Figure 25 (below). A modern reproduction of the Odd-Jobs.

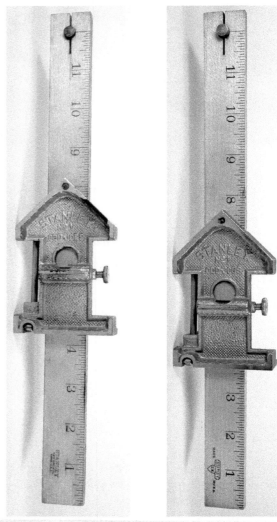

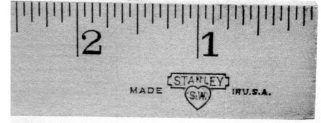

The Odd-Jobs tool remained a multi-use tool until 1935, when it was discontinued. Stanley had manufactured the various types of the Odd-Jobs, wonderful and interesting multi-use tool, for forty-eight years. Another version is now being reproduced by a different manufacturer (Figure 25).

Notes

1. *Iron Age Magazine* 38, no. 15. (October 7, 1886): 29.
2. The Odd-Jobs in this article have been "typed" according to the latest research by the author. Previous type studies of the Odd-Jobs, by the author, are obsolete. This article presents an additional type.
3. "S" and "B" casting marks are generally thought to denote the foundry where the main casting was poured.

The Development of Stanley Zig-Zag Rules

Stanley Tools started in October 1854, as A. Stanley and Company, doing business out of New Britain, Connecticut. At that time, folding rules were its only product. In 1858, A. Stanley and Company merged with Hall and Knapp, another hardware firm, to form the Stanley Rule & Level Company. This "new" company continued to manufacture rules and, in the 1860s, began to diversify its tool line by adding planes and levels.

Boxwood and ivory folding rules were the only type of rules widely used throughout the late-nineteenth century. By the mid-1890s, Germany was making an edgewise folding rule of a different design (Figure 1). The German rule joint consisted of two plates, one of which had four slots on one plate, with two pair perpendicular to each other, and a pressed friction bar on the other plate, which acted like a spring. This bar went into the slots or recesses on the first plate. This was a total "friction joint." It did not contain a separate spring.

About 1898, Justus A. Traut, one of Stanley's inventors and contractors, saw a potential market for this new rule and called it to the attention of Stanley's management and president (Charles A. Mitchell) who, seeing and recognizing the need for continued growth of Stanley, acquired the American manufacturing rights from the German owners.[1] Thus, in March 1899, Stanley became the first United States company to make spring-joint rules (although the first rules had friction joints). Stanley immediately called the new rule the "Zig-Zag." Zig-Zag, and the initials ZZ, were registered as a trademark with the U.S. Patent Office on December 26, 1899 (nos. 33,953 and 33,954).[2] The Zig-Zag and ZZ trademarks had been in use since March 1899 (Figure 2).

The first Zig-Zag rules that Stanley produced had steel spring joints made the same way as the German joints described above. These rules also had, on the end sticks, a tip invented by Justus A. Traut on June 5, 1900 (no. 650,879) (see Figures 3 and 4). Later, these tips were changed to a half-round shape (Figure 5).

On August 18, 1900, Charles E. Ricker, an employee of Justus Traut, applied for a patent for a totally different joint for Zig-Zag rules. (At this time, Stanley was still using the contract system, where Stanley supplied the machinery, supplies and raw materials, and the contractor supplied the labor.) Ricker's patent was granted on March 12, 1901 (Figure 6), and is characterized by scallop-shaped, crimped

Figure 1 (above). A German folding rule showing the new joint—a friction joint—introduced in the mid-1980s.

Figure 2 (below). Stanley's Zig-Zag rule, with the ZZ trademark. This rule had a spring joint.

edges on the metal joint and D-shaped spurs punched into the plates to press into the wood sticks to prevent slippage (Figure 7). These joints were only manufactured for a very short time. Quickly, the joints were changed to a straight crimp on the sides, as shown in Figure 8.

By August 1900, Stanley was offering six Zig-Zag rules, nos. 02 through 08, in lengths of 2 to 8 feet and in metric/English with an M after the number (Figure 9).

Justus A. Traut, seeing he could improve these rules, filed a patent on May 20, 1901, for friction plates to be attached to the rules to save the marking (see Figures 10 and 11). This patent was granted on October 21, 1902 (no. 711,547).

Frank L. Traut, also working for Stanley Rule & Level Company, received a patent on November 11, 1902 (no. 713,255), for a rivet joint (see Figures 12 and 13).

CONTINUED PAGE 50

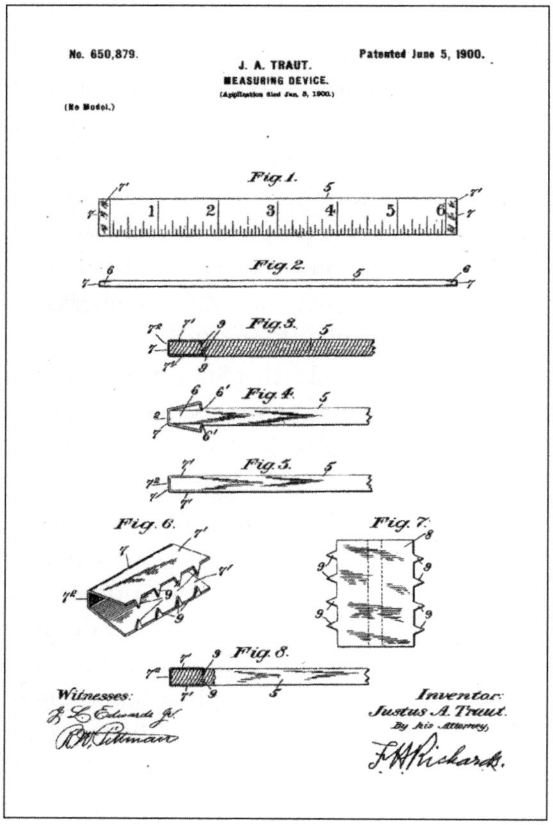

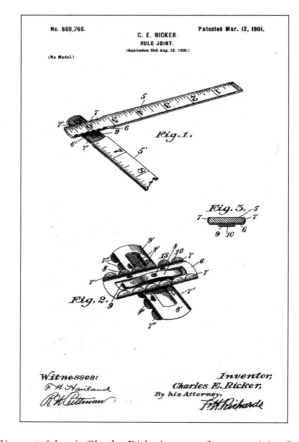

Figure 3 (above). The patent for Justus A. Traut's rule. Traut invented a tip for the end sticks.

Figure 4 (below, top). Detail of Traut's tip.

Figure 5 (below, bottom). Traut later designed a new, half-round tip.

Figure 6 (above). Charles Ricker's patent for a new joint for Zig-Zag rules.

Figure 7 (below). Ricker's joint has scallop-shaped, crimped edges and D-shaped spurs to prevent slippage.

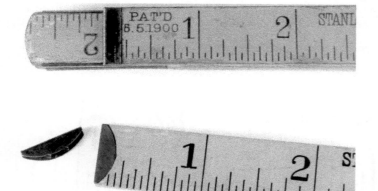

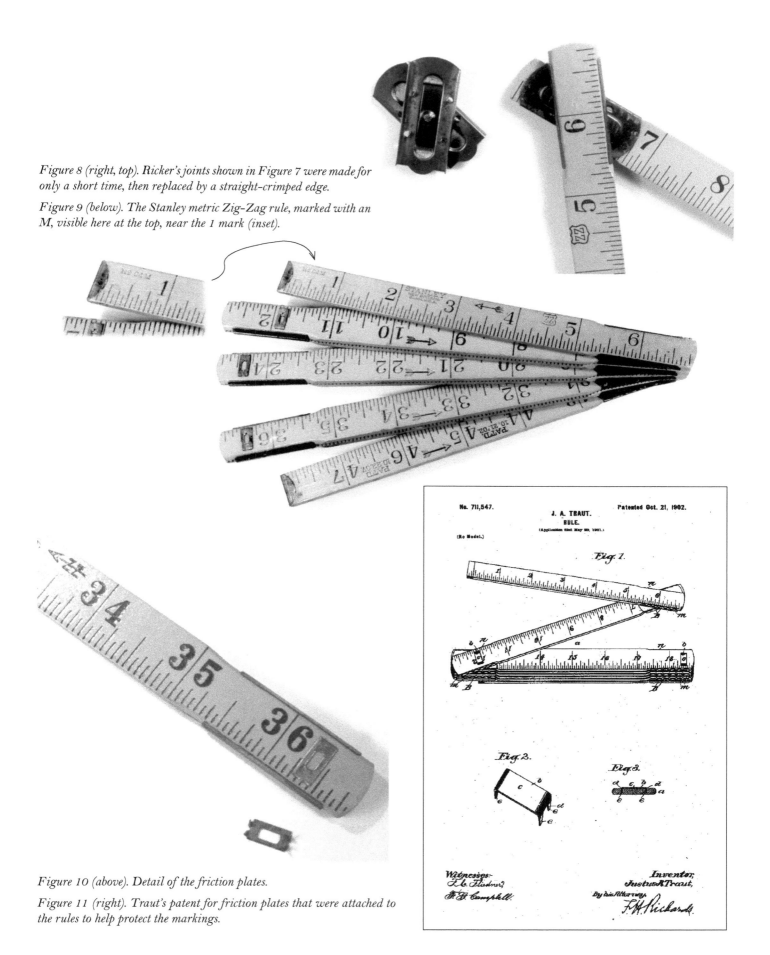

Figure 8 (right, top). Ricker's joints shown in Figure 7 were made for only a short time, then replaced by a straight-crimped edge.

Figure 9 (below). The Stanley metric Zig-Zag rule, marked with an M, visible here at the top, near the 1 mark (inset).

Figure 10 (above). Detail of the friction plates.

Figure 11 (right). Traut's patent for friction plates that were attached to the rules to help protect the markings.

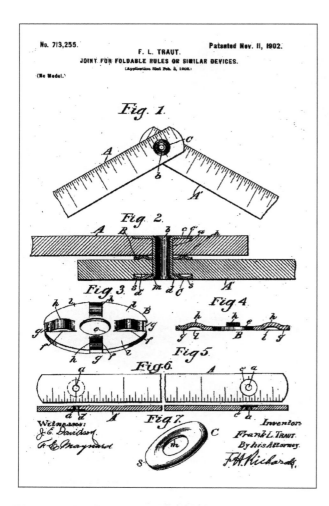

Figure 12. Frank Traut's patent for a rivet joint.

Figure 13. A Zig-Zag rule from the Victor line. It used Frank Traut's rivet joint.

This joint was used on a second quality line of Zig-Zag rules called the Victor rules. Since Stanley devoted a complete department for manufacturing these rules at very reasonable prices, it undoubtedly increased the demand and general use of folding rules. Figure 14 shows Frank Traut's 1902 rivet-joint patent with a later improvement (c. 1904). Justus and Frank Traut together obtained a patent on December 16, 1902 (no. 716,150), for a rule extension feature, which allowed the user to slide the end stick out for inside measurement (Figures 15 and 16).

Also, at the same period of time, Justus and Frank Traut were refining the rivet joint on Zig-Zag rules. Their patent, issued on July 21, 1903 (Figure 17), shows a reinforcing rivet joint with cleated plates that strengthened the rivet hole. The common problem on the earlier patent was that through use the rivet hole would elongate and cause the rule to lengthen when extended, making the measurement inaccurate. The features of this patent were to overcome and strengthen the wearing qualities of the joint and to make readability better by clear gradu-

ations on the rule stick at the joint. Actual examples of Zig-Zag rules with this joint have not been observed by the author, to date. Another feature of this patent was the use of protuberances, which interlocked into holes in the joint plates to keep an extended rule straight when open.

CONTINUED PAGE 52

Figure 14. Frank Traut's 1902 rivet-joint patent with later improvements.

Figure 15 (above). A Stanley Zig-Zag with Justus A. and Frank L. Traut's rule extension.

Figure 16 (below, left). Justus A. and Frank L. Traut's patent of December 16, 1902, for a rule extension.

Figure 17 (below, middle). Justus A. and Frank L. Traut's patent of July 21, 1903, for a rivet joint.

Figure 18 (below, right). Justus Traut's rivet-joint patent of July 1906.

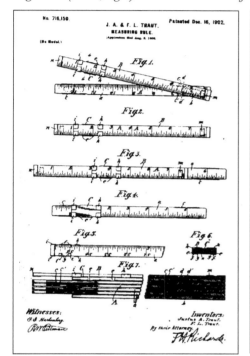

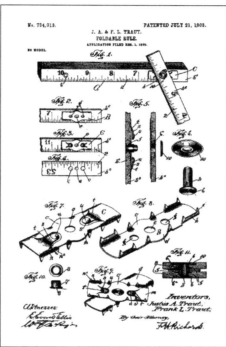

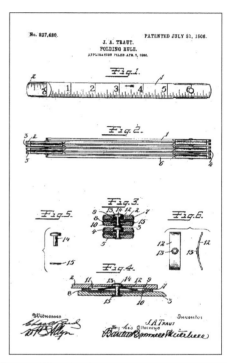

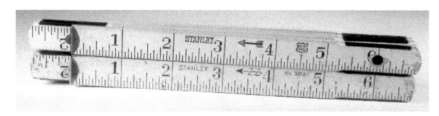

Figure 19 (above). Two rules showing the Stanley trademark and the Irvin Besse directional arrows.

Figure 20 (right). Irwin Besse's patent of October 22, 1907, which was for directional arrows on a rule to indicate the direction of the end of the rule from which a measurement had been taken

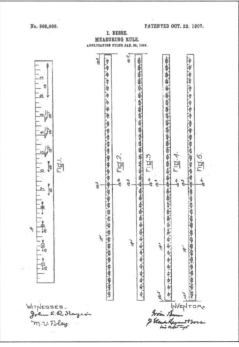

Another improvement to the rivet-spring joint was patented by Justus A. Traut on July 31, 1906 (no. 827,480). Called the basic rivet-joint patent, it was used by Stanley on all its later rivet-joint rules (Figure 18). These rivet joints had D spurs in the plates and were basically the same as the October 21, 1902, concealed-joint patent (Figure 11), except the rivet extended through the rule stick and the heads formed the strike plates for the rule. (Rivet-joint rules do not use strike plates; concealed-joint rules do.)

Zig-Zag Rule Symbols and Ball-Lock Spring Joints

The Stanley trademark consisting only of the "Stanley" name had been used on Zig-Zag rules since 1897. But, it wasn't until October 15, 1907, that a registered trademark (no. 29,747) was issued for it (Figure 19). Shortly thereafter, on October 22, 1907, Mr. Irvin Besse, of Newburyport, Massachusetts, was granted patent no. 868,905 for symbols or arrows painted on rules (Figure 20). Their purpose, he explained,

...is adapted to suggest by its indication of direction the end of the rule from which a measurement is taken in measuring from a given point...[3]

Besse must have been an employee of Stanley because this patent had been filed on January 29, 1904, and these directional arrows were shown on the rules fairly soon after in Stanley's 1905 catalog (no. 34). Both the now officially registered Stanley trademark and Besse's directional arrows can be seen in Figure 19.

Stanley continued to expand its Zig-Zag rule line by adding more models. In 1905,

Figure 21 (above). In 1907, Stanley introduced a 4-inch fold, narrow rule. Previous models had all been 6-inch fold models. At top is a white-enamel no. 603 model; on bottom is a yellow-enamel no. 302.

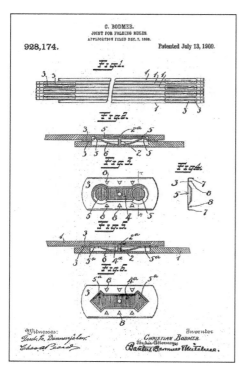

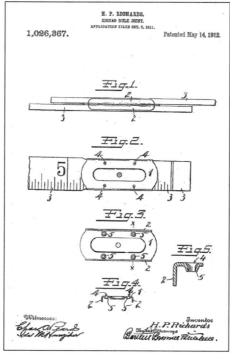

Figure 22 (far, left). Christian Bodmer's patent of July 13, 1909, for a ball-lock joint for a rule. Stanley still uses this feature in its rules.

Figure 23 (left). H. P. Richards's May 14, 1912, patent for eyelet spurs. The patent dealt with a quicker method of making the spurs.

Figure 24 (below). An example of the new spur.

new spur

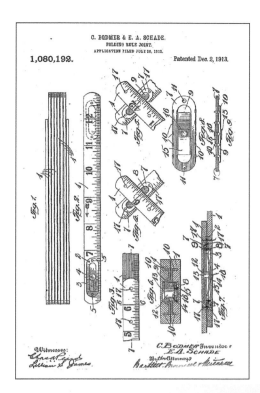

Figure 25 (left). C. Bodmer and E. A. Schade's patent of December 2, 1913, for a rule joint.

Figure 26 (below). Stanley offered four basic methods of marking its rules (top to bottom): Regular with the markings on the outside of the rule; Style T where the foot marking is larger than the inch marking; Style F with marking on the inside of the rule; and Style M with metric marking on one side and inch markings on the other.

Stanley offered twenty-eight different models including metric/English markings. All were 6-inch fold models.

Stanley introduced the 4-inch fold, narrow Zig-Zag rules in the 1907 (no. 34) catalog (Figure 21). The 4-inch fold size was obviously copied from the German rules. (German manufacturers were the first to use this size fold.) Offered in 2-, 3-, and 4-foot lengths, model nos. 302, 303, and 304 were yellow enamel, and nos. 602, 603, and 604 were white enamel.

The number of rules Stanley offered in the 1907 catalog had increased to thirty-six different models or sizes.

On July 13, 1909, Christian Bodmer of Stanley was granted a patent (no. 928,174) for the improvement of spring joints. This joint consisted of plates with recesses and tenons featuring a ball-lock device with a leaf-spring load (Figure 22). It's a feature still used on Stanley rules today. Hubert P. Richards of Stanley received a patent, no. 1,026,367, on May 14, 1912 (Figure 23), for a quicker method of making the spurs for holding the friction plates to the rule sticks. This consisted of four eyelet spurs (Figure 24) instead of the D-punch spurs (Figure 27, left side).

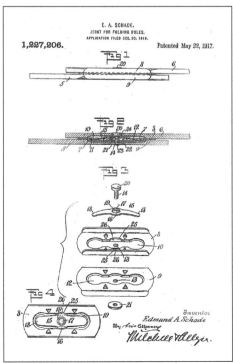

Figure 27 (above). In 1916 Edmund A. Schade reshaped Christian Bodmer's ball lock joint to help prevent it from stretching. On left is the older joint; at right is the improvement.

Figure 28 (right). Schade's patent for the joint improvement.

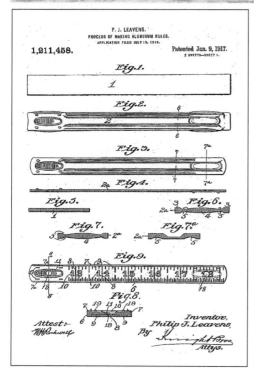

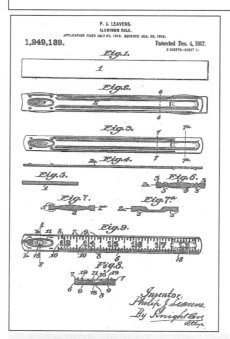

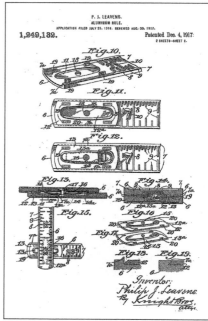

Figure 29 (above). The raised graduations and numerals on the aluminum Zig-Zag rule.

Figures 30a and 30b (left). P. J. Leavens patent of January 9, 1917, for the process of making aluminum rules.

Figures 31a and 31b (below). The patents shown in Figures 30a and 30b were granted to Leavens for the process of making aluminum rules. On December 4, 1917, the actual rule received patent no. 1,249,132.

Figure 32 (bottom). Examples of Leavens's style of Stanley aluminum Zig-Zag rules (model nos. 424, 425, and 426).

Christian Bodmer and Edmund A. Schade again combined their talents and received a patent (no. 1,080,192) on December 2, 1913, for another folding-rule joint. On this joint, the tenon-and-mortise plates did not wrap around the rule stick. This joint was attached to the rule stick through five pointed fastening tangs located on each side of the plates and pressed into the wood sticks (Figure 25).

By 1915, the Stanley Company offered 135 different rules with four basic styles of figuring: Regular, Style T, Style F, and Style M (Figure 26).[4] The Regular style was marked at 1, 2, 3, 4, etc. on the outside of the rule. Style T marked each foot with a larger figure than the inch mark. On Style F, the numbers commenced on the inside of the rule, allowing the rule to lie flat, and it marked each foot with 1F, 2F, 3F etc. Style M had regular English marking on one side and metric marking on the other side.

By 1916, Edmund A. Schade was working on an improvement on Christian

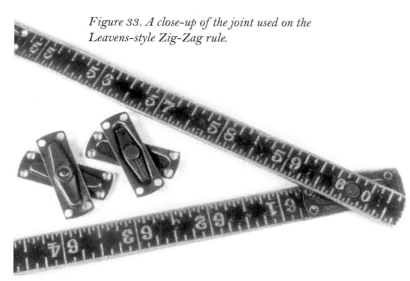

Figure 33. A close-up of the joint used on the Leavens-style Zig-Zag rule.

Bodmer's ball-lock joint of 1909. Schade found that if he reshaped the spring it would help prevent the rule joint from stretching. (Compare the springs in Figure 27; the earlier spring is on the left and the later one on the right.) He received a patent on this reshaped spring on May 22, 1917 (no. 1,227,206) (Figure 28). Unfortunately, this feature cannot be seen from outside the rule joint.

Meanwhile, another man with an inventive mind had worked out a new process for making rules by using aluminum strips that were subjected to a blanking die and finishing die, which produced a rule stick with the graduations and numerals raised above the rule surface (Figure 29). Patent no. 1,211,458 for the rule-manufacturing process was granted on January 9, 1917 (Figure 30a and 30b), and on December 4, 1917, patent no. 1,249,132 (Figure 31a and 31b) for the rule itself was granted. The inventor was a well-known New Jersey businessman, Philip J. Leavens of Bridgeton, who, in 1911, sold the Stanley Company his business of Jersey vises. Leavens later acquired the Gage Tool Company (April 1917); he then sold that business to Stanley in 1919. Sometime during the period of 1917 to 1919, Leavens sold his aluminum rule patents to Stanley. These rules, Stanley nos. 423 through 426, were offered by the Stanley Company as early as 1919 (Figure 32). Figure 33 illustrates a close-up of the joint used on Leavens-style rule. The Leavens aluminum Zig-Zag rules were manufactured by Stanley from 1919 to 1935.

New Models of the Zig-Zag Rules Following the Merger of the Stanley Companies

On May 1, 1920, the Stanley Rule & Level Co. and the Stanley Works merged, and with this merger new models of Zig-Zag rules emerged and a refinement of the rule line began. A new trademark was also instituted—a heart with the letters SW inscribed in it. The SW stood

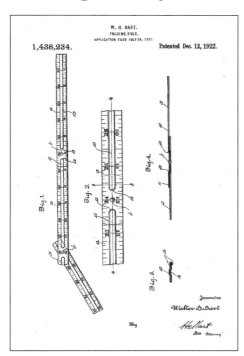

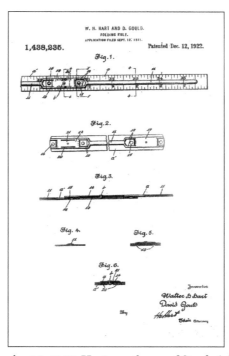

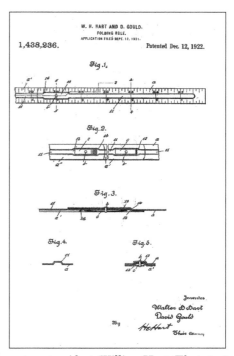

Figure 34 (left). Walter H. Hart's patent of December 12, 1922. Hart was the son of Stanley's long-term president, William Hart. The patent was for a rolled-aluminum rule.

Figures 35 and 36 (middle and right). Hart, along with David Gould, filed this patent, which concerned the same rule as the one in Figure 34, except this combined patent has a separate spring that fitted into the corrugated groove.

Figure 37. The rule patented on December 12, 1922, became Stanley's model no. 413.

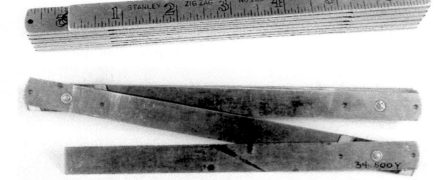

Figure 38. Stanley's model no. 126, a 6-foot rolled-aluminum Zig-Zag rule. This rule had still another type of joint.

Figure 39. This prototype of a rolled-aluminum Zig-Zag from the model shop is unmarked and is dated circa 1928.

for the Stanley Works; the heart commemorated William H. Hart, who had been president of the Stanley Works for over thirty years (1884–1916) and was much admired by everyone including the employees of the company. By 1919, the Stanley Company had already started to refine its Zig-Zag rule line and to eliminate similar styles. The number of different models of rules offered dropped from a high of 135 rules in 1915 to 113 rules in 1920. However, aluminum being lightweight, strong, and rustproof, as well as a new material for tools, continued to catch the eyes of the inventors and the public.

On July 28,1921, a Stanley employee, Walter H. Hart (the son of William H. Hart) filed a patent for a resilient rolled-aluminum rule with a stiffening corrugation extending length-wise through the rule and acting at the joints as a friction joint (Figure 34). On September 12,1921, Walter H. Hart and David Gould filed two combined patents (Figures 35 and 36) concerning this same rule but added a separate spring that fitted into the corrugated groove. A pivot rivet held the sections together forming a spring joint. The three

patents were granted on December 12, 1922. This rule, Stanley's no. 413 (Figure 37), had rolled markings on it.

Stanley, again, offered another aluminum Zig-Zag rule in its June 1929 catalog, a rolled-aluminum rule (model nos. 124, 125, 126). This rule had still another type of rivet joint with recessed plates. The patentee of this joint is still uncertain. These rules were only available up until 1939 (Figures 38 and 39). Henry S. Walter and Christian Bodmer of Stanley received a patent (no. 1,562,933, Figure 40) on November 24, 1925, for a hook, a finger-like attachment that was permanently attached to the end of the rule stick (Figure 41). This folded out and could be hooked over an edge for measuring something that was longer than arm's reach. Stanley offered hooks on at least sixteen different models in its 1927 catalog. By 1929, the popularity of this feature had dropped, and only eight models were available with the hook. From 1937 to 1941, only the nos. H808, H266, and H266F 6-foot rules still had this feature.

Stanley also produced in 1929 an aircraft gas gauge,

CONTINUED PAGE 59

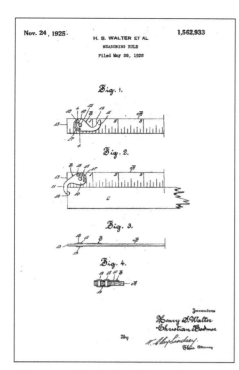

Figure 40 (left). Henry S. Walter's patent of November 24, 1925, for a finger-like attachment at the end of the rule stick. The hook made it easier to measure something longer than an arm's reach.

Figure 41 (right). Examples of rulers made from Walter's patent. On left is the H806, a yellow "Victor" rule; on right is the H106, a white ruler, circa 1929.

Figure 42 (below). Stanley's catalog 129 (2nd edition, 1929) included a special insert (catalog page 20A) showing an aircraft gas gauge.

Figure 43 (right, top). The Stanley aircraft gas gauge no. 184, circa 1929, was designed for measuring fuel in aircraft fuel tanks. Notice there is no metal end cap on the rule stick in order to prevent sparks when in use.

Figure 44 (right, bottom). A close-up of the gas gauge showing the side marking "STANLEY Aircraft."

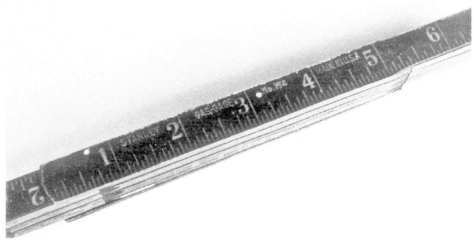

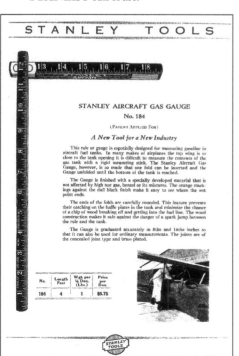

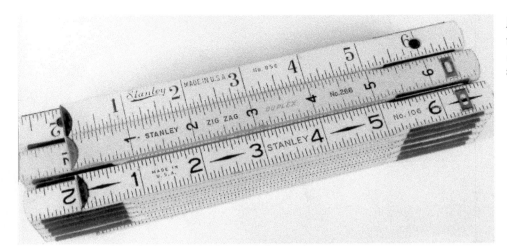

Figure 45 (left).Three rulers showing the various markings on Stanley's rulers of the 1930s. From top to bottom are the standard marking, the duplex, and the gothic.

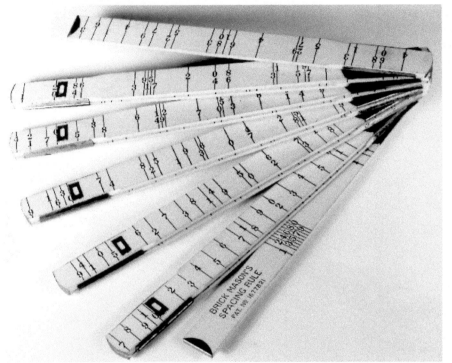

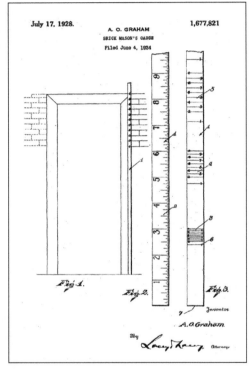

Figure 46 (above, left). Stanley's brick mason's rule (no. 267) showing the markings. Graham's patent for the rule is shown in Figure 47.

Figure 47 (above). Graham's patent for the brick mason's rule.

Figure 48 (left). Stanley engineer's rule. These rules were graduated in tenths and hundredths of a foot. On top is the "Victor" Zig-Zag no. 816, circa 1909, and below is the same model from circa 1930s.

CONTINUED FROM PAGE 56

model no. 184 (Figure 42), using E. A. Schade's patented ball-lock joint (patent no. 1,227,206; May 22, 1917) (Figure 43). This rule was marked "STANLEY Aircraft" on the side (Figure 44).

Stanley, up until 1930, used the four types of markings, except for special rules, discussed earlier in this series. During the 1930-1940 period, however, the marking styles changed (Figure 45). The "standard" marking was similar to the previously named "regular" marking. Two new markings were added. The "duplex" had vertical figures and graduations on all edges, so it would be easy to read in any position. The "gothic" had large, open figures horizontally and graduations on all edges.[5]

Another type of rule offered was a brick mason's spacing rule (Figure 46). This marking was patented (no. 1,677,821) on July 17, 1928, by Andrew O. Graham of Fort Worth, Texas (Figure 47). Stanley acquired the patent and started offering this type rule in the early 1930s as its model no. 167.

The engineer's rule, another Zig-Zag marking, was graduated in tenths and one-hundredths of feet and marketed as model nos. 814, 815, and 816. These rules were manufactured from about 1909 through the 1940s (Figure 48). Stanley also made metric and other interesting rules.

The Zig-Zag Rule Outside North America

The Stanley company was (and remains) the world's largest tool manufacturer. Its markets were not solely in the United States and Canada but were found throughout the world. To meet the demands of foreign countries, especially those countries using different units of measurement, Stanley manufactured rules specifically for those markets.

Folding rules made with metric measurements (two- and four-fold boxwood rules) were manufactured by Stanley as early as the 1860s. When Stanley began to manufacture Zig-Zag rules in 1899, it was only natural that the company should consider making metric models available. Stanley first offered in 1901 a metric Zig-Zag that had concealed joints and orange-enamel sticks. Designated model no. 04M, it was a basic model no. 04, an early Stanley Zig-Zag 4-foot rule, but with inches on the outside and metric measurements on the inside (Figures 49 and 50).

By 1902, Stanley had started manufacturing a Zig-Zag rule with white enamel, model no. 104. This rule was exactly like the no. 04 model except for the white-enamel color. Stanley then began offering these rules in metric measurement as no. 104M. By 1908, two more metric rules were added to the line. With these new rules the only difference from the older models was the use of the less expensive rivet joints instead of a concealed joint. The rivet, however, came through the surface, making it harder to read the scale. These 4-foot metric/English Zig-Zag rules were designated no. 404M for the yellow enamel and 504M for the white enamel.

By 1911, Stanley had expanded its metric/English line of rules to include four different length rules with both concealed joints and rivet joints, available in white or orange enamel. The orange-enamel, concealed-joint rules came in four sizes, 3-, 4-, 5-, and 6-foot lengths numbered

Figure 49 (above). The Stanley no. 04M Zig-Zag rule showing English marking.

Figure 50 (below). The same model ruler, 04M, showing the inside metric scale.

Figure 51 (top). Two Stanley orange-enamel, concealed-joint rules, no. 06M. The top rule shows the metric side, the bottom the English inches.

Figure 52 (above). Three Stanley rivet joint Zig- Zag rules. The no. 806E-M (top) is a 6-foot rule with the English scale visible. Stanley continued to make this model into the 1970s. The no. 804E-M (middle) is a 4-foot rule. At bottom is the inside metric scale of an 804E-M.

Figure 53 (below). The Stanley model no. 7022M-E, 4-inch fold with ⅝-inch wide sticks, circa 1920s.

03M, 04M, 05M, and 06M, respectively (Figure 51). Likewise, nos. 103M, 104M, 105M, and 106M, respectively, were for the concealed-joint white-enamel rules. Stanley made these same lengths (3-, 4-, 5-, and 6-foot) available with rivet-joint Zig-Zags. These were designated nos. 803M, 804M, 805M and 806M for the orange enamel and nos. 853M through 856M for the white-enamel (Figure 52). All

of these models were available through the 1920s and into the 1930s with some models, like the 806M (in later years labeled 806E-M), produced into the 1970s.

In 1919 and into the 1920s, Stanley made a series of metric only and metric/English rules with 4- inch folds in two widths. The all metric model, no. 313M, and the metric/English model, no. 311M, had ⁷⁄₁₆-inch-wide sticks (rather than the more commonly found ⅝-inch width) and were orange enamel. The 723M was 1 meter in length and metric on both sides. The 722M and 7022M-E, with metric/English scales, were orange with ⅝-inch width sticks (Figure 53).

No. 713M was 1 meter in length and had metric on both sides. No. 712M, a metric/English, orange Zig- Zag, had a long fold of 6½ inches with six sticks making up the rule (Figure 54). The regular Zig-Zag had 6-inch folds. This style Zig-Zag was also available in white enamel, numbered 763M for all metric and 762M for the metric/English version (Figure 55).

A 2-meter, metric/English Zig-Zag was also produced in both orange and white enamel. The orange-enamel no. 714M had twelve sticks and a 6½- inch fold (Figure 56). Likewise, the 764M 2-meter, white, metric/English rule also had a 6½-inch fold with twelve sticks (Figure 57). Both the 714M and the 764M were concealed-joint rules. For a short time in the early 1920s, Stanley offered a 2-meter rule, no. 764M-10, that had ten sticks with 8-inch folds and concealed joints (Figure 58). The no. 864M-10 was the same rule as the 764M-10, except that it had rivet joints instead of concealed joints (Figure 59).

Stanley also manufactured, in 1919 and through the 1920s, rules with metric, English, and Burgos scales. These rules were for use in California, Mexico, Central and South America, and other Spanish speaking countries.

During the period of the Spanish Empire (1513-1834), standard measuring systems were mandated many times for its provinces, including Mexico, but the local governments generally ignored the mandates, causing confusion and disruption in commercial trading. Uniformity began when Mexico and Spain adopted the metric system in 1867, but prior to that, linear measurements called Burgos were used. The standard for this length was kept in Burgos, Spain, and thus the name. One Burgos was equivalent to ¹⁵⁄₁₆ of an

CONTINUED PAGE 62

Figure 54 (top). Two Stanley no. 712M Zig-Zag rules with 6½-inch folds. The metric side is shown on the top rule and the English measure on bottom.

Figure 55 (above). The same 1-meter rule as shown in Figure 54 in the white-enamel version. The all metric rule (top) is the 763M. Below it are two examples of the no. 762M, one showing English measure and the other metric.

Figure 56 (below). Two examples of the Stanley no. 714M, a 2-meter, orange-enamel Zig-Zag rule. The rule on top shows the metric side and below it is the same model showing the English side.

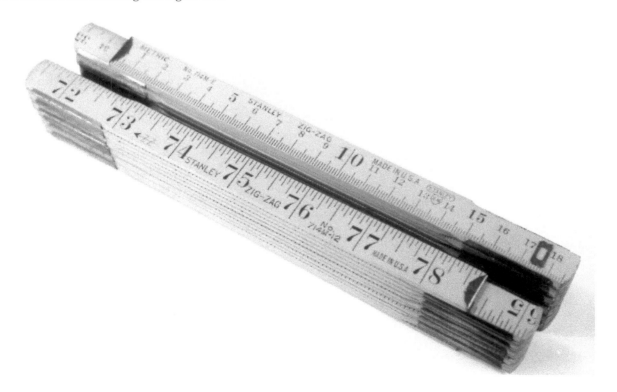

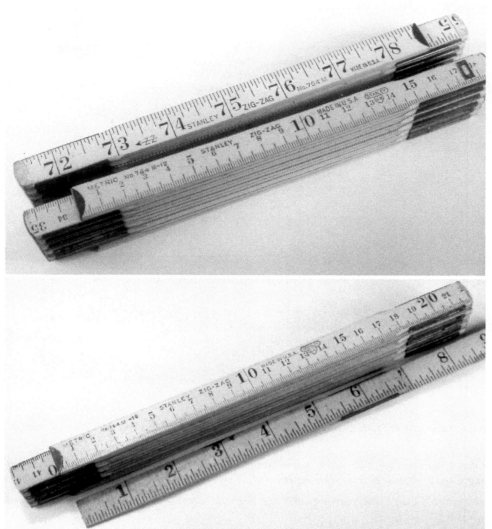

English inch.

The Spanish-speaking colonies, including Mexico and countries in Central and South America, used the Burgos system of measurement. California, which had been a part of Mexico from 1828 until 1846, when it declared itself an independent republic, (it gained statehood in 1850), also used this measurement. When the metric system was adopted by Spain and Mexico, it took years for people throughout these countries to change to the new system. Thus, Stanley manufactured a number of different models of Zig-Zag rules with three scales, English, metric, and Burgos, for that market.

In 1919, Stanley manufactured two metric/English/Burgos Zig-Zags with 4-inch folds. The no. 321M had ⅞₆-inch-width sticks, and the no. 721M (or MB-E) model had a ⅝-inch-wide stick that was 1 meter long (Figure 60). Stanley also made a Zig-Zag, known as 711M, that had 6-inch folds and was 1 meter in length. There was also model no. 734MB-E, an orange-enamel, 4-foot rule with metric/Burgos on one side and English measurement on the other side (Figure 61). Stanley continued to make Burgos rulers until 1950.

Another fascinating line of Zig-Zag rules that Stanley manufactured were the Cyrillic rules in Werschock and Sajen, pre-Revolutionary Russian (1917) units of measurement. According to *Webster's Unabridged Dictionary*, Sajen is a Russian measure of about seven English feet. For Sajen units, an English rule 7-feet long was divided into 100 parts, making each part approximately ⅞ inch. A 7-foot rule in Werschock units was divided into 48 equal parts, which is about 1¾ inches

Figure 57 (top). Stanley no. 764M Zig-Zag showing English measures on the top rule and metric on the bottom.

Figure 58 (above). Stanley no. 764M-10. This model had ten sticks and 8-inch folds.

Figure 59 (below). Stanley no. 864M-10 with rivet joints and 8-inch folds.

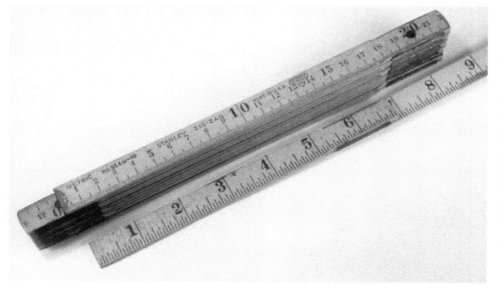

per segment.

The words Werschock and Sajen are archaic Cyrillic (Russian) words. These units of measure fell into disuse following the 1917 Revolution. This rule could be called a "transition" rule, as it shows the two old units of measures—Werschock and Sajen—the metric, and also the English measure. Most Russians today know only the metric system. However, individuals born before the Russian Revolution knew only the old measuring system, and individuals born after the Revolution would have been in a transition period. Russia officially changed from the old system to the metric system after 1917. The government set a timetable for the institution of the metric system, but the old measurements continued in use. Another deadline for conversion was set, as were penalties for not conforming, but it was another fifteen years before the changeover occurred around 1935 when the old Werschock and Sajen measurements were discontinued. Some people continued to use the measurement anyway, while the metric system was used by the younger people. The examples in Figures 62, 63, and 64 were probably exported between 1924-1935. They are both stamped with Stanley's well-known "sweetheart" logo (the letters SW inside a heart). The heart appearing under the notched rectangle (appearing between the 6 and 7 mark in Figure 64) was used beginning around 1924. The sweetheart logo was discontinued in 1935.

Stanley manufactured at least seven models of the Cyrillic Zig-Zags. Model nos. 790M and 791M were 42-inch long rules with Wer-

Figure 60 (top). Two examples of Stanley no. 721MB-E—metric/Burgos/English Zig-Zag with 4-inch folds. On the rule on top are the metric and Burgos units. The bottom rule is unfolded to show the English units of the same model rule. Burgos rules were used in Spanish-speaking countries.

Figure 61 (above). The no. 734MB-E metric/Burgos and English Zig-Zag rules with 6-inch folds.

Figure 62 (below). The Stanley 790M Cyrillic Zig-Zag that shows both the Werschock and Sajen scales. The rule is 42 inches with 7-inch folds.

Figure 63 (above). Stanley no. 790M Cyrillic Zig-Zag showing the metric/English side.

Figure 64 (below). Stanley no. 793M Cyrillic Zig-Zag with white enamel and 7½-inch folds.

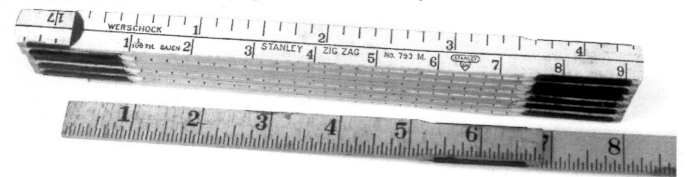

schock and Sajen measurements on the outside and metric/English on the inside. The 790M had orange-enamel (Figures 62 and 63). The 791M was white enamel. Nos. 792M and 793M (Figure 64) were 84-inch long rules with the Werschock/Sajen and metric/English scales. No. 792M was orange enamel, and the 793M was white enamel.

Stanley also manufactured two other Cyrillic Zig-Zag rules in 1-meter lengths, with the same configurations mentioned before. The 794M (Figures 65 and 66) was orange-enamel and no. 795M was white enamel. Also manufactured was a 2-meter length Zig- Zag in orange enamel, designated no. 798M with the same four scales, Werschock/Sajen and metric/English.

I have addressed here the type of Zig- Zag rules that Stanley manufactured in measurements other than the English inch. I did not, however, cover every model made because this treatise was not conceived to be a checklist of all models.

Notes

1. Robert K. Leavitt, "History of the Stanley Works," *Stanley World* (New Britain, Connecticut: The Stanley Works, 1951-1956), 74.
2. *Official Gazette*, vol. 89 (Washington: U.S. Patent Office, 1899): 2,652.
3. *Official Gazette*, vol. 130 (Washington: U.S. Patent Office, 1907): 2,202.
4. *Stanley Tools Catalog* no. 34 (New Britain, Connecticut: The Stanley Rule & Level Company, 1915), 16-17.
5. *Stanley Tools for Carpenters and Mechanics*, Catalog no. 34 (New Britain, Conn.: The Stanley Rule & Level Plant of the Stanley Works, January 1937), 16.

Figure 65 (above). The metric/English side of Stanley no. 794m Cyrillic Zig-Zag with orange enamel and 6½-inch folds.

Figure 66 (below). The same rule as shown in Figure 66 showing the Wershock and Sajen rules.

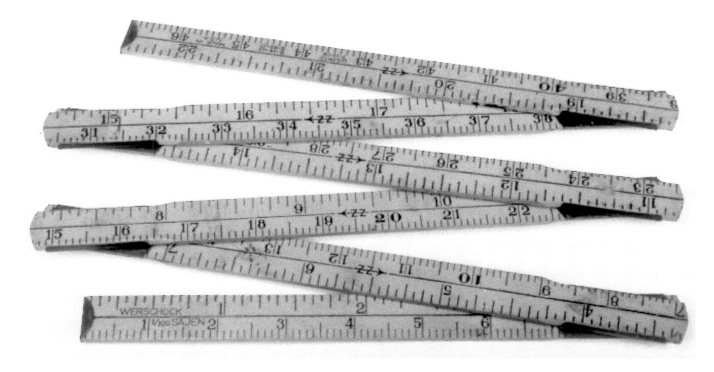

Figure 1 (above). A 3-foot rule, no. 403, advertising Timms, Cress & Co. As with other advertising rules of this time, it is marked with the company's name on both outside sticks.

Stanley Advertising Zig-Zag Rules, Their Variety and Types

Following the introduction of its trademarked Zig-Zag spring-joint rules in March 1899, Stanley began to expand its line of rules.[1] By 1906, Stanley began to offer advertising rules; the first advertisements were on the new rivet-joint rules. Figure 1 shows model no. 403, an orange enamel, 3-foot Zig-Zag made for Timms, Cress & Co. This rule used Justus Traut's basic rivet patent of July 31, 1906, as the patent number shown on it indicates, and it illustrated the typical way advertising rules were marked with the advertiser's name on both outside sticks.

Advertising rules were available in a variety of sizes. Figure 2 shows three rules, a 3-foot, a 4-foot, and a 5-foot

model (nos. 503, 504, and 505), in white enamel. The 3-foot rule (no. 503) is marked "J. W. Paxson Foundry Equipment, Co., Philadelphia" on both outside sticks in the same manner as the no. 403 (Figure 1). The 4-foot rule (no. 504) advertised "Cream City Sash & Door Co." and the 5-foot (no. 505) was marked "Dearborn Boiler Compounds." All these rivet rules had a very similar advertising makeup, with uppercase lettering in the same type face and placed in the same position. The only variance was with the rule itself, the model number, enamel color, and size of the printed advertising.

In 1907, the concealed-joint rules in orange enamel were available for advertising. These rules had patent

Figure 2 (right and detail below). Three different sizes (3-foot, 4-foot, and 5-foot) of the same model of Zig-Zag rules. The detail shows the companies' names: "J. W. Paxson Co., Foundry Equipment" on the 3-foot; "Cream City Sash & Door Co." on the 4-foot; and "Dearborn Boiler Compounds" on the 5-foot rule.

Figure 3 (left, top). A Stanley no. 03, 3-foot, orange-enamel rule marked "Compliments of Chapman Valve Mfg. Co."

Figure 4 (left, bottom). Three no. 04, 4-foot rules advertising a brick company and two carriage manufacturers.

dates of October 21, 1902, and October 22, 1907, marked on them and directional arrows on the sticks. Figure 3 shows a model no. 03, 3-foot rule with "Compliments of Chapman Valve Mfg. Co." marked on it in a manner similar to the rivet rules mentioned above. Figure 4 shows three no. 04, 4-foot, orange-enamel advertising rules with the same type of one-line advertisement. One is for a fire brick company, and the other two are for carriage makers.

While Stanley was offering metric rules only in the 4-foot length in 1907, they were available with advertising. All the rules illustrated up to this point had the same advertising line on both sides of the rule; however, the 04M metric rule, (Figures 5a and b) had advertising only on the English marked side. Figure 5a shows the side with the English marking and the advertising line, "Fred W. Wolf Co., Chicago, USA." Figure 5b shows the reverse side with the metric markings.

Another variation, illustrated in Figures 6a and b, show a no. 105, white-enamel Zig-Zag with the same patent dates as the rules in Figures 3, 4, and 5a and b. However, the advertising on this rule reads "Made For People Who Want The Best Sunshine Heaters." on one side, and "It is a Good Rule—To Always Buy Sunshine Heaters" on the reverse. Not only are the messages different on each side, but the advertising line is also printed in two type sizes and faces.

Figures 5a (right, top) and 5b (right, bottom). This no. 04m 4-foot rule has English markings on one side and metric on the other. The advertising appeared only on the side with the English markings.

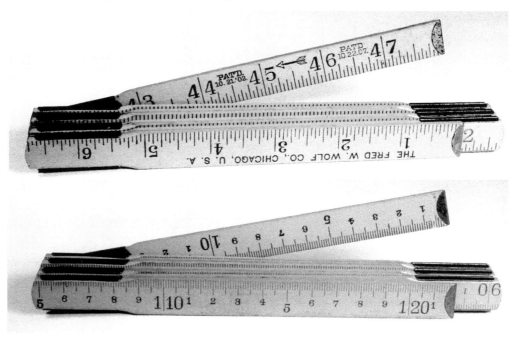

MADE FOR PEOPLE WHO WANT THE BEST SUNSHINE HEATERS.

IT IS A GOOD RULE—TO ALWAYS BUY SUNSHINE HEATERS.

Figures 6a and b (left). A Stanley no. 105 that shows a different advertising slogan on each side.

From 1908 to 1910, the advertising messages printed on the rules continued to be one-line inscriptions. Some were marked with just the company name and address (Figure 7). Others had the company, its address, and what it made, such as the model "U" injectors manufactured by the Desmond-Stephan Manufacturing Company of Urbana, Ohio (Figure 8). The no. 04 rule in Figure 9 has the descriptive, catchy slogan, "Use The Best-Berry Brothers' Varnishes."

One unique 3-foot, no. 103 Zig-Zag rule, has no advertising *per se*. Instead, the rule is a commemorative item imprinted with regular English markings on the front side and the menu for the New England Hardware Dealer's Association Annual Banquet on March 23, 1911, on the reverse (Figures 10a and b).

By 1912, 6-foot rules were being offered with a different set-up, single and double lines of advertising with two type sizes, such as the no. 106 rule illustrated in Figure 11. However, the normal advertising set-up throughout the 1910s and the early 1920s is the single-line message on both sides (Figure 12), except for the previously described metric rules, which only had the one line on the English marking side. The four-fold, 2-, 3-, and 4-foot rules also carried advertising, usually in one line. (Figure 13 illustrates a typical version.)

In 1927, Stanley made its 6-foot, model no. H106 Zig-Zag, the rule with H. S. Walter and Christian Bodmer's patented hook, available with advertising (Figure 14) in two sizes of type on two lines.

CONTINUED PAGE 70

THE CENTRAL CONNECTICUT BRICK CO., NEW BRITAIN, CONN.

"WELLER MANUFACTURING CO., CHICAGO."

THE STRONG-SCOTT M'F'G. CO., MINNEAPOLIS, MINN.

THE DESMOND-STEPHAN MFG. CO., URBANA, OHIO. MODEL "U" INJECTORS.

USE THE BEST.—BERRY BROTHERS' VARNISHES.

Figure 7. Examples of rules showing one-line advertising with name and address only.
Figure 8. This Stanley no. 404 advertises not only the company, but also its product.
Figure 9 (left). A catchy slogan was printed on this model no. 04.

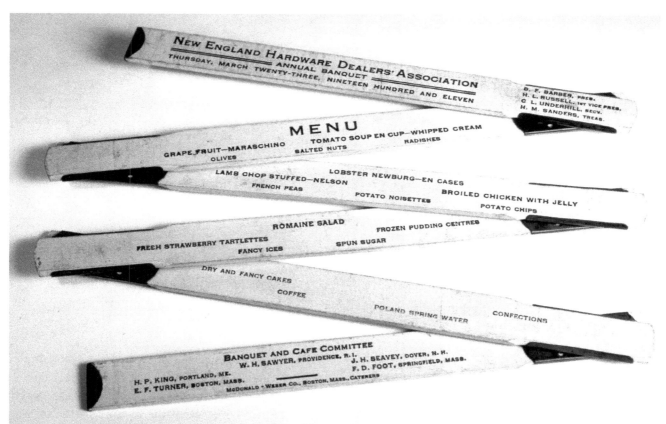

Figures 10a and b (left and above). The face side (at left) of a commemorative model no. 103 rule. This rule was made for the New England Hardware Association's annual banquet in 1911. Printed on the reverse side (above) is the menu for the banquet.

Figure 11 (left, top). This example shows a model no. 106 with single and double lines of advertising for the Nelson Company, a plumbing and heating supply company.

Figure 12 (left, bottom). These examples, including one for Hammacher Schlemmer & Co., are typical of the style of Stanley's advertising rules in the 1910s and early 1920s.

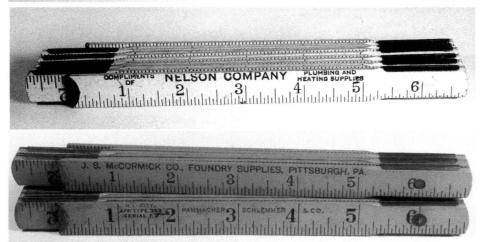

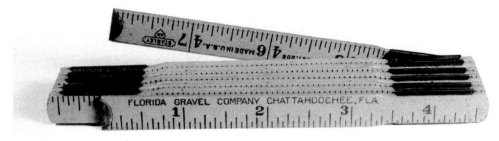

Figure 13 (right, top). A typical 4-foot rule from the 1910s and 1920s.

Figure 14 (right, bottom). The Walter and Bodmer hook patent Zig-Zag rule with two lines of advertising in two different type sizes.

By the 1930s, Stanley advertising rules were available in one- and two-line messages using one or two sizes of type in different color inks. Mint green, green, red, and black inks seem to have been most prevalent. Figure 15 shows the variety of colors and designs. Another style of advertising was also available in the 1930s on Stanley's brick mason's rule, model no. 167. The advertising message in this case is a single line of red print down the middle of the face stick with vertical numbers and the message printed between the inch graduations (Figure 16 a and b). In the late 1930s, Stanley's sales representatives for foreign markets even utilized the Zig-Zag

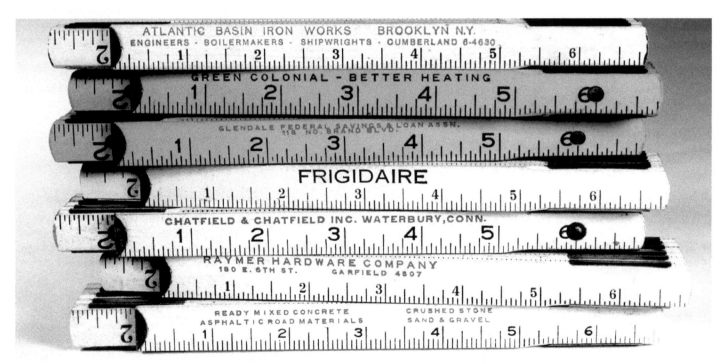

Figure 15. Stanley's Zig-Zag advertising rules made in the late 1920s and early 1930s showing a variety of sizes and print colors. The rule on top is mint-green ink on white enamel. The "Green Colonial—Better Heating" rule is appropriately printed in green ink on orange enamel, and the "Glendale Federal Savings & Loan" rule has red ink on orange enamel. The "Frigidaire" rule is black ink on white. The bottom three rules are all red ink on white enamel. Each shows a variation in the type set up—single line, double line with different type sizes, and double line using the same type.

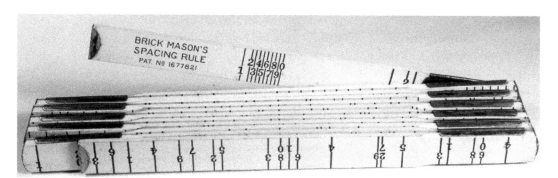

advertising rule as a business card with orange-enamel and green print. Figure 17 illustrates a metric/English no. 7012 M-E rule.

As the popularity of the tape measure grew, it became the preferred means of advertising. As a result advertising Zig-Zag rules began to decline. Ultimately, they became a thing of the past and another collector's item for the future.

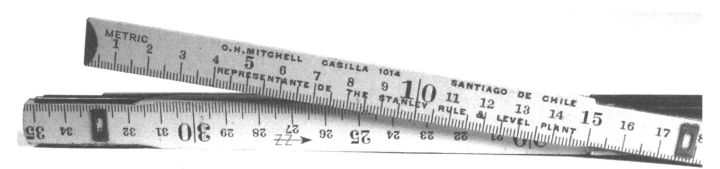

Figure 17. Stanley didn't forget its foreign clients. This metric ruler advertises a distributor for Stanley in Santiago, Chile. The ink is green on the orange-enamel rule.

Stanley Tapes Measure the World

The Stanley Company began making rules in 1850, when Augustus Stanley founded A. Stanley & Co. to manufacture boxwood and ivory rules. At this time in history, folding rules were the only type of rules in use. They continued to be manufactured well into the twentieth century.

In 1899 the Stanley Rule & Level Company began manufacturing a totally new style of rule that had been introduced in Germany a few years before. This rule, known as the Zig-Zag rule, gained large popularity between 1910 and 1935, with many styles being manufactured. However, the drawback of both of these types of rules was that they required two hands to open. The Zig-Zag was also somewhat bulky to carry.

With this overview, I will begin the story of a new rule, one that would ultimately become the tape measure as we know it today. It begins with Hiram A. Farrand, an engineer from Merchantville, N.J., a small town near Camden (Figure 1).

For years, many inventors dreamed of a rule that would be universal in its application—flexible for measuring curves and angles and rigid for measuring straight surfaces. Farrand was one of those inventors who dreamed of such a rule. He started working on this dream about 1902. It would take him twenty-five years to make it a reality. "I had to sweat and study and pore over volumes on metallurgy," he said, "as well as scrimp and save to purchase materials. Finally, I went to the bottom of things and set up a laboratory in my cellar. After digging into metallurgy, chemistry, and a variety of research, I succeeded in producing a rule which would perform as I had dreamed it would."[1]

Finally, on October 23, 1919, Hiram Farrand filed his first rule patent, no. 1,402,5899 (Figures 2a and b). He wrote in the application,

> [T]his invention relates to a measuring tape made of metallic ribbon curved to have a concavo-convex section and sufficiently flexible to permit of its being rolled or coiled. Its stiffness and resiliency being sufficient to cause it to remain in or return to a straight or unrolled condition when it is released or free to move.

The object of this invention was to provide a simple inexpensive holder for the reception of a coil of tape or concavo-convex rule which would permit it to be coiled up by the exertion of a force applied tangentially of the coil, the arrangement being such that the tape may be easily detached from the holder when desirable.

On January 3, 1922, Farrand received the patent he filed in 1919. Sometime between 1922 and December 1926, he relocated to Berlin, N.H. There Hiram experimented with and invented six arrangements for controlling resilient rules, filing patent applications from 1926 through 1929. All six received patents, but two were significant for their controlling devices.

Figure 1. Hiram A. Farrand.

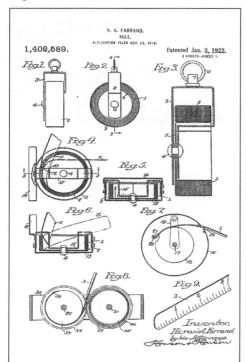

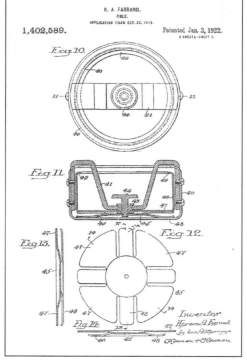

Figures 2 a and b. Farrand's first patent for a tape measure.

His patent (Figure 3) of March 31,1931, no. 1,799,044, was the basic patent for the case of his Model C medium-price line of tape rules (Figure 4). Farrand's patent of no. 1,799,094, also filed on March 31., 1931, was the basic patent for the case of his Model A rules, which were his top-of-the-line tapes (Figures 5a, b, c, d, and 6 a, b).

On October 21, 1926, Farrand filed patent no. 1,828,401 (Figure 7) for "increasing the strength and resiliency of the spring of which the rule is composed; for preventing corrosion; for producing color contrast thereon, for creating on the rule a reflecting and light diffusing surface by a metallic plating applied by the electroplating process." The metallic plating was either nickel or chromium, which presented a hard, wear-resistant surface capable of being highly polished. The patent had another important feature. Farrand succeeded in making the spring stronger by improving the process of marking the graduations on it. With this patent the marks were made on the spring with a non-conducting material before placing the spring in the electro-plating bath. The spring was stronger because before Farrand's invention, all concavo-convex rules had to be etched, which weakened the spring by removing metal at the etched locations. Farrand received this patent on October 20, 1931.

On December 18, 1931, Farrand sold his business to the Stanley Works. As the Stanley Works reported in *Tool Talk*, "Mr. Farrand was as anxious to successfully retire from business as Stanley was to increase its line of desirable and superior tools."[2] Mr. Farrand had good patents and had completed valuable development work; Stanley had the marketing and manufacturing experience and equipment to further develop the Flexible-Rigid rules.

The Stanley Works purchased everything that Farrand had concerning rules including machinery. However, they did not purchase the buildings. Stanley agreed to give a royalty on all patents for the life of the patent or until 1939, whichever came later, and Farrand agreed to give Stanley use of anything he invented relating to tape rules.

At the time of the acquisition Hiram Farrand had three different models and sixteen different rules in the line. A Model A72, 6-foot rule in brass is shown in Figure 8. Figure 9 illustrates a

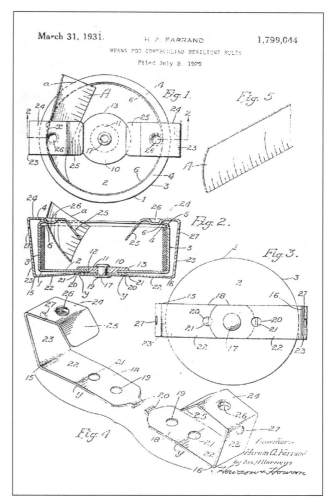

Figure 3. The patent for the basic case used in the Model C tape rule.

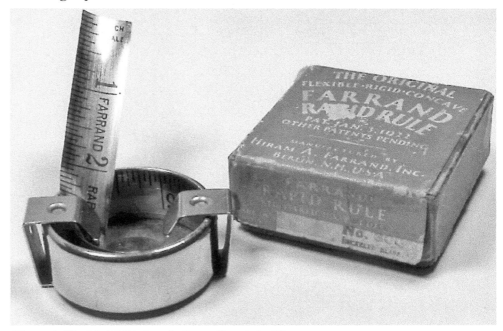

Figure 4. The Model C tape rule, the medium-priced line.

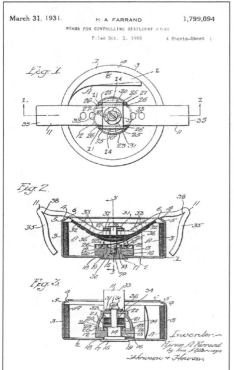

Figure 5a

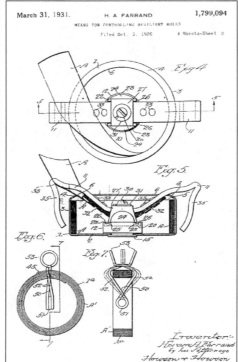

Figure 5b

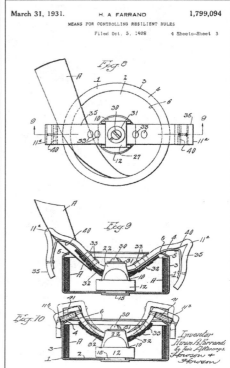

Figure 5c

Figures 5a, b, c, and d (below). The patent drawings for Farrand's basic patent for the case of his Model A rules, his top-of-the-line tapes, which are seen in Figures 6a and b.

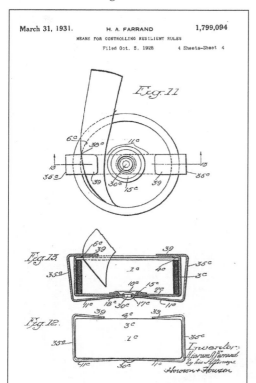

Figure 5d

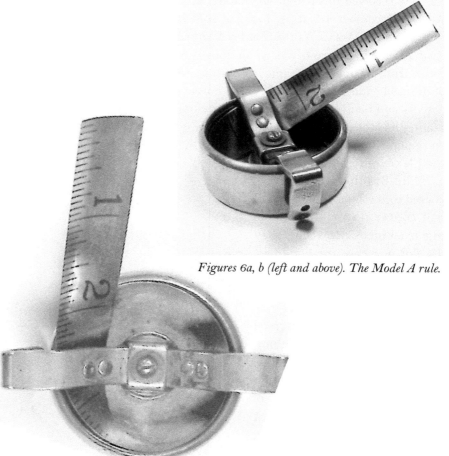

Figures 6a, b (left and above). The Model A rule.

Model A72 with a nickel-plated case. Farrand also manufactured metric tapes as shown in Figure 10, which is a A6M Double Meter tape with nickel blade. The A6MR was a 2-meter, rust-resistant metric rule.

The Model C line had a slightly cheaper case (see Figure 4). No. C72 was a 6-foot tape with a nickel blade. The Model C72R had a galvanized, rust-resistant blade. The Model C was also available with an 8-foot tape marked on both sides. This rule is known as Model C96.

The Model D line had the "Feather-weight" case. Figure 11 shows a no. D72 6-foot rule, which was invented by Farrand and filed with the Patent Office in 1932 (no. 1,994,339). The patent was granted in 1935 (Figure 12).

All of these rules were offered by Stanley beginning in January 1932 and were sold to 1938.

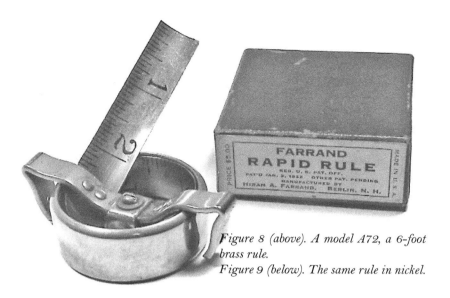

Figure 8 (above). A model A72, a 6-foot brass rule.
Figure 9 (below). The same rule in nickel.

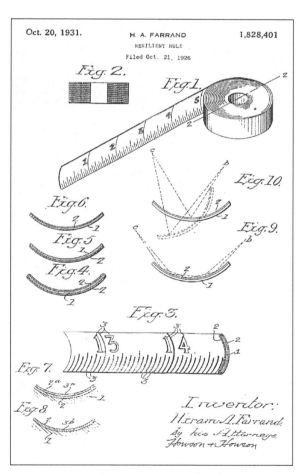

Figure 7. Farrand's patent that introduced a new method for making the marks on the tape. Previously they had been etched into the surface, which weakened the material. With Farrand's new patent, the marks were made on the spring with a non-conductive material before placing it in the electroplating bath.

Figure 10 (above). The A6M Double Meter tape with nickel blade.

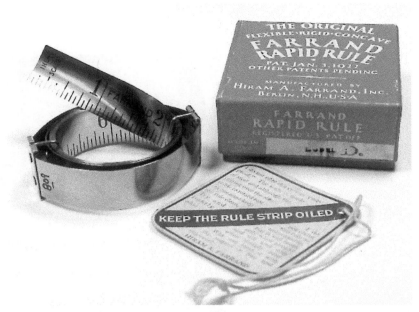

Figure 11. A 6-foot Model D with a Featherweight case.

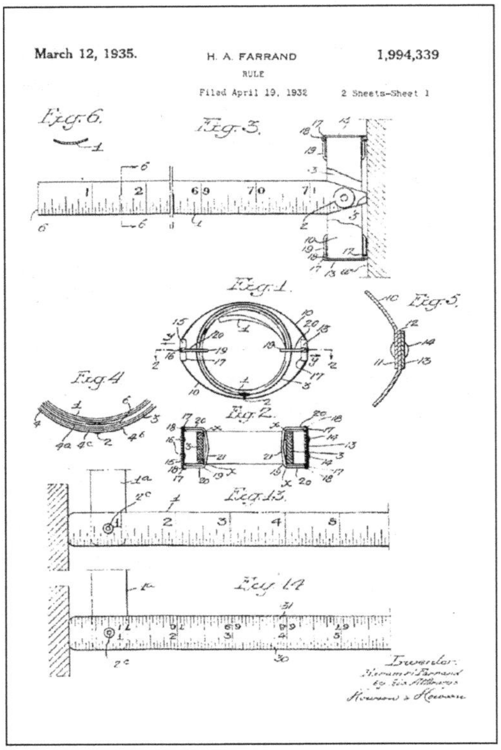

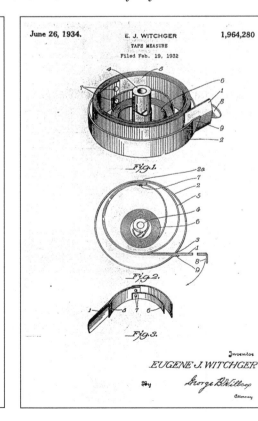

Figure 12. The patent for the Model D.

The Pull-Push Rules

Farrand's rules launched Stanley into the tape rule business. Initially, Stanley offered Farrand's line of rules, but at the same time, Stanley engineers had quickly developed a new line called Pull-Push rules.

The Pull-Push rules utilized three elements: Eugene Witchger's patent (no. 1,964,280, which had been assigned to the Lufkin Rule Company of Saginaw, Michigan), Farrand's concavo-convex spring or tape, and Fred Volz's

patent (no. 2,013,322, Figure 13) for a coilable measuring device including the case. Stanley and Lufkin made an agreement whereby Stanley paid Lufkin a royalty for use of Witchger's patent and, similarly, Lufkin paid Stanley a royalty for the use of Farrand's cross-curve blade patent.

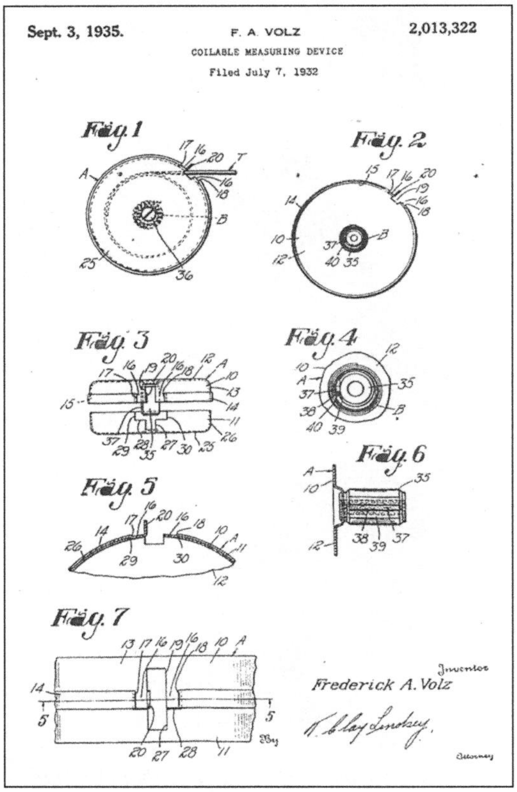

Figure 13 (far left). Volz's patent for a coilable measuring device.

Figure 14 (left). Witchger's patent that enabled the tape to retract. The patents were first used in the Four-Square Pull-Push rules (Figures 15 and 16).

It is believed that the companies had an understanding that no other company would be licensed by either firm.

Witchger's patent (Figure 14) was for an improvement in the drum, where a coil spring and a casing constituted a tape controller enabling the concavo-convex tape ribbon to retract into the drum. This was first used on the no. 1166 Four-Square Pull-Push rules (Figure 15). This model also was Stanley's first advertising tape rule, as illustrated in Figure 16. Notice the hook on the end of the tape, which was patented by Maxwell A. Coe, one of Stanley's inventors. He filed for this patent for abutment and hook on rules (Figure 17) in June 1932.

Frederick Volz's design (no. 1,983,202, February 10, 1933, Figure 18) provided a snap redraw when the rule was almost closed, keeping it closed, an improvement on his earlier patent (Figure 13). The winding mechanism (or spring winder) was attached to the tape rule inside the case. This was the major difference from Farrand's rule. Volz's tape rule could not be pulled entirely out of the case. The cases were made by a forming and blanking machine. They were stamped, blanked, and formed in one operation from either steel or brass sheets of a heavy uniform gauge. The blades were made by rolling steel through a precision rolling mill, which gradually reduced the thickness of the steel to five thousandths of an inch (.005). This was done by cold rolling, which extended the steel in length only. The .005-inch strip steel next went through a slitting machine, which sheared it to the desired width. The resulting sharp edges were then filed to a safe edge in a cleverly constructed filing machine. Next, the steel was tempered by a special controlled heat treatment that gave it "life" or spring. From there, the tape went into an oxidizing oven that gave it a dark blue finish. The tape went through a series of inspections for finish, straightness, width, and thickness, and samples of each coil were sent to the laboratory for hardness and bend testing for temper.

Next, the coils of steel were cut to length, cleaned, and curved in a rolling machine to the concavo-convex shape. The blades were cleaned again, and printed on a highly developed printing machine, using accurate steel printing dies and special solvent-resisting baking ink. Each blade then was placed into metal tubes and baked in an electric oven to dry and toughen the ink.

Figure 15 (above). Stanley no. 1166: Four-Square Pull-Push tape rule.

Figure 16 (below). Stanley no. 1166: Four-Square advertising tape rule. The hook on the end of the tape was patented by Maxwell A. Coe.

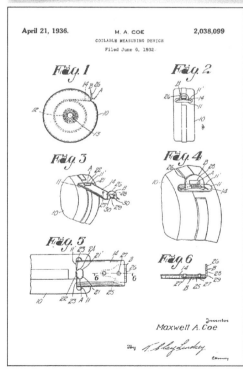

Figure 17. Coe's patent for abutment and hook on a tape rule.

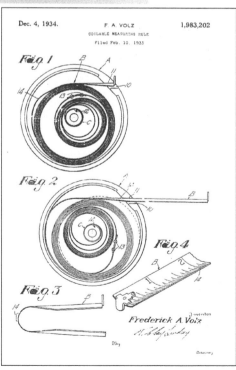

Figure 18. Volz's patent for a winding mechanism in a tape rule.

The blade was next dipped into a chemical solution, which removed the blue finish except where it was printed. The tape rule was next electroplated with nickel, which only built up on the bare blade, leaving a bright, silvery background. Finally, the blade was coated with a tough, protective layer of clear lacquer. A hook was then secured to the blade. The finished blade was next wound into the case, completing the rule.[3]

In July 1932, Stanley offered no. 1166 and no. 1266 tape measures. The no. 1166 was 2 inches in diameter and contained a ½-inch wide, 6-foot tape rule graduated on both edges (Figure 15). The no. 1266 tape was the same as the no. 1166, but was 2⅛

Figure 19 (above). The Stanley no. 1266 tape rules. The rule at top shows an advertising tape graduated on one edge, while the tape at bottom is graduated on both edges.

Figure 20 (below). Two versions of the 1266A tape measure. The top is nickel-plated, while the tape below has the gun-black finish.

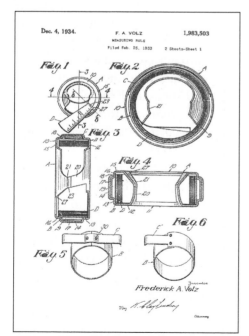

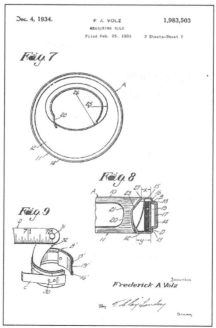

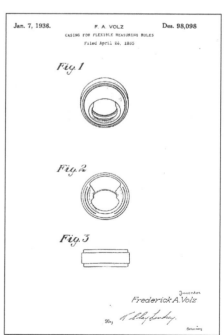

Figures 21 and 22 (above, left and middle). Volz's patent no. 1,983,503 for a detachable-blade, Pull-Push rule, that became Stanley nos. 3206 and 3306.

Figure 23 (above, right). The design patent for the casing for models 3206 and 3306.

Figure 24 (above, left). No. 3206, chrome-plated, detachable-blade rule. Figure 25 (above, right). No. 3306, the detachable blade in gun-black finish.

inches in diameter and had a ⅝-inch wide blade. It was initially graduated only on one edge. Later, it was graduated on both edges (Figure 19).

The nickel-plated no. 1266A was the same size as the no. 1166 (2-inch diameter) and was graduated on only one edge. Later models were graduated on both edges (Figure 20). Gun-black finish was also available. Stanley also produced models no. 1268 and no. 1266E, which were the same size as the no. 1266, except no. 1268 was an 8-foot rule and 1266E was a 6-foot engineer's rule.

Frederic Volz filed another patent (no. 1,983,503, Figures 21 and 22) in February 1933, for Pull-Push rules with detachable blades, which was used on nos. 3206 and 3306. A design patent for the cases for nos. 3206 and 3306 was filed and issued in 1936 (D 98,098, Figure 23).

The chrome-plated no. 3206 (Figure 24) and gun-black finish no. 3306 (Figure 25) rules were introduced in September 1933, together with the nickel-plated no. 3506 (Figure 26), which had an octagonal case. This case

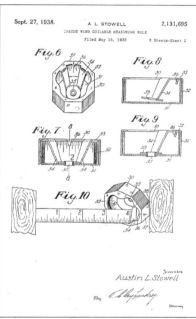

Figure 26 (above). No. 3506 was introduced at the same time as the 3205 and 3306. This model had an octagonal case, patented by Austin L. Stowell (Figure 27 left).

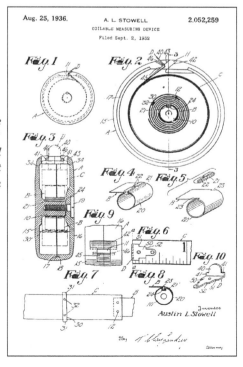

Figure 28 (left). The Stanley SS "Stanlex" no. 7886. This model used Austin Stowell's patent no. 2,052,259 shown in Figure 29 (right).

Green Composition Case — Durable and attractive green "Stanlex" composition case. Nickel plated blade.

No.	Length	Each
7886	6 feet	$1.20

Figure 30. The model H3306, so named because of the hook on the end of the blade.

Figure 31. This tape with a hook on the blade has an octagonal case.

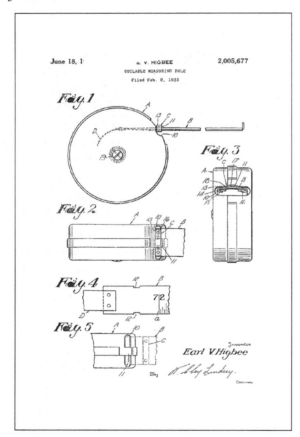

Figure 32. Earl Higbee's patent for controlling the tape in a coilable measuring rule. The Higbee patent allowed the tape to stay in a particular position without retracting. Volz's patent no. 1,983,202 (Figure 18) could also lock in position.

was invented by Austin L. Stowell, who filed the patent on May 15, 1935 (no. 2,131,695, Figure 27).

Also introduced in September 1933 was a new line of ½-inch wide tapes with composition cases colored in red, green, and yellow known as no. 7886 (Figure 28). These composition case rules were called "Stanlex" Pull-Push rules. They utilized Austin Stowell's patent no. 2,052,259

(filed September 1932) for composition cases and coilable rule (Figure 29).

By April 1934, Stanley had introduced the model nos. 3206, 3306, and 3506 Pull-Push rules with a hook on the tape end. This was designated by placing an "H" on the catalog number. However, the rules were merely placed in the same case as the no-hook models. Shown in Figure 30 is an H3306 Pull-Push rule with a gun-metal finish. Figure 31 shows an H3506 octagon tape rule case with a hook on the blade end (see also Figure 26).

Between 1932 and 1935 two patents were used for controlling the tape when it was drawn out. This enabled the tape to stay at a particular position without retracting into the case. One patent was by Frederick Volz (no. 1,983,202, Figure 18) and one by Earl Higbee (no. 2,005,677, Figure 32).

Improving the Winding Mechanism

Beginning in the mid-1930s, Stanley's engineers, having gained a foothold into the tape rule market, could turn their attention to refining the tape rule through innovation and improvements to the winding mechanisms. By March 1935, Stanley had introduced the "target" case models—removable-blade Pull–Push rules nos. 7406 and 7506. These rules were both 6 feet, with the no. 7406 (Figure 33) boasting a chromium-plated case with red and black enamel-filled decoration. The no. 7506 had a gun-black steel case with red-enamel-filled design (Figure 34). They resembled a target, thus the name. Another term often describing these rules is a "bull's eye" rule.

These target tapes, patented by Austin Stowell of Stanley (design patent no. D98,554, Figure 35, and patent no. 2,131,694, Figure 36a and 36b), were close-cased rules. These rules had a hubless design, which had a coil-

CONTINUED PAGE 82

Figure 33. Stanley no. 7406, the chromium-plated "target" tape, so called because the black-enameled outer ring resembled a target.

Figure 34. A Stanley no. 7506 with a gun-black finish and a red-enameled outer ring. The tapes were also called "bull's eye" tapes.

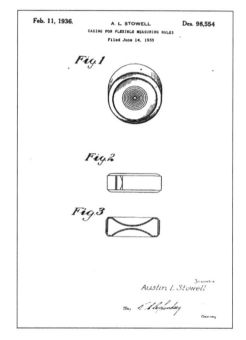

Figure 35. Austin Stowell's design patent for target tape rules.

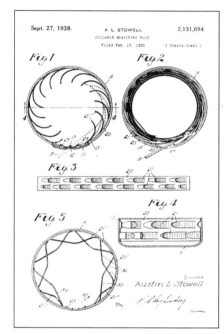
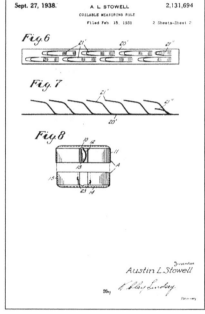

Figures 36a and 36b. The patent for the coiling mechanism, a double row of protruding spring fingers, used in the target tapes.

Figure 37. The target tape model 7506 was continued until 1948, when it was changed to a vertical read tape. "Target" rings were still etched in the case, but the enameled decorations had been eliminated.

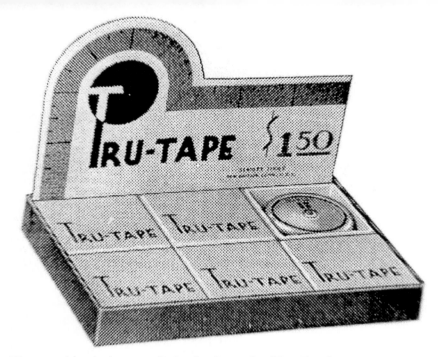

Figure 38 (above). A counter display for the popular "Tru-Tape."

Figure 39 (above). A 6-foot model 7566 Tru-Tape with a gun-black steel case.

Figure 40 (below). Model 7466, a 6-foot Tru-Tape with a nickel-plated case.

Figure 41 (bottom). Model 7363, a 3-foot, chromium-plated brass-case tape rule.

ing medium of a double row of protruding spring fingers fitted around the inside of the case, against which the blade coiled. No. 7406 was permanently discontinued on December 21, 1942. Target rule no. 7506 was continued until 1948, when the tape was changed to a vertical read and the enameled decorations were eliminated (Figure 37). The case was redesigned in 1950.

In July 1936, Stanley introduced a line of 1⅝-inch diameter tape rules that were smaller in size. The company advertised them as "vest pocket rules" and "the rules that women raved about for making sewing and knitting measurements." This size rule, called "Tru-Tape" (Figure 38) was made in five models. The 3-foot, no. 7563, and the 6-foot, no. 7566 (Figure 39) were finished in a gun-black steel case. No. 7466 was a 6-foot model manufactured in a nickel-plated steel case (Figure 40). The 3-foot model no. 7363 (Figure 41) and the 6-foot model no. 7366 had chromium-plated brass cases. By 1938 the nos. 7363 and 7366 cases were being manufactured in stainless steel with the Four-Square symbol on one side (Figures 42 and 43).

In late 1937, Stanley introduced a Pull-Push rule based on patent no. 2,131,695, filed by Austin Stowell, that would allow the user to take an inside reading (Figure 44). The case was open, which allowed the user to read the marking on the tape that was still inside the case, providing a direct read. Frederick Volz improved this concept (Figure 45) and the resulting rule was the no. 6386 direct-read rule (Figure 46). These rules were first offered in both nickel and gun-black finish.

By 1938 the blades of the direct-read rules were printed with black over a white background (Figure 47). This model, no. 6386, was the first used by Stanley of a tape with a white background. The idea was patented by Adolf Keuffel and Walter Gotham of the Keuffel & Esser Company of Hoboken, N.J. (patent no. 2,089209, Figure 48). The patent pertains to creating a steel tape with a pigment imprinted with graduations, and then placing the protective coating over the entire tape. Stanley, recognizing the advantage of the clarity of a tape with a white back-

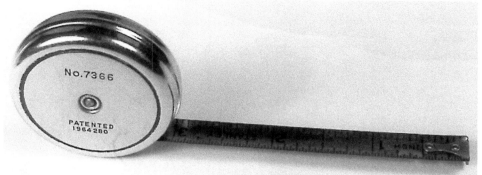

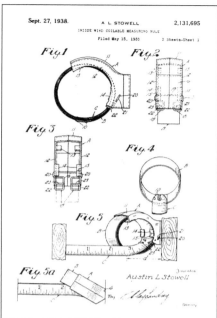

Figure 42(above). A model 7366 Tru-Tape with a stainless-steel case.

Figure 43(below). The reverse of the same tape showing the Stanley "Four-Square" symbol.

ground, made an agreement with Keuffel & Esser on Keuffel and Gotham's patent, similar to an agreement it had made with the Lufkin Rule Company.

As the Pull-Push rules started to gain in popularity, Stanley saw a market in producing rules imprinted with a company's name and used for advertising or promotional sales. Thus Stanley offered most of its tape rules in four styles of business imprints. Figure 49 shows an example of a model no. 7566 with a Type A imprint, stamped with type, advertising a furniture company. On Type B models the imprint was stamped with plates. Figure 50

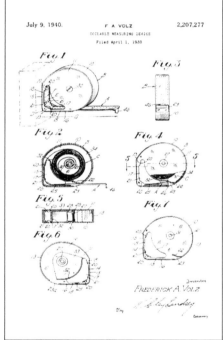

Figure 44 (right, top). Austin Stowell's patent for a direct-read tape.

Figure 45 (right). Frederick Volz improved the Stowell patent in 1940.

Figure 46 (left). Two tapes based on the Volz patent. On the left is model 6386N, a nickel-plated tape. and on the right is model 6386, a gun-black tape.

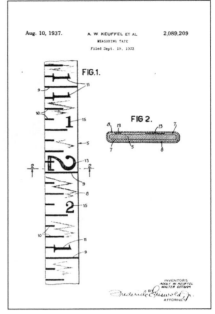

Figure 47 (above). Stanley model 6386, an inside-read rule with a white background on the tape.

Figure 48 (right). Adolf Keuffel's and Walter Gotham's patent pertaining to pigment imprinting graduations on tape rules.

Figure 49 (below). Stanley model 7566 with a Type A imprint, stamped with the name of a furniture company.

shows two no. 1266 tapes—one advertising Buster Brown shoes and the other a paint and varnish company. Type C imprints were etched on the case as shown in Figure 51 on two examples of model 1166. One promotes a coal company and the other a sashmaker.

Sometime after December 1935, Stanley's inventors, Albert Stanley Duncan and Austin Stowell, invented a unique inside and outside tape rule with direct read (patent no. 2,127,443, Figure 52). Duncan and Stowell utilized Earl Higbee's coilable case design for winding the tape and added an inside reading feature. This direct-read rule is known as the X1266 (Figures 53 and 54) and was manufactured for a very short time. Both Frederic Volz and Stowell made additional patents in 1937 (patent no. 2,156,905, Figures 55a and b), but the idea apparently was soon dropped.

Frederick Volz filed a patent in 1937, which was granted in May 1939, for an improvement to the winding mechanisms in tape measures. This improvement controlled the tape so that when pulled out it would

Figure 50 (left, top). Examples of Stanley model 1266 tape rule with the Type B stamp advertising.

Figure 51 (left). Two examples of the Type C etched design advertising on model 1166 rules.

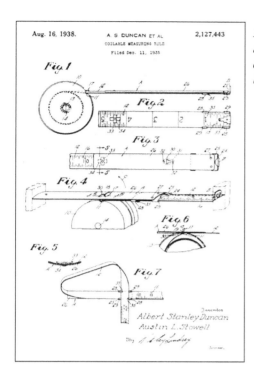

Figure 52 (left). Albert Stanley Duncan and Austin Stowell's patent for inside and outside tape rules. The model X1266 was based on this patent.

Figure 53 (above). Stanley's model X1266 inside and outside tape rule, front side.

Figure 54(left) The reverse side of the inside and outside tape.

stop when extended, but still could be retracted with little difficulty (Figure 56).

In 1939 Stanley came out with its first automatic rule. Figure 57 illustrates a 6-foot rule, no. 1260, which was marketed through Stanley's Defiance line. The coil mechanism inside the case had a ratchet clutch that was disengaged when a button in the center of the side of the case was pushed, thus retracting the blade. The rules were produced with a nickel-plated case, except during the war years when the case was finished in gun-black (Figure 58). Stanley also introduced the no. 1261 (Figure 59), which was a removable Pull-Push rule.

In 1940 and 1941, Stanley manufactured a 6-foot model no. 7366 tape commemorating the London Air Lift

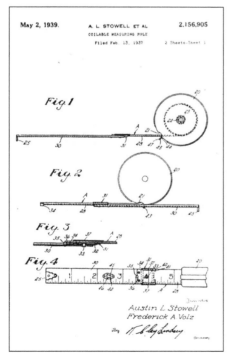

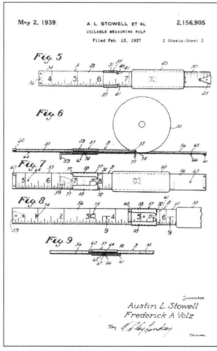

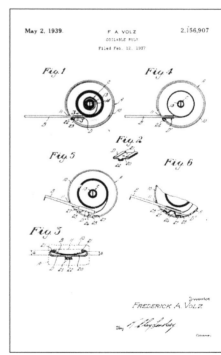

Figures 55a and 55b. Austin Stowell and Frederick Volz's improvement on the inside and outside tape.

Figure 56. The 1939 Volz patent for a winding mechanism for tape measures that allowed the tape to stop when extended, but could retract with little difficulty.

Figure 57 (left). Stanley Defiance model 1260 automatic tape rule. Pushing the button in the center disengaged the ratchet clutch.

Figure 58 (below, left). During World War II the nickel-plated case of model 1260 was replaced with a gun-black case.

Figure 59 (below, right). Stanley Defiance model 1261 with a removable Pull-Push tape.

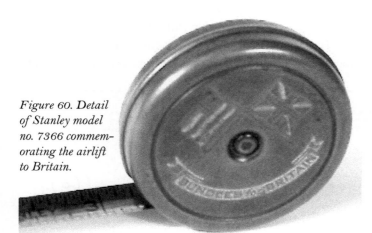

Figure 60. Detail of Stanley model no. 7366 commemorating the airlift to Britain.

(Figure 60). The tape is imprinted "Bundles for Britain" and shows a United States flag and the Union Jack.

During World War II, Stanley discontinued most tape rules except nos. 1266, 1266A, E, and M, 1268, and 6386. They reintroduced most rules after the war, but nos. 3206, 3306, 3506, 7406, and 7886 were permanently discontinued on December 21, 1942.

The D-Style Tape

In 1949 Stanley, utilizing Austin Stowell's patent of September 27, 1938 (Figures 36a and b), added another Pull-Push rule to the Defiance line. This was the no. 1262 (Figure 61), which had a removable blade and was shaped

Figure 61 (above). The Stanley Defiance model 1262. This model, with its D-shaped case, launched Stanley into a completely new rule design.

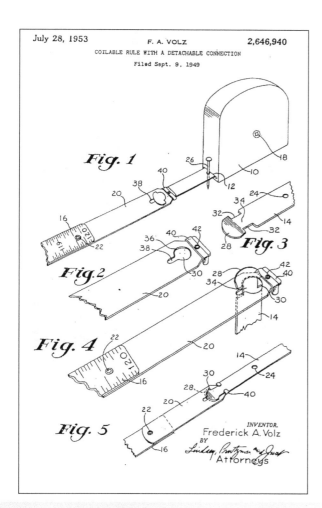

Figure 62 (left). Frederick Volz's patent for a detachable tape rule.

Figure 63 (above). A no. 346, 6-foot retractable, detachable tape rule with a nickel-plated blade.

Figure 64 (below). Stanley no. 346W, 6-foot tape with white-enamel blade.

Figure 65 (above). Stanley no. 348W, 8-foot white-enamel tape with original orange and blue box.

Figure 66 (below). Stanley no. 346W made for retailers in the Hardware Division.

like the letter D, lying on its side. Stanley called them the "D-style" case. This rule style launched Stanley into a completely new rule design. Retractable tape rules, up to 1949, were permanently secured to a winding mechanism inside the rule casing. If they broke or were damaged the tape rule usually had to be discarded.

Frederick Volz filed a patent (no. 2,646,940) in September 1949 for a retractable tape rule in which the blade was detachable (Figure 62). This resulted in a type of tape introduced in May 1950 as Pull-Push replaceable-blade rules. These tapes—nos. 346 (Figure 63), 348 and 3410—had a nickel-plated blade and were made in 6-, 8-, or 10-foot lengths. White-enamel blades also were offered at an additional cost of twenty cents per rule; these rules had a W prefix on the end of the model number (Figures 64 and 65). Stanley also made the no. 346 for the Hardware Division to give out to hardware dealers (Figure 66). The no. 6386 direct-reading rule was given a new Art Deco D-shape design in 1950 (Figure 67).

In August 1948 Stanley introduced the no. 546 6-foot and the no. 548 8-foot rules (Figure 68). These were 1⅛-inch diameter, nickel-plated cases with a ½-inch attaché blade. These rules replaced the 1266A and were advertised as watch-size rules for men or women.

Stanley's no. 7506 Pull-Push rule with removable tape was streamlined into a more modern case design (Figure 69). By 1954 this rule had its case redesigned

Figure 67 (above). Front and verso of the no. 6386, direct-reading rule with D-shape Art Deco design.

Figure 68 (right). Stanley no. 546, "watch-size" 6-foot tape rule.

REMOVABLE BLADE
Nickel Plated Steel Case, 2³⁄₁₆ Inches Diam. Blade, ⅝ Inch Wide

Blade can be removed from case and used for end-to-end measurements and for inside measurements. Blade is nickel plated and has vertical markings.

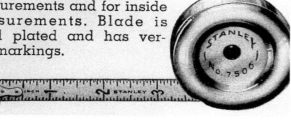

Figure 69 (above). A catalog illustration for the no. 7506 Pull-Push rule with removable tape.

Figure 70 (above). Stanley no. 7506 showing the 1954 redesigned case, Pull-Push, 6-foot rule.

Figure 71 (left). An illustration of a no. 556 D-style tape with brushed-satin finish.

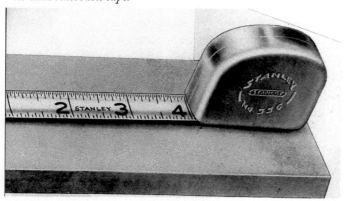

with a metal decal in the center (Figure 70). Stanley also introduced the nos. 556 and 558 style of D tapes around 1950 (Figure 71).

These models had replaceable blades and nickel-plated, brushed-satin finish steel cases. Another tape rule introduced in 1950 was the Featherlite Pull-Push rule no. 636W. This rule was 6 feet long and had a lightweight 1¾-inch diameter case made of red and black plastic and a ⅜-inch white blade. These rules exist with the face side in red or black (Figure 72).

In 1952 a Defiance line of tape rules was introduced. The cases were die-cast with chromium finish. They were available in 6-, 8-, and 10-foot lengths, numbered 1206W, 1208W, and 1210W (Figure 73).

By 1953 the decal of the face of the no. 636 was changed to include a feather and the word "Featherlite" (Figure 74). The same year,

Figure 72. Examples of the no. 636W Handyman tapes with box.

Figure 73. Stanley's Defiance tapes nos. 1206W and 1208W.

Figure 74. Stanley's no. 636W Featherlite tape with a feather on the decal.

Figure 75. Stanley's tape models nos. 1206W, 1208W, and 1210W.

Figure 76 (above). The Stanley Handyman automatic tape rule, no. H1260.

Figure 77 (below). An illustration of Stanley's automatic tape rule no. 736W.

Figure 78 (right). Stanley no. 3610W, a tape rule with "true read mouth," double scale, and ¾-inch wide blade.

AUTOMATIC

Spring return blade controlled by push-button on case. Tough plastic case is red and black.

Stanley introduced the grade nos. 1206W, 1208W, and 1210W Pull-Push rules with D-shaped cases. They were available in 6-, 8-, and 10-foot lengths (Figure 75). Apparently, the Defiance line had been discontinued.

In 1954 Stanley began promoting the Handyman line of tools. The "Handyman" name was a trademark of North Brothers of Philadelphia, which was purchased by Stanley on May 1, 1946. The Defiance no. 1260 automatic rule was renumbered to H1260 (Figure 76). The Featherlite rule line had an additional rule added known as no. 736W automatic rule, which had a spring-return blade controlled by a push button on the case (Figure 77).

A new D-style rule, the no. 3610W, was introduced in November 1954. This rule had a ¾-inch wide double scaled blade with a "true reading mouth," which was recessed allowing the user to see the graduations and numbers on the rule clearly (Figure 78).

In 1955 Austin Stowell filed a design patent for a plastic display box with a magnifying glass (D181,321; Figure 79). This was known as the "Magna View Box" and all the 1200 series rules were marketed in this box (Figure 80). Beginning sometime in 1955, all of the nos. 1206W, 1208W, 1210W, and the new 12-foot, 1212W, were manufactured with the "true reading mouth" (Figure 81). Also at about the same time, a no. 3612W rule came on the scene. This tape was 12 feet long with a ¾-inch-wide blade. With the introduction of the "true -reading mouth" feature, Stanley was required to make the die-cast case a little higher. The older 1200 series D cases were used on a new line of tapes known as the "Pacemaker" rules. These were available in 1955 in four lengths numbered A06W, A08W, A010W, and A012W and did not include the "true-reading mouth" (Figure 82). Metric sizes were also available in models ME06 and ME010, which were 2-meter and 3-meter rules, respectively.

United States Patent Office

Des. 181,321
Patented Oct. 29, 1957

181,321

COMBINATION MAGNIFYING GLASS AND DIS-
PLAY BOX FOR RULES AND THE LIKE

Austin L. Stowell, New Britain, Conn.

Application November 2, 1955, Serial No. 38,701

Term of patent 7 years

(Cl. D80—5)

FIG. 1

FIG.2

Figure 1 is a perspective view of the combination magnifying glass and display box for rules and the like showing my design with the box assembled and lying in a horizontal position.

Figure 2 is a perspective view as disassembled with the cover and base thereof turned on end to stand in a vertical position.

I claim:

The ornamental design for a combination magnifying glass and display box for rules and the like, as shown.

References Cited in the file of this patent
UNITED STATES PATENTS

D. 172,724   Polk _____ July 27, 1954
660,782   Strumpell _____ Oct. 20, 1900

OTHER REFERENCES

Modern Packaging Catalog, 1948, p. 333 and p. 528, top center.
Modern Packaging Catalog, 1954, p. 293, No. 30, p. 299, top.

Figure 79 (left). Austin Stowell's design patent for a plastic display box (shown in Figure 80).

Figure 80 (above). A "Magna View Box" with a no. 1210W tape rule inside.

Stanley was now well into producing tape rules and was ready to enter into the manufacture of steel long tapes. March 1959 brought a new line of tapes known as "white" tapes. These rules were manufactured in 25-, 50-, 75-, and 100-foot lengths and 30- and 50-meter lengths and were ⅜ inches wide. White tapes were numbered 6325, 6350, 6375, and 63100.

The cases were made of steel and covered with a long-lasting, coated fabric (Figure 83). Two other lines of D-style rules were also introduced in 1958. The first line was a red and black plastic model available in three lengths, numbered 646W, 648W, and 6410W. It was advertised as colorful, lightweight, durable, and economical in price (Figure 84). Each size was available in either a black or red front.

The second line was the Glide-O-Matic series of tape rules (Figure 85). These were manufactured in four lengths: 6,

Figure 81 (above). Stanley nos. 1206W, 1208W, and 1210W tapes with "true read mouth."

Figure 82 (below). Stanley Pacemaker rules, nos. A06W, A08W, A010W, and A012W (left to right).

Figure 83 (above). Stanley's steel long tape nos. 6350 (10 feet), 63100 (100 feet) and 63166MR (20 meters).

8, 10, and 12 feet, and featured a push-button lock and an inside-reading scale on the underside of the blade. They also had automatic glide return and scribers to mark your work (Figure 86). These Glide-O-Matic tapes were offered until late 1962, when a new line of rules was introduced that would change the history of the tape measure for the next thirty years.

Stanley Tapes of the 1960s and 1970s

William G. Brown of Stanley filed a patent (no. 3,121,957) in July 1959, for encasing a metal rule with a plastic film (Figure 87). This was a significant patent because it solved a common problem—Stanley rule blades received a lot of friction on the edges and the graduations would become unreadable. With this patent, a tough film of plastic called Mylar® was wrapped around the blade, making it substantially free from frictional resistance to coiling and uncoiling and highly resistant to rust and corrosion, chemicals, solvents, and staining. This new Mylar®-coated blade was advertised under the trade name of "Life Guard.™" While Brown's patent was not granted by the U.S. Patent Office until February 1964, Stanley had begun producing Mylar®-coated tapes by 1961.

A new D-style tape for use by masons was introduced in January 1960. Known as nos. MM10W and MA10W tape rules, they were ten feet long and featured modular spacing and brick spacing scales (Figure 88).

In January 1961, Stanley introduced a new style measure that had a different shape to it. I call it the "square-

Figure 84 (top). Stanley red and black plastic tapes, nos. 648W and 6410W.
Figure 85 (above). Stanley's "Glide-O-Matic" rules, nos. 346W, 348W, and 3410W (left to right).
Figure 86 (right). Closeup of Stanley "Glide-O Matic" 648W tape showing inside-read scale (in red). The arrow points to the scribers.

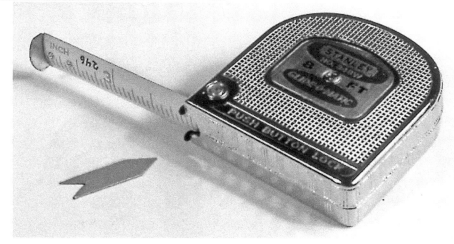

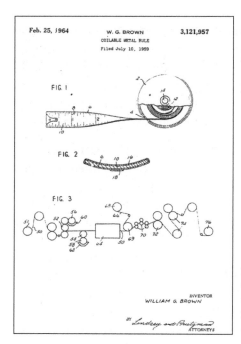

Figure 87 (left). William Brown's patent for encasing a metal rule with plastic film.

Figure 88 (right). The MM10W and MA10W tape rules that featured modular spacing and brick spacing scales.

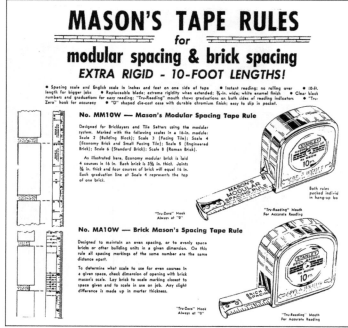

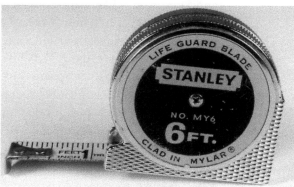

Figure 89. A "square round" tape introduced in 1961.

Figure 90. The LifeGuard™ in the 10- and 12-foot lengths.

Figure 91 (above). The LifeGuard™ in the MA10Y brick mason's models.

Figure 92. In 1964 the decal on the MY series was changed. (below)

round." Stanley manufactured these tapes in two different lines, both of which were available in 6-, 8-, 10-, or 12-foot lengths and 2-meter length (Figure 89). The MY series had LifeGuard™ blades. When first introduced, the face decals had black centers surrounded by a yellow border indicating a LifeGuard™ yellow blade was inside. The 10- and 12-foot lengths (Figure 90) were also available in ¾-inch widths. The MY series also included two brick mason's models, denoted by nos. MM10Y and MA10Y (Figure 91). The decal on the MY series was changed in 1964 to a black/white/yellow background (Figure 92).

In May 1963, Stanley introduced three more D-style tapes with ½-inch white blades. No. A06W was a 6-foot length and nos. ME05 and ME010 (Figure 93) had metric lengths. These tapes had a black background on the face decal. At the same time, a ¼-inch wide

CONTINUED ON PAGE 94

Figure 93. The D-style tapes were introduced with a black background decal.

Figure 94. The TY series with the three-color decal.

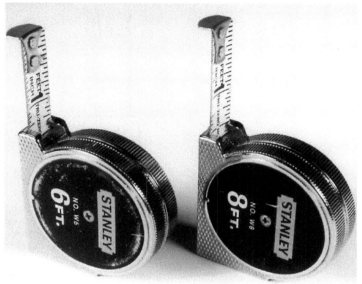

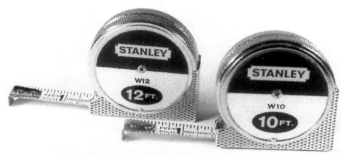

Figure 95 (left). The W series of "square-round" tapes continued to be produced in the ½-inch width only.

Figure 96 (above). The W series decal was changed in 1964.

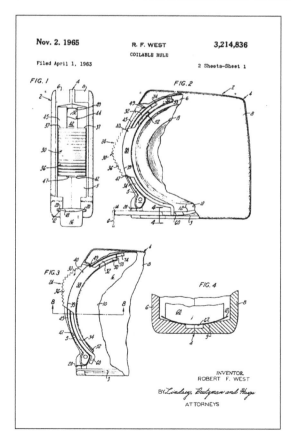

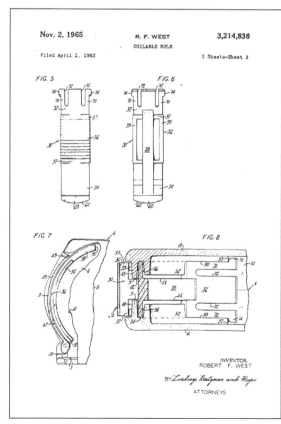

Figures 97 and 98 (left). Robert West's patent for a new shape for a rule and a clamping mechanism for holding the blade when extended.

Figure 99. An example of West's patent—the renowned Stanley Powerlock™.

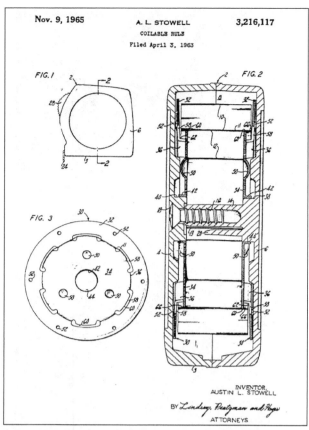

Figure 100. Austin Stowell's patent for a mechanism to improve the coiling of the tape.

pocket Pull-Push rule, with LifeGuard™ tapes—known as the MYT series—was introduced in 6-, 8-, and 10-foot lengths. A TY series was offered in 2-meter lengths. The cases had a three-color (black/yellow/white) decal background (Figure 94).

The W series of "square-round" rules used an older white blade and was available in ½-inch width only in 6-, 8-, 10-, and 12-foot, and 2-meter lengths (Figure 95). The original decal had a black background, but that was changed to a black and white background in 1964 (Figure 96). Brick mason's rules were not offered in the W series. LifeGuard™ yellow, steel long tapes were offered in 1964, in 50- and 100-foot lengths.

A major change in tape rules came about in April 1963, when Robert West of Stanley Tools filed a patent (no. 3,214,836) on a totally new concept in tape measures (Figures 97 and 98). This patent would reshape tape measures to the present day.

West's patent was for the shape of the rule and for

a clamping mechanism for holding the blade when extended. This became the world famous Powerlock™ tape (Figure 99), which also featured LifeGuard™ rules.

About the same time as West's patent was filed, Austin Stowell of Stanley patented an improvement in the coiling mechanism inside the Powerlock™ rule (no.

Figure 101 (above). The Powerlock™ line as offered in 1964 with the power return based on Stowell's new coiling mechanism. The rule extended to the left when facing the decal. This design would later change.

Figure 102 (left). The Powerlock™ layout tape with its special "write-on-blade" feature.

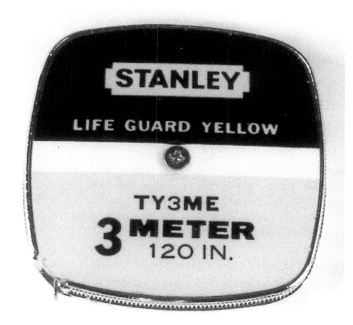

Figure 103. The TY3ME tape, a ¼-inch tape in the Pull-Push line.

Figure 104 (above). In 1967 Stanley introduced a new line of tapes with a V-shaped case.

Figure 105 (below). The Stanley no. W312 V-style tape with a white blade. The V-style tapes extended to the right when facing the decal, the opposite of the new Powerlock™ tapes.

3,216,117) (Figure 100). The Powerlock™ power return rule was first offered in 1964 in six lengths, which were 6-, 8-, 10-, and 12-foot lengths in the ½-inch blade and 10- and 12-foot in the ¾-inch blade width (Figure 101). Note that the rule extended to the left when facing the decal.

A new Powerlock™ layout tape was introduced in 1964, which was designed with a special "write-on-blade" feature. The user simply marked on the rule with a pencil and, when finished, wiped it off. This rule, no. 61-312, was a ¾-inch wide, 12-foot long model (Figure 102). In January 1965, Stanley added a 3-meter tape to its ¼-inch Pull-Push line, numbering it TY3ME (Figure 103).

A new style of rule was introduced in 1967 with a totally different look, which replaced the "square-round" MY and W series of tape measures. The model numbers were the same but the look was different. I refer to it as the "V-style" tape. V-style tapes were made in both a ½-inch-wide model in 8-, 10-, and 12-foot lengths and a ¾-inch-wide model in 10- and 12-foot lengths. The V-style tapes had LifeGuard™ yellow tape and were numbered MY8 through MY312 (Figure 104). These tapes were also available with white blades in the same sizes denoted by number W6, W8, W10, W12 and W312 (Figure 105). Both V-style tapes extended to the right when facing the decal, which was the opposite of the new Powerlock™ tape rules.

Also in 1967, Stanley introduced three steel long tapes. The first was the "Steelmaster" line, made with a chrome,

Figure 106 (above). The Steelmaster line had a chrome-plated zinc, die-cast case available in 50- and 100-foot lengths and in metric models.

Figure 107 (below). In 1968 Stanley changed the face look of its ¼-inch MYT line pocket tapes. See Figure 94 for the older style.

Figure 108. The 1968 Powerlock™ layout rule with the redesigned decal. Compare to the original Powerlock™ tapes in Figures 101 and 102.

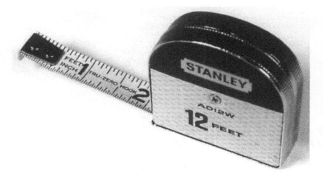

Figure 109. In 1968 the decals on the D-style tapes were also redesigned.

Figure 110. Stanley Powerlock™ rules. The older style from 1963 (left) and the newer from 1970. On the 1963 Powerlock™ the tape extends from the left. On the newer model it's to the right. Note too the change in how the models were identified after Stanley began to use EDP numbers.

zinc, die-cast case in 50- and 100- foot lengths and in metric models. These tapes were Stanley's top of the line and had a ⅝-inch LifeGuard™ yellow blade (Figure 106).

The second style of long tapes was the "Jobmaster" line. Available in 25-, 50-, 75-, and 100-foot lengths, these tapes had a black, zinc die-cast case with a white blade. They were numbered 6325, 6350, 6375, 63100 and replaced the original series of long tapes introduced in 1957, which had the same numbers.

The third style long tape was an economy line, also with a die-cast case available in 50- and 100-foot lengths. Numbered 62-050 and 62-100, these tapes were advertised as a "long distance" tape for homeowner or professional and sold at a popular price.

Also introduced in 1967 were the Powerlock™ models 61-110 and 61-112 rules, which were 10- and 12-feet long and had decimal fraction scales instead of the standard scale.

Stanley decided in 1968 to change the face look of its ¼-inch MYT line of Pull-Push pocket tapes. Figure 107 shows the new look for these rules.

June 1968 saw the redesign of the original decal of the 61-312 Powerlock™ rule, giving it a brighter, classier look (Figure 108). Also, a new line of D-style tapes were offered in the usual 6-, 8-, 10-, and 12-foot lengths with a white blade and a smart-looking face. They were numbered A06W, A08W, A010W, and A012W (Figure 109).

In 1970 and 1971, Stanley began to list its rules with an Electronic Data Processing (EDP) number, which Stanley used to identify each individual type of tool to help in inventory control. For example, the 8-foot Powerlock PL-8 became 33-208 (Figure 110). The Powerlock™ line began to have many size additions and the rule numbers were slowly changed from the old number to the EDP number listed on the rule face. As the Powerlock™ tape rules were changed over to the new EDP numbers, the case was redesigned so that the tape extended to the right when facing the decal (Figure 110) similar to the "V" series rules.

From its introduction in 1964, the Powerlock™ tape rule revolutionized the tape rule industry. It became known as the "Badge of the Professional." Powerlock™ is still being produced today, thirty-eight years later, but with improved winding mechanisms to accommodate longer rules.

Tape measures have come a long way since Farrand's original patent of the 1920s. Today, the tape rule has made the folding rule and the Zig-Zag rule obsolete. Tape rules are, today, Stanley's top-selling tool thanks to Mr. Farrand's revolutionizing measuring tapes.

Notes

1. *Tool Talk*, no. 10 (New Britain, Conn.: Stanley Tool Works) 1938.

2. *Tool Talk*, no. 10.

3. *Tool Talk*, no. 10.

Figure 1. Stanley's imprinted tape rules were quite popular among businesses as advertising vehicles, including at Stanley itself. From the time Stanley introduced advertising imprints on its tapes, the company met the demand with new, imaginative designs. Stanley promoted its own business with this tape rule, a model no. 1166, that was etched with the phrase "A good rule at any time."

Stanley Advertising and Imprinted Tape Rules

Stanley's purchase of Hiram A. Farrand, Inc. of Berlin, New Hampshire, on December 18, 1931, not only added new measuring instruments—tape rules—to Stanley's line but also a new and effective advertising item—imprinted tape rules (Figure 1).[1] Tape rules with advertising, within one decade, would supersede the Zig-Zag rule as the most popular Stanley promotional item.

When Stanley purchased the company, Farrand already had been offering its tape rule with advertising engraved on the barrel side of the case (Figure 2). Hand engraving, however, was expensive, and by 1934, Stanley was promoting inexpensive, imprinted tape rules to its customers.

Three types of imprinted messages, designated types A, B, and C, were offered. Type A had a stamped-with-type imprint, as shown in the model no. 7566 tape rules in Figure 3. These tape rules have the stamped imprint filled in with white enamel on gun-blued cases. Figure 4 is a model no. 6386, direct-read tape, Type A stamped-with-type imprint. Figure 5 shows a Four-Square no. 1166 advertising tape with a Type A imprint with black fill, but with the Four-Square logo in red.

The Type B imprint is stamped with a plate. The model no. 7566 rule shown in Figure 6 has a nickel finish

and black infill. Variations on this style were also available. Shown in Figure 7 are three no. 1266 tape rules with the Type B imprint, one with red and two with black infills.

Figure 2. The Farrand Company had been offering imprinted tape rules when Stanley purchased the company in 1931. This Farrand tape promoted the Western Rawlplug Co.

Figure 3 (above). Two examples of model no. 7566 tape rules with the Type A, stamped-with-type imprint.

Figure 4 (below left). Another example of the Type A imprint on a model no. 6386 rule.

Figure 5 (below, right). The imprint on this no. 1166 Four-Square rule has black fill, and the Four-Square logo is in red.

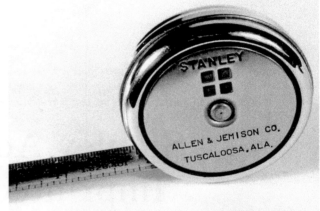

Figure 6 (above). An example of the Type B imprint on a model no. 7566 rule.

Stamped-with-type imprints are made by setting up steel type in much the same way a printing press is set up. The words are then stamped into the rule case blank. With a stamped-with-plate imprint, a die plate is made, which is then used to strike the plate. Die plates cost more to make. The advertising on steel tape rule faces (not the advertising on the edges, however) is done before the two case halves are die formed into the case design. The case blank is really a flat, circular disk, which for the rule in Figure 3 would be 2⅛ inches in diameter with a ⅛-inch hole in the center. For the tape in Figure 5, the blank would have been 2½ inches in diameter.

Stanley also offered Type C imprint tape rules. These rules had the imprint etched into the face of the tape case. Figure 8 shows two no. 1666, 6-foot tapes with Type C imprints, and illustrates the variety obtainable through Stanley. Both have black-enamel infill. Etching was more expensive, but the design possibilities were unlimited.

Not only were the Type C imprinted rules available in the ½-inch blade width size but also in the smaller, ⅜-inch wide blade model nos. 7366 and 7466. Figure 9 shows a no. 7366 stainless case with Ross Engineering imprinted with a blue-enamel background. The Type C etched imprint rules allowed for intricate designs, if desired. In Figure 10 is a no. 7466 with a very intricate design with a black-enamel background. The model no. 1166 in Figure 1 is another example of how interesting the etched models could be. Stanley promoted itself on this rule with the slogan "A good rule at any time"

Figure 7 (left). Three model no. 1266 tape rules with the Type B stamped-with-plate imprint. The Stein, Hall and Buster Brown Shoes tapes have black infill; the Pioneer Paint & Varnish Co. is red. Note how Buster Brown took advantage of the rivet to complete the word "shoes."

Figure 8 (right). These two model no. 1666 tapes have the Type C etched imprint.

Figure 9 (below). Imprinting was available on many models, including model nos. 7366 and 7466 with their ⅜-inch wide blades. The example shown is a no. 7366, with a blue-enamel imprint.

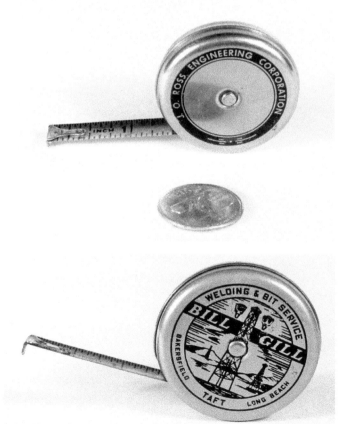

Figure 10. One of the advantages of the Type C design was that it allowed for intricate designs on the rules such as this one for Bill Gill Welding and Bit service.

and "Buy Stanley," which incorporated a clock face. Again, the background is black enamel. The no. 1166 tapes in Figure 11 show variations of the Type C imprint that take advantage of the available advertising space, utilizing not only the border of the tape case, but also the center.

These three imprint types were offered throughout the 1930s and World War II. With the improvement of the tape measure Stanley's new line of Defiance "Pull-Push" rules, nos. 1260 and 1261, were available with one, two, or three lines of advertising on the rim of the rule case with the imprint filled in with the color of the advertiser's choice (Figure 12). When Stanley introduced the Defiance D-style no. 1262 case in 1949, advertisers had the option of an imprint around the rim as well.

Over time, the D-style tape rule was refined from the pressed-metal style to a chrome-plated, die-cast case. With this change, the center of the case in model nos. 1206, 1208, and 1210 had a screwed-on plate that was marked with the name, model number, and length of tape rule. First marked as Defiance in 1951, this tape was soon updated to a "Stanley Grade" tool with the same numbers.

By 1953, these tape measures, which cost $1.38 to $1.84 each, depending on the length of the tape, were available with advertising name plates instead of the Stanley name plate. The name plates could be either

Figure 11 (left). Two examples of Stanley model no. 1166 rules with the Type C imprint. The advertising text was placed not only around the edge, but in the center as well.

Figure 12 (below). A Stanley no. 1261 Defiance Pull-Push tape with the advertiser's name imprinted around the rim and filled in with red.

lithographed or etched; etching cost 54¢ extra. In 1951, the J. Fegely & Son Hardware Company of Pottstown, Pennsylvania, celebrated its one-hundredth anniversary by distributing a Defiance model no. 1206. The rule had a lithographed plate with a red background that advertised the anniversary (Figure 13). These rules were also available in an etched plate, which made the words or design stand out with a recessed background. With this technique, an infinite number of creative advertising logos or designs could be made with any color background desired. Figure 14 shows three examples of

Figure 13 (right). The J. Fegely & Son Hardware Company had this Defiance tape no. 1206W lithographed with its name to celebrate its one-hundredth anniversary.

Figure 14 (left). Three examples of the D-style tape, model no. 1206W, with etched advertising plates.

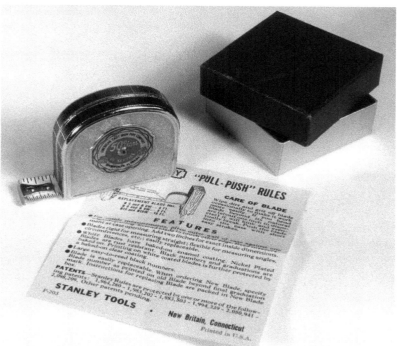

Figure 15(above). A Stanley no. 1210w, 10-foot, D-style tape with an etched plate.

Figure 16 (right). A gold-plated Stanley no. 1210W with an etched plate.

D-style, etched-plate, die-cast tape rules, all no. 1206W. These tapes were also available with blue and silver gift boxes. A 1210W, 10-foot advertising tape is shown in Figure 15 with a silver background, etched plate with red lettering.

By January 1954, Stanley D-style tape models 1206W, 1208W, and 1210W were available with a gold-plated case at an extra charge of 35¢ each. When in 1955 the American Cast Iron Pipe Company wanted to mark fifty years of service, the company chose the gold-plated option with an etched plate on a Stanley no. 1210W 10-foot, D-style tape rule (Figure 16). The normal rule of this type would have cost $1.84 in 1955. This advertising tape would have cost the American Cast Iron Pipe Company $2.73 ($1.84 for the basic tape; 35¢ for the gold plated case; 54¢ for the etched advertising plate) if purchased in a lot of 100 to 249.

Also available in imprinted models in 1954 was Stanley's Featherlite Pull-Push tape rules no. 636W or with diameter scale denoted as no. 636WD. Tape rules with diameter scales could be used to wrap around any round object and would then give the object's diameter. Either scale was the same cost. These tapes were offered with etched plates, etched plates and reverse-side stamping, or stock plates and reverse-side stamping with colored plastic cases. Shown in Figure 17 is a no. 636WD tape with a blue case and etched plate. Figure 18 illustrates a

Figure 17 (above). Stanley no. 636WD tape rule with diameter scale and etched plate.

Figure 18. Stanley no. 636W tape rule with a stock plate and reverse side stamping.

Figure 19 (above). In 1963 Stanley was able to use a new material, Mylar®, in producing imprints. This Stanley no. MYT6 (left) and MYT8 (right) have Mylar®-coated imprints.

stock plate with reverse-side stamping for a 1955 Detroit convention. The lettering is gold on red.

In 1963, a new model, a wide-pocket tape, was introduced by Stanley known as the MYT series.[2] The imprints on these rules were printed on the face and then covered with a polyester film called Mylar®. Available in 6, 8, and 10 feet, these rules (Figure 19) had a 1⅝-inch square billboard face for an advertising message. Two-color faces were available for an extra charge. Instead of the standard chrome case, a gold-plated case was available as another option.

The new Powerlock tape rules were available in 1964 with advertising on a 1¼-inch-diameter circular name plate protected by a Mylar® film. These nameplates had a two-color imprint with any color background and any color copy. A three-color copy was available for an additional charge. Shown in Figure 20 are a 12-foot, PL12 and an 8-foot, PL8 Powerlock tape rule with advertising.

Stanley continues to manufacture tape rules for promotional advertising in selected models today, and they are still a long-lasting and effective way to promote a company.

Figure 20. A Powerlock PL12 (left) and a PL8 (right) with Mylar®-coated imprint plates.

Notes

1. Walter W. Jacob, "Stanley Tapes Measure the World, Part I," *The Chronicle* 53, no. 4 (2000): 163–167.
2. For more information on stock models see Walter W. Jacob, "Stanley Tapes Measure the World," *The Chronicle* 54, no. 4 (2001): 154–159.

The Turn of the Screw:
The History of Stanley Screwdrivers

Screwdrivers, earlier known as turnscrews, have been around since at least the fifteenth century. At first, screwdrivers were very scarce because screws were so expensive to manufacture. But the beginning of the nineteenth century saw the arrival of machine-manufactured screws. As the per-piece cost of screws came down, their use increased, and with that, the need for more screwdrivers.

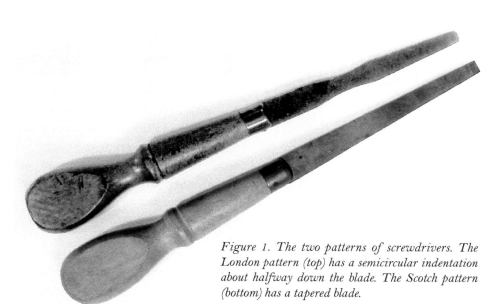

Figure 1. The two patterns of screwdrivers. The London pattern (top) has a semicircular indentation about halfway down the blade. The Scotch pattern (bottom) has a tapered blade.

Until the 1840s, screws had a flat or blunt tip, which necessitated drilling a lead hole, first in order to start the screw. Early screws had their heads slotted by hammering a knife edge into a red-hot screw head.

The screwdriver was flat, and the tip was ground or beveled on both sides almost to a point to fit the V-slot. When the first machine-made screws came out, their heads were slotted with a saw.

Finally, machinery was developed to make the screws with a gimlet point. Then the price of the screws came down, and the practicality of their use improved, especially with the use of butt hinges.

With advances in screw manufacturing, more screwdrivers began to appear. Up until the 1850s, screwdrivers had a flat blade with a turned handle that was flat on two sides. These common flat-blade screwdrivers were made into two patterns—the London pattern and the Scotch pattern—that evolved over time (Figure 1). The London

pattern had a semicircular dip on the sides, about halfway down the blade. The Scotch pattern was a straight, tapered blade.

It wasn't until 1870 that Stanley entered into the screwdriver business. Up until then, there were only fifteen United States screwdriver patents. The earliest known United States patent was issued in 1852. The patent dealt with a screwdriver attachment to a brace. All the others, with two exceptions, were concerned with either leverage attachments or early spiral screwdriver designs, and had nothing to do with improving the basic, centuries-old design.

On July 23, 1867, J. A. Ayres of Hartford, Connecticut, patented an improved screwdriver (Figure 2). His patent dealt with improving the tip by cutting a dovetail cross section on the end. When the screwdriver was used, it bit into the slot, reducing slip out. This idea, of course, didn't last because the tip of the screwdriver broke at the dovetail.

The other patent, by J. P. Curtiss, was for an improvement in screwdrivers by securing the shank in a solid handle (Figure 3). The blade was cut out by means of the usual die and punch. The tang, or shank, that went into the solid handle was notched and recessed on each side. A hole was drilled in the center of the handle, wider than the notched shank, but not all the way through. The shank was then driven into the end and molten lead and antimony were poured into the hole on the side, thus securing the metal part of the screwdriver. The resulting accumulation of metal was then shaved off to finish the screwdriver. Figure 4 shows an early Stanley screwdriver with a Curtiss patent and a flat handle.

Stanley cast-steel screwdrivers, with the Curtiss patent, started showing up in its 1870 catalog. It is unclear whether Curtiss was employed by Stanley or whether the company secured his patent. In any event, the fact that his design appeared in Stanley catalogs before the patent was issued, suggests Curtiss was employed by Stanley.

The design of this screwdriver was the London

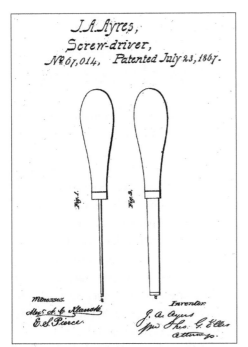

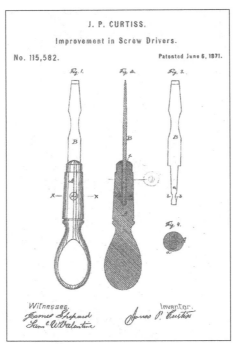

Figure 2 (above, left). J. A. Ayres's patent for an improvement in screwdrivers.

Figure 3 (above, right). J. P. Curtiss's patent for an "Improvement in Screw Drivers," a new way of attaching the handle to the blade. Figure 4 shows an example of this screwdriver.

pattern. It was first made with wrought-iron ferrules (patented by S. N. Chapin), but by the end of 1870, it was changed to a brass thimble or ferrule (Figure 5).

These screwdrivers were initially offered in sizes 2 through 10 inches and 12-inch lengths. By 1871, a 1½-inch length had been added to the line, and flat or oval handles for each size were offered.

An 1872 Stanley advertisement noted: "By the aid of improved machinery we are now producing a screwdriver which is superior to any other in the market—and at the prices paid for the ordinary tools."

By 1874, Stanley was offering its screwdrivers in no. 1 grade with Curtiss's metallic fastening and in no. 2 grade without the metallic fastening at a discount price. Oval handles were discontinued at this time (Figure 6).

Shortly afterward, around 1876, the no. 1 was sold with black-enameled handles only. In 1879 Stanley eliminated the no. 2 grade screwdriver and offered the no. 1 grade in varnished and black-enameled handles (Figure 7).

Stanley, in 1888, finally began numbering its screwdrivers. The no. 64 had a varnished handle and was a solid cast-steel screwdriver with patent metallic fastening. The no. 75 is the same screwdriver but had black-enameled handles. Both the no. 64 and no. 75 are the London patterns. Another screwdriver, no. 86, was introduced with polished handles and no metallic fastening. It did not have Curtiss's patent. This screwdriver had the Scotch pattern blade.

The no. 75 screwdriver, with black-enameled handle, was discontinued in 1892. Only the no. 64 with varnished handle and the no. 86 in the Scotch pattern remained in the catalogs. The no. 64 screwdriver was changed to a

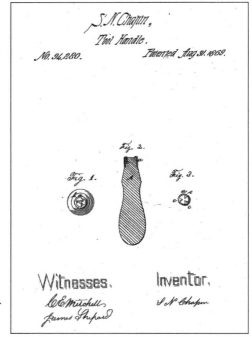

Figure 4 (above). Stanley screwdriver with the Curtiss patent marked on the blade (see inset).

Figure 5 (right). S. N. Chapin's patent for a screwdriver handle.

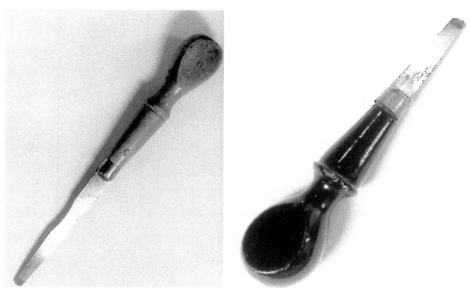

Figure 6 (above, left). A Stanley no. 1 grade screwdriver with a Curtiss patent fastener.

Figure 7 (above, right). Stanley screwdriver with black-enameled handle.

Scotch pattern in 1919. Both the no. 64 and no. 86 were discontinued in 1927 (Figure 8).

George E. Wood

George E. Wood of Southington, Connecticut, filed his first screwdriver patent on October 2, 1900 (Figure 9). This patent was for an improvement in the construction of a screwdriver. Mr. Wood claimed in this patent that:

> ...the combination with a metal shank having its handle end formed with one or more integral, laterally-extending wings, of a wood handle formed with a central longitudinal bore or passage for the said shank, and with a trans-

verse slot located in its outer end, and intersecting the outer end of the said bore or passage, and receiving the wing or wings of the shank.[1]

He assigned this patent to the Acme Manufacturing Company of Southington, Connecticut.

Shortly after George E. Wood was granted patent no. 671,039 on April 2, 1901, he went into business with John Hurley to manufacture screwdrivers. They set up a shop in Plantsville, Connecticut, and named the new company using their last names. The founding of the Hurwood Manufacturing Company marked the beginning of the "solid-bar screwdriver." Solid-bar screwdrivers had a blade that ran all the way through the handle in one piece. In earlier screwdrivers, the blade went only part way up the handle and when used hard would come out of the handle. This and later patents solved that problem.

Herbert S. Pullman, employed by Hurwood, filed a patent on July 14, 1902, and granted on February 23, 1904, that took Wood's 1901 patent one step further (Figure 10). Pullman made a slight change to the crosspiece in the handle and added integral wings on the shank under the bolster. This patent was assigned to the Hurwood Manufacturing Company.

Figure 8. The Stanley no. 64 and no. 86 screwdrivers with their boxes. These examples were made after 1919 in the Scotch pattern.

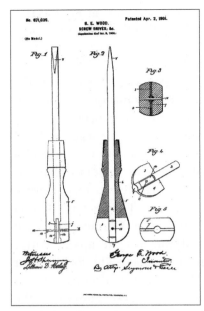

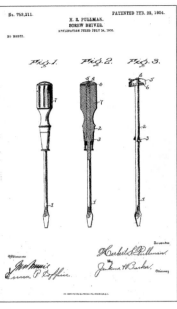

Figure 9 (far left). George E. Wood's first patent.

Figure 10 (left). H. S. Pullman's patent, assigned to the Hurwood Manufacturing Company.

Figure 11 (right). This screwdriver, patented by Wood, did not have its tip made until the handle was finished.

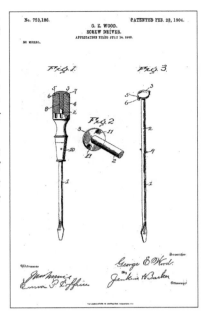

George E. Wood filed two more patents on July 14, 1902. (I believe that Herbert Pullman's and George E. Wood's July 4, 1902, patent were all filed at one time, since the witnesses and attorneys are the same on all patents.) Mr. Wood's patents provided for a solid bar with a solid head. Patent no. 753,186, granted February 23, 1904, had two-prong extensions from the head, which extended into the wood handle (Figure 11).

In manufacturing the screwdriver, the forged solid bar would not have the screwdriver tip forged until it was inserted through the wood handle and the ferrule. After the handle portion was finished, the tip of the screwdriver was made.

Mr. Wood's second patent (no. 765,302) filed on July 19, 1904 (Figure 12), provided for a different arrangement. The solid bar had a round head with no prongs but "…recesses are formed in the shank from which spurs are formed along the length in any desired number." These spurs would, when driven through the wood handle, prevent the handle from turning during use. As stated in Stanley's 1938 publication *Tool Talks*: "George E. Wood can truly be called the father of the modern screwdriver for it seems to mark the starting point of this tool's present numerous applications."[2]

The hardware trade immediately recognized Hurwood's quality, and sales of its screwdrivers increased to a point that the company moved to a larger plant in 1903.

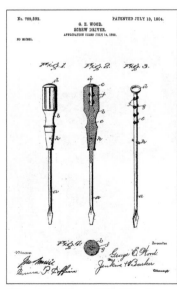

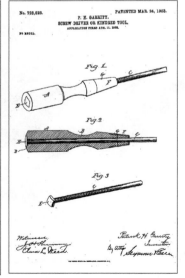

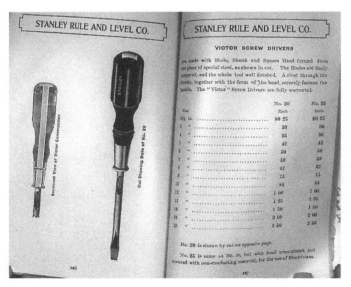

Figure 12 (above, left). Wood's second patent, which used spurs to prevent the handle from turning during use.

Figure 13 (above, right). Garrity's patent, which became the basis of the Victor line of screwdrivers.

Figure 14. The 1905 Stanley catalog illustrating the Victor no. 20 and 25 screwdrivers.

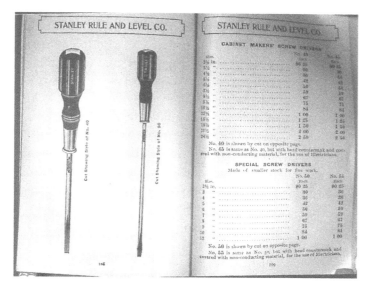

Figure 15 (above). Victor screwdrivers no. 40, 45, 50, and 55, as described in the 1905 catalog.

Figure 16 (below). The Victor Machinists', Junior, and Handy screwdrivers from the same catalog.

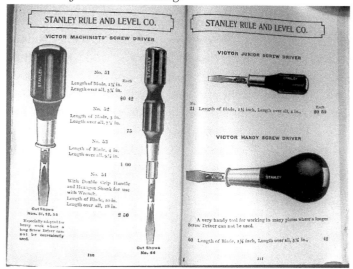

Patrick H. Garrity of Waterbury, Connecticut, filed an application on August 11, 1902 (Figure 13) for a variation of George E. Wood's patent. Garrity's patent provided for a screwdriver shank with a solid, square head that was recessed into the top end of the handle. This invention was granted a patent on March 24, 1903.

Figure 17. The Stanley Victor Handy screwdriver, no. 60.

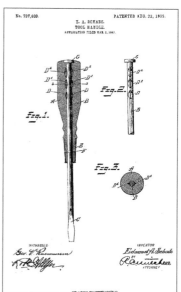

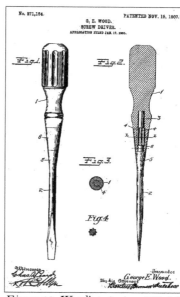

Figure 18. Edmund A. Schade's patent of August 22, 1905.

Figure 19. Wood's patent no. 871,154 granted November 19, 1907.

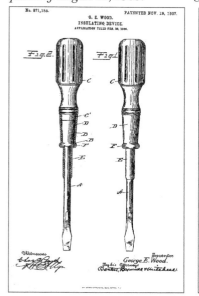

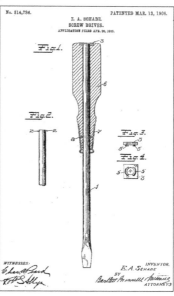

Figure 20. Wood's patent with a rubber insulating jacket.

Figure 21. Schade's patent had a round shank recessed on the top.

Garrity's patent was apparently purchased by Stanley before 1905 because his patent was used on a line of Stanley screwdrivers known as "Victor" screwdrivers that were offered in Stanley's 1905 catalog no. 34. Figure 14 shows pages 106 and 107 of that catalog, describing the various sizes available for the no. 20 and 25 Victor screwdrivers. Pages 108 and 109 (Figure 15) of that catalog describe the Victor cabinetmaker's line and special screwdrivers. In addition to the standard and cabinetmaker's screwdrivers, Stanley also manufactured Victor machinist's screwdrivers (Figure 16), which were extra heavy in construction. Also offered at the time, was a small 1½-inch screwdriver, called the Victor Junior, and a Victor Handy screwdriver designed to be used in tight places (Figure 17).

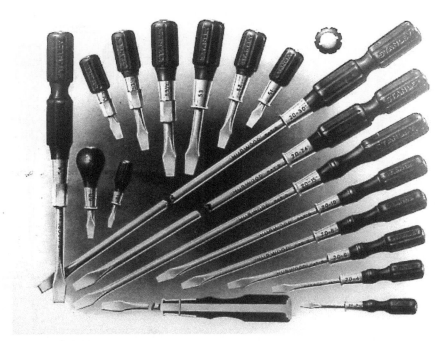

Figure 22. The Hurwood line of screwdrivers as shown on a Stanley hardware store advertising sign circa 1910.

Stanley was now offering these Victor screwdrivers in addition to its no. 64 and no. 86 flat-blade screwdrivers. A medium-grade screwdriver series, known as the Defiance brand, was offered in 1905. These screwdrivers had round shanks fastened to a wood handle by a pin through the ferrule. The shank did not go all the way through the handle. They were offered in no. 70 for regular pattern and no. 75 for the cabinetmaker's model.

Stanley was, apparently, trying to compete with the Hurwood Company and, in so doing, Edmund A. Schade filed an application for a patent on March 7, 1903. This patent was granted on August 22, 1905 (Figure 18) and was similar to George E. Wood's patent (Figure 12). Mr. Schade's patent provided for the solid shank in the handle to be made with a series of lateral projections or wings graded in size toward the head.

Meanwhile at the Hurwood Company, the sales of its screwdrivers were increasing at such a rate that the lack of adequate production equipment left the company unable to fill orders. This, coupled with management problems, led to the sale of the company to the Stanley Rule & Level Co. in 1904. Wood, because of his knowledge of the manufacturing of screwdrivers, was hired by Stanley as superintendent of the screwdriver division. He held this position until his retirement, about 1923.

Wood, now working for Stanley Rule & Level, filed an application on January 17, 1905, for another screwdriver patent (Figure 19). Granted on November 19, 1907, this patent provided for a tapered ferrule with a ribbed screwdriver shank seated into a wood handle.

One month later on February 28, 1905, Mr. Wood filed another patent for a screwdriver with a rubber insulating jacket covering the ferrule and the upper part of the shank (Figure 20). The handle's exposed grip portion was made of non-conducting material. This patent was granted on November 19, 1907.

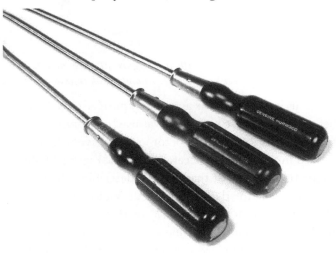

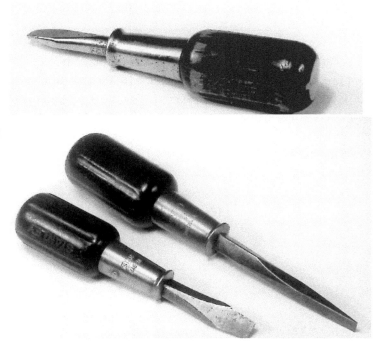

Figure 23 (above). Hurwood no. 20 screwdrivers in the 8-, 10-, and 12-inch lengths.

Figure 24 (right, top). Stanley Hurwood no. 51 machinist's screwdriver.

Figure 25 (right, bottom). Hurwood no. 52 machinist's screwdriver.

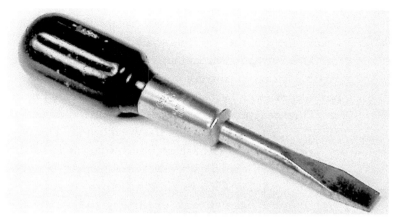

Figure 26. Hurwood machinist's screwdriver (nos. 51 and 53) with square shanks, manufactured after 1934.

Edmund A. Schade on April 20, 1905, filed another patent application for the construction of a screwdriver that retained strength, rigidity, and durability but was also economical to manufacture. This patent, granted March 13, 1906 (Figure 21), provided for a screwdriver with a round shank recessed on the top and held in the handle top by an angular metal cap that slid in from the side.

Stanley, after the purchase of the Hurwood Company, redesigned the Victor line of screwdrivers with George E. Wood's 1904 patented solid-bar design (Figure 11). This screwdriver set the standard for fine quality screwdrivers. The Victor line was renamed "Hurwood." The model numbers were kept the same, but the construction was changed to the Hurwood-design style.

The Stanley Hurwood line (Figure 22) consisted of the no. 20 and no. 25 screwdrivers, which were made in blade lengths from 2½ to 30 inches. Figure 23 shows three no. 20 screwdrivers with 8-, 10-, and 12-inch blades. The no. 25 series was the same as no. 20, except it was insulated for electrical work. The no. 40 and no. 45 screwdrivers had cabinetmaker's tips, and both were available with blade lengths from 2½ to 24½ inches in length. The no. 45 was the electrician's insulated screwdriver. Cabinet screwdrivers were made the same as standard models except the tips did not flare out at the sides. Smaller diameter shanks were offered on the no. 50 and no. 55 screwdrivers. These screwdrivers were made for fine work. The no. 55 was the same as the no. 50 except it was insulated. Blade lengths ranged from 2½ to 12 inches.

Stanley Hurwood machinist's screwdrivers were made extra heavy for rigid work. The no. 51 had an overall length of 5¼ inches with a ⅜-inch-diameter blade width and a shank length of 1¾ inches (Figure 24). The Hurwood no. 52 had a 3-inch blade, a ⁷⁄₁₆-inch diameter and an overall length of 7¼ inches (Figure 25). Another screwdriver was made the same as a no. 52, but had a ½-inch diameter blade and the blade length was 4 inches with an overall length of 9½ inches. This model was designated no. 53. The nos. 51, 52 and 53 had round shanks until 1934, when extra heavy square blades were provided (Figure 26). Hurwood's no. 54 screwdriver (the vertical screwdriver on the left side of the photo seen in Figure 22) was 18¼ inches long with a double-grip handle. The blade was 8 inches in length and ½ inch in diameter. A hexagon shank was near the ferrule, for use with a wrench.

In the Hurwood machinist's line of screwdrivers there were also three screwdrivers with hexagon shanks near the ferrule. Designated numbers 51½, 52½, and 53½, they were similar to the no. 51, 52, and 53, but they had slightly shorter blades and were heavier in weight (Figure 27). Figure 28 illustrates the Stanley Hurwood name marked on the shanks of the early examples.

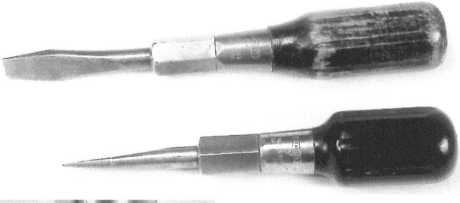

Figure 27 (above). Hurwood machinist's screw-drivers nos. 52½ and 53½.
Figure 28 (left). This close-up shows the Stanley Hurwood name as stamped on early screwdrivers.

The 100 Plus Screwdrivers

The Hurwood name, by 1909, had become the recognized standard for screwdrivers, and Hurwood-style screwdrivers remained Stanley's top-of-the-line screwdriver to the late 1920s. Hurwood no. 20 remained in production until 1987. Throughout the 1910s and into the 1920s, more inventions were created leading to the development of the 100 Plus screwdriver.

These inventions meant improvements could be made. Wood went on to patent a new design of tool handle for screwdrivers with his patent of February 23, 1909 (Figure 29). The patent provided for an offset bend in the shank that slid in a slot in the wood handle. This prevented the shank from turning in the handle when the screwdriver was turning the screw.

Charles E. Mitchell, an engineer at Stanley, was also trying to improve the screwdriver structurally. Apparently, Stanley was having problems with users striking the screwhead with the handle of the screwdriver to start the screw. This resulted in the wood handle splitting. Mitchell's patent of April 13, 1909 (Figure 30), increased the strength of the handle by placing a holding pin through the ferrule, handle, and shank. A reinforcing ring was pinned at the midpoint between the ferrule and the handle top.

At the same period of time (1909), the blades were being manufactured out of cold-rolled steel. But the cold-rolling process required that the steel be annealed or softened to keep the metal flexible and not brittle. This process oxidized and discolored the metal. Stanley found that if it carefully controlled a special gas used for heating the metal then oxidation was overcome. Thus, a smooth finish was achieved at a lower cost.

George E. Wood patented, on August 5, 1913, an improved method of forming tools and avoiding injury to the screwdriver handle during the operation (Figure 31). The method he invented consisted of forming a head on a rod. This was then inserted into a formed handle and shouldered at the head. A ferrule was next placed over the rod and tightened against the wood handle. The shank was swaged, thereby securing the ferrule and handle.

George E. Wood's son, George A. Wood, patented an improved process for making screwdrivers on May 11, 1915 (Figure 32). Wood's patent provided for securing the wood handle to the shank

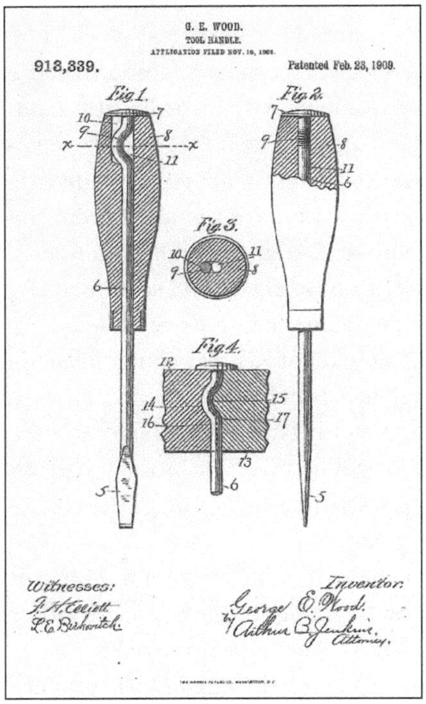

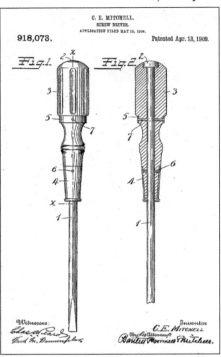

Figure 29. Wood's design for an offset bend in the shank.

Figure 30. Charles E. Mitchell's patent strengthened the handle of the screwdriver.

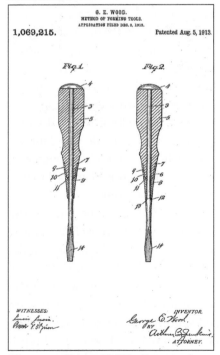

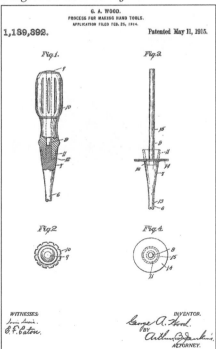

Figure 31. George E. Wood's patent for an improved method of forming tools.

Figure 32. George A. Wood (George E.'s son) was granted a patent to improve the process of securing the handle.

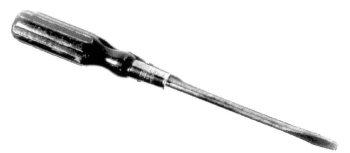

Figure 33. The Defiance, a less expensive line of screwdrivers.

Figure 34. The Stanley Four-Square screwdriver with a 2½-inch blade.

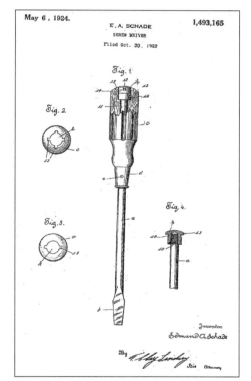

Figure 35. Edumund Schade patent of May 6, 1924. With this new patent the blade could be hardened in its entirety.

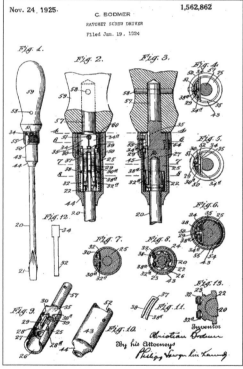

Figure 36. The Bodmer patent for a ratchet screwdriver.

with no perceptible line of division between the ferrule and bolster. In this patent there is no head on the shank and the handle is secured by other means.

The improvements brought about by both Mitchell's and the two Woods' patents, while initially created for screwdrivers, ended up being applied to chisels as well.

While all this engineering was taking place, the Hurwood line of screwdrivers, however, remained the same throughout the teens and into the 1920s.

During this period a less expensive line of screwdrivers, named "Defiance," was produced. Defiance screwdrivers were manufactured in a standard tip (no. 70) (Figure 33) and a cabinetmaker's tip (no. 75), and both had red handles. Sizes ranged from 2½- to 18-inch blade lengths. The Defiance screwdrivers had a squared shank at the end that was forced into the handle. Then a pin was placed through the ferrule, handle, and shank to secure it.

In 1923, Stanley introduced the Four-Square line of household tools. With this line, four screwdrivers were offered. They were made in 1½, 2½-, 4-, and 5-inch blade lengths (Figure 34). The Four-Square screwdrivers were basically a Defiance no. 70 screwdriver but with a reshaped wood handle. The Four-Square screwdrivers remained in production to 1935.

Edmund A. Schade patented, on May 6, 1924 (Figure 35), a different arrangement for securing the handle to the shank. His approach was that the shank had the head end threaded to accept a cap. The cap had any amount of lugs

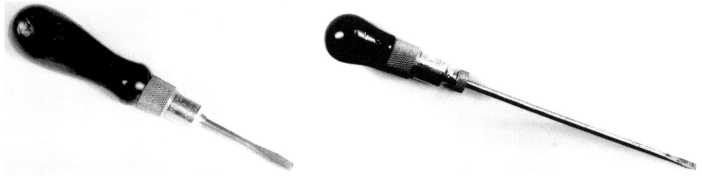

Figure 37. The Stanley no. 215, a ratchet screwdriver based on Bodmer's patent.

Figure 38. The 216, a ratchet screwdriver with a cabinet tip.

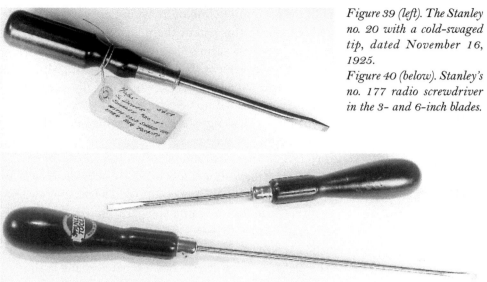

Figure 39 (left). The Stanley no. 20 with a cold-swaged tip, dated November 16, 1925.
Figure 40 (below). Stanley's no. 177 radio screwdriver in the 3- and 6-inch blades.

radio screwdrivers, which meet the demand for radio work of all descriptions (Figure 40).[3] These screwdrivers had a %64-inch diameter shank and a cabinet tip. They were made in blade lengths of 2, 3, 4, 6, and 8 inches, and had handles with a fluted part near the ferrule, so that delicate adjustment of a screw could be made. These screwdrivers remained in the Stanley line until 1964, when their handles were replaced with plastic. They continue in the Stanley line today.

On February 10, 1927 (Figure 41), Christian Bodmer, an engineer at Stanley, filed the patent that introduced the bolster-type construction on a screwdriver. In this type of construction, the shank of the screwdriver was forged and knurled on the handle receiving end and then tempered to the desirable hardness. This shank would then be driven into a bolster, which had ribs on its outer side. The shank and bolster, with an insulating washer, were next driven into the handle through the previously fitted ferrule. The insulating washer was part of the patent and would be used on the new 100 Plus line of screwdrivers. This patent was granted on July 16, 1929, but the bolster part wouldn't be used until 1932.

which prevented the wood handle from turning (usually two or four). The main feature of this patent was that the blade in its entirety could be hardened and finished, ready for sale and then placed in the handle. Once in the handle, it would be pinned through the ferrule. Hardening of the entire blade reduced or nearly eliminated the blade bending while being used to pry something.

While Stanley engineers were working on ways to make their tough screwdrivers tougher, Christian Bodmer of Stanley filed, in January 1924, a patent for a ratchet screwdriver (Figure 36). This patent would launch Stanley as a competitor with North Brothers' "Yankee" brand of ratchet screwdrivers. These Stanley screwdrivers would be designated Stanley's no. 215 and 216 ratchet screwdrivers. These ratchet screwdrivers were nickel-plated and had rosewood handles. No. 215 (Figure 37) had a standard tip and was offered in six sizes ranging from 2- to 8-inch blades. The no. 216 (Figure 38) had a cabinet tip and was offered in five sizes ranging from 2 to 6 inches.

Stanley, by the mid-1920s, was experimenting with cold-swaged tips on its screwdrivers, after the blade went through regular forging. Figure 39 shows a 5-inch no. 20 Stanley screwdriver with a cold-swaged tip dated November 16, 1925. The model no. 20 was its standard type Hurwood screwdriver.

The year 1925 would see the introduction of Stanley's no. 177

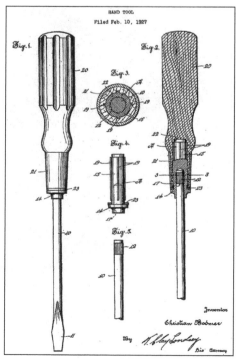

Figure 41. Bodmer's patent of July 16, 1929, which had a bolster-type construction.

In 1927 Stanley introduced the 100 Plus (Figure 42). These screwdrivers had a forged, one-piece, tempered blade including a bolster and special wings on two sides. The handles were hickory with leather washers at the top, similar to a chisel handle. The one-piece shank and bolster, with an insulating washer, was driven under pressure into the handle through a ferrule. Figure 43 illustrates a salesman's cutaway model next to a complete screwdriver. Notice the wings through the ferrule in the cutaway. The 100 Plus line claimed to have the strongest handles on the market to withstand pounding. The 100 Plus models included the no. 1001 with standard tip and the no. 1003 with cabinet tip.

The no. 680 square-shank Heavy-Duty screwdriver (Figure 44) was also introduced in 1927. These were heavy-duty screwdrivers with a similar construction to that of the 100 Plus line but with a square shank that could be gripped with a wrench. These were advertised as "made especially for garage mechanics, millwrights and others who require a screwdriver that will stand up under severe usage."[4] Handles were made of hickory with leather washers. No. 680 screwdrivers were made in 4-, 6-, 8-, 12-, and 16-inch lengths.

Stanley's 1931 automotive catalog introduced the no. 270, a 25¢ cent screwdriver for home use; it was Stanley's

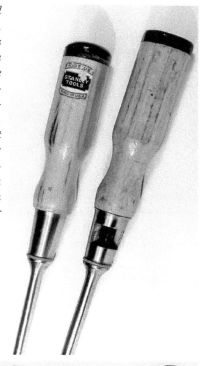

Figure 42 (left) and Figure 43 (right). The Stanley 100 Plus screwdriver, which had a forged, one-piece tempered blade including a bolster and special wings on two sides. Figure 42 is a first production. Figure 43 shows a second production example next to a salesman's model with a cut away revealing the construction.

first multi-color tool line.[5] They were advertised to be the best 25¢ screwdrivers produced. The handles of these screwdrivers were colorful with two-color combinations. They came in red and black, orange and black, green and black, yellow and black, and blue and black (Figure 45). They were offered in 4-, 5-, and 6-inch shank lengths and were ¼ inch and $\frac{5}{16}$ inch in diameter.

In 1934, the no. 270 screwdriver handle was changed to a natural color, and the number of sizes increased to eight, starting with the 2½-inch blade length. The largest was 12 inches. A new screwdriver (no. 1070) with a smaller handle used the two-color combination. It was offered at a very inexpensive cost and was cheaper than the no. 270.

Another screwdriver, called the Grip-E-Grip, was introduced by Stanley in July 1931. This utilized Emerson Warner's patent for a unique hand grip. Warner's patent, filed July 26, 1930, provided for grit-like sand to be applied in the lacquer finish on the handle of screwdrivers to enable a user with oily hands to get a better grip when using the tool. Warner's patent was granted May 1932 (Figure 46). The Grip-E-Grip screwdriver was numbered no. 700 and was first approved by the operations committee, Department 58 of Stanley Tools, on September 9, 1930. The handles of these screwdrivers were available in four colors—red, orange, green, or blue—and had the words "Grip-E-Grip" on the handle (Figure 47). Six blade lengths were offered from 3 to 10 inches. The Grip-E-Grip was discontinued in 1933.

In 1932, Stanley also introduced a new handle material that was advertised to be tough, non-flammable, and a perfect insulator against electricity. The new line, designated no. 1002, was called "Lastex" (Figure 48). They were available in six sizes, the usual 4-, 5-, 6-, 8-, 10-, and 12-inch lengths. The tips were cross-ground to prevent slippage when in use. This was the first use of cross-grinding, which is an operation that produces crosswise ridges on the tip. This prevents the screwdriver from climbing out of the screw slot. Stanley claimed it was "one of the most important mechanical improvements ever made in the screwdriver and was originated by Stanley."[6] The Lastex line was discontinued in December 1936.

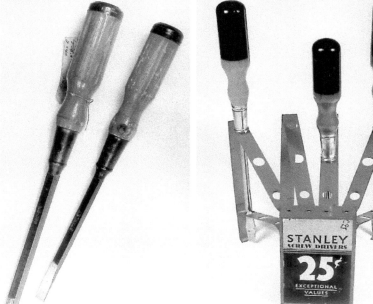

Figure 44 (left). Stanley's Heavy Duty no. 680 in the 6- and 8-inch sizes. Figure 45 (right). An original hardware store display stand showing Stanley's no. 270 screwdrivers.

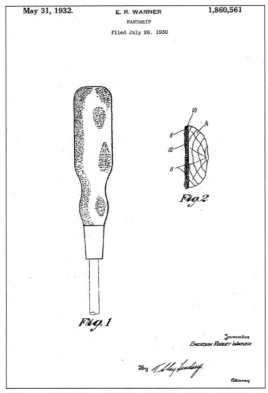

Figure 46. Emerson Warner's patent for a handgrip.

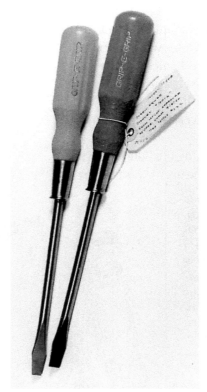

Figure 47. Examples of Stanley's no. 700 Grip-E-Grip screwdriver in the 6-inch size with orange and red finish.

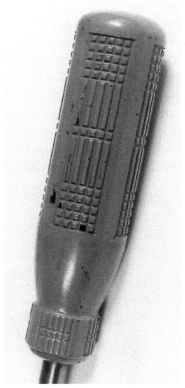

Figure 48. Stanley's "Lastex" handle used on no. 1002 screwdrivers.

Specialized Screwdrivers

Although based on Christian Bodmer's patent of July 16, 1929, the 100 Plus screwdrivers used only part of Bodmer's patent—the outside ferrule and the insulating washer, not the bolster that was included in the patent. Bodmer's patent called for a knurled shank, which could be driven under pressure into the bolster. Apparently, tests showed that under severe usage this design was not substantial enough.

Harris Cook, another inventor at Stanley, patented an improvement (Figure 49) on Bodmer's patent by forming four wings and grooves on the shank, which was then driven into the bolster. The bolster had two rings formed on it.

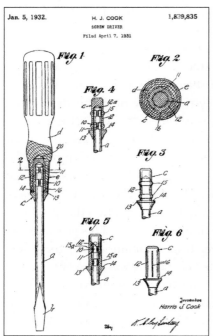

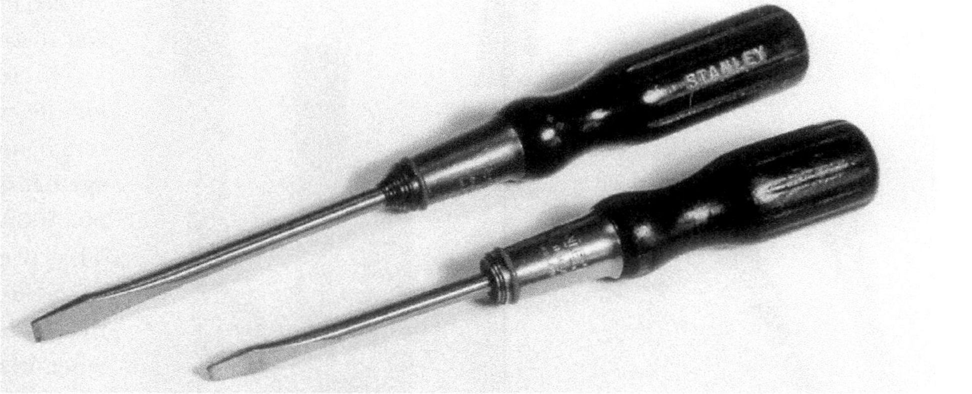

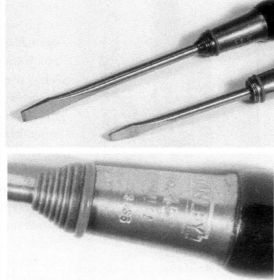

Figure 49 (far left). Harris J. Cook's patent of January 5, 1932.

Figure 50 (above). The Hurwood bolster-type screwdriver no. 25, developed by Harris J. Cook with 3-inch and 4-inch blades.

Figure 51 (left). A close-up of the ferrule on the bolster-type screwdriver shown in Figure 50.

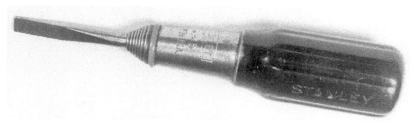

Figure 52 (above). Stanley's no. 45 cabinet tip, 1½-inch blade screwdriver.

Figure 53 (below). Stanley made the no. KS 6854 especially for the Bell Telephone Company. Note the "Bell System" mark.

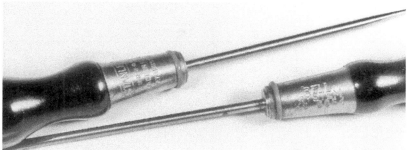

These rings lined up to the grooves of the shank when the bolster was inserted into it. After the shank was driven into the bolster, the bolster was placed into a die that squeezed the rings into the grooves and wings of the shank. It also placed four ribs on the outside of the bolster. The shank and bolster were next inserted with an insulating washer into the handle and ferrule and driven tight, thereby preventing axial movement between shank, bolster, and handle. Beginning in 1934, this new bolster-type construction was used on upgraded screwdrivers, nos. 25, 45, and 55.

The Hurwood bolster-type construction no. 25 screwdriver featured a standard tip (Figures 50 and 51) and was available in 2½-, 3-, 4-, 5-, 6-, 8-, 10-, and 12-inch blade lengths. This type screwdriver was also manufactured with a parallel-sided cabinet tip (Figure 52) in 1½-, 2½-, 3-, 4-, 5-, 6-, 8-, 10-, and 12-inch blades. Cabinet tips are parallel-sided blades that do not flare out at the tip and are the same diameter throughout the shank.

A light-duty, small-blade, bolster-type screwdriver—designated no. 55—was made for electrical work and for small screws. This screwdriver had a smaller standard tip with a ⁵⁄₁₆-inch-diameter blade and was produced in lengths 1½ to 12 inches.

The Bell Telephone Company was quick to see the quality of this type of screwdriver and had Stanley manufacture for them a special screwdriver with a 3½-inch blade, ⅛-inch diameter shank, and a cabinet tip. These screwdrivers were marked KS 6854 and Bell System (Figure 53) and were perfect for telephone line work.

Around 1935, Stanley engineers also experimented with a pear-shaped handle for the no. 25 screwdriver (Figure 54). Apparently, production costs were too high and it never went into full production.

Another experimental screwdriver, made in about 1935, is shown in Figure 55. This Hurwood no. 20, with an 8-inch blade, was fitted with a maple handle lacquered in satin black and grooved in a diamond pattern to improve the grip. It made a very interesting screwdriver, but it probably didn't make it out of the production shop.

On December 26, 1933, Austin Stowell of Stanley filed a patent for a spark-testing screwdriver (Figure 56). The patent was granted on July 21, 1936, but production had obviously begun in 1934. The nos. 88, 1011, and 1014 screwdrivers are illustrated on page 105 of Stanley's 1934 catalog (Figure 57).

The no. 1011 screwdriver had a standard tip and a pocket clip. It was kept in the Stanley line until 1955. The no. 1014 had a cabinet tip and remained in Stanley's line until 1971, when it was renumbered no. 66-140, which was produced until 1989. In 1960, Stanley added the same screwdriver under the Stanley Handyman logo as no. 3014 (Figure 58). These screwdrivers had a clear plastic and red handle.

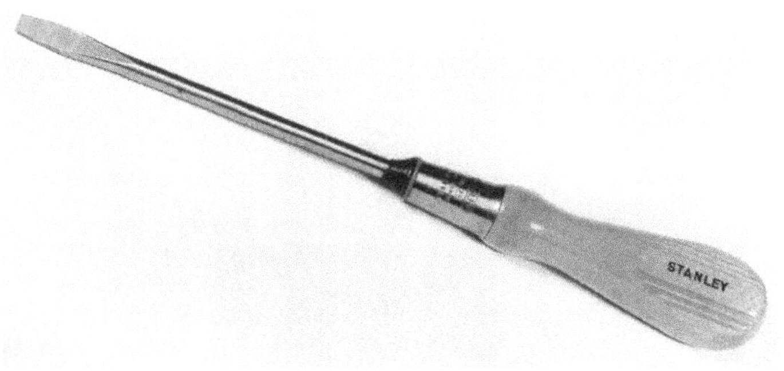

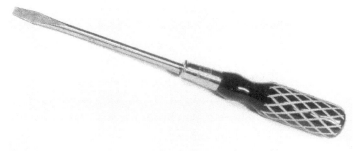

Figure 54. The no. 25 screwdriver with the experimental pear-shaped handle was manufactured circa 1935, but was never placed into production.

Figure 55. The no. 20 screwdriver had an 8-inch blade and the experimental maple handle that was lacquered in satin black and grooved in a diamond pattern. This Hurwood screwdriver probably was also not mass produced.

On July 3, 1934, Henry Phillips of Portland, Oregon, filed two patents for a "means for uniting a screw with a driver" (Figures 59a and b and Figure 60). These patents were granted on July 7, 1936, and were the beginning of the Phillips-head screw. Mr. Phillips assigned the patent to his company, the Phillips Screw Co., incorporated in Wilmington, Delaware. On January 15, 1935, Henry Phillips filed two additional patents concerning the Phillips head screw and driver (Figures 61 and 62). The Phillips-head screw had a tapering recess that extended into the upper portion of a screw head, which has alternating ribs and flutes. Today these screws have taken over the market in fastening devices, not only on screws but on small bolts as well. Phillips's patents also claimed the driving tool used on these Phillips-head fasteners.

Henry Phillips saw the potential use of his invention, but he also knew that success of this invention would only happen if he licensed out his patent for other companies to use. Stanley, seeing the potential of the Phillips-head screw, applied for Phillips's license and received license no. 1.

Stanley's interest was not in manufacturing the screws but in making screwdrivers to use with them. With the no. 1 license in hand, Stanley quickly developed a Phillips-head screwdriver and offered it to the trade beginning in April 1937. The no. 2701 through 2704 models were screwdrivers meant for general use (Figure 63). The no. 2701 had a no. 1 size tip; no. 2702 had a no. 2 size tip; no. 2703 had a no. 3 size tip; and no. 2704 had a no. 4 size tip. These were different size Phillips recesses (Figure 64).

At the same time, a heavy-duty model was made and bore Stanley numbers 2501 through 2504. Also introduced were two stubby screwdrivers, one with a 1-inch blade and a Phillips no. 1 tip. The other was a 1½-inch shank and a Phillips no. 2 tip. They were numbered 2711 and 2712 (Figure 65).

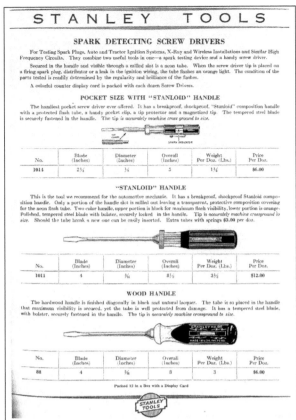

Figure 56 (above). Austin Stowell's patent for a spark-testing screwdriver. Although the patent is dated 1936, production began in 1934 as evidenced by Stanley's 1934 catalog (Figure 57 at right).

Figure 57 (right). Page 105 from Stanley's 1934 catalog, no. 134.

Figure 58. The Stanley Handyman, no. 3014, spark-test screwdrivers on a display card.

Another interesting screwdriver was invented by Austin Stowell of Stanley. He filed a patent in February 1937 (Figure 66) for a screwdriver with a light inside it to illuminate a screw head while using the driver. His patent was granted in May 1939, but Stanley manufactured and offered the screwdriver for sale beginning in October 1937 as its no. 1021 "Flash-lite" screwdriver, with an octagonal brass case. It had a 2-inch, cabinet-tip blade and a total length of 5⅝ inches (Figure 67). This screwdriver was discontinued in 1941. At the same time, a no. 1020 Flash-lite screwdriver was offered, which also had a cabinet tip, but had a 5-inch blade and was 10½ inches in length. The case was a "Stanloid" black and amber composition. This screwdriver used two batteries and was discontinued in 1940 (Figure 68).

By the end of the 1930s, Stanley created another interesting screwdriver for use by electricians and auto mechanics. It was called Stanley's Jack Knife screwdriver no. 1022 (Figure 69) and was manufactured from 1939 to 1941. It had a 4-inch, parallel-tip blade. This screwdriver was basically the no. 45 bolster-type screwdriver (described on page 109) with a thicker ¼-inch diameter blade and a 2-inch jack knife fitted to the handle.

Also in 1939, Stanley experimented with two other Jack Knife screwdrivers. One had a composition Stanloid handle with a push-button locking mechanism to remove the knife from the handle. The other was a no. 70 standard-tip screwdriver with a 6-inch blade, ⁵⁄₁₆-inch diameter, and a friction fit removable jack knife in the handle (Figure 70).

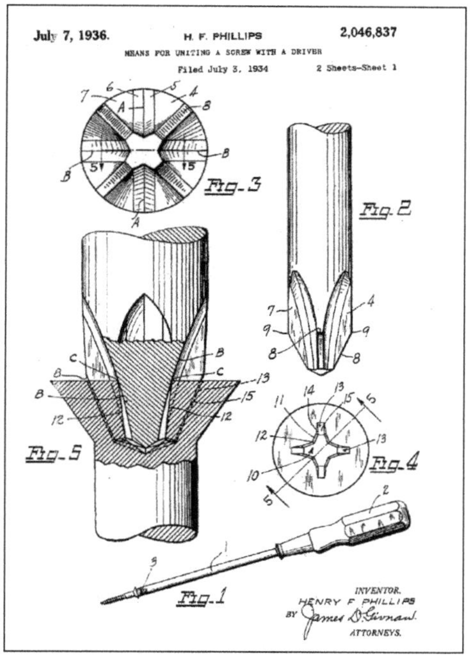

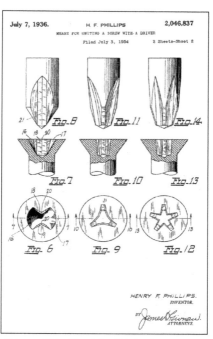

Figure 59a. Henry Phillips's patent 2,046,837 of July 7, 1936, for the Phillips screw and driver.

Figure 59b. Sheet 2 of patent 2,046,837 for Phillips's screw and driver.

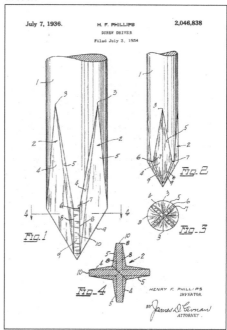

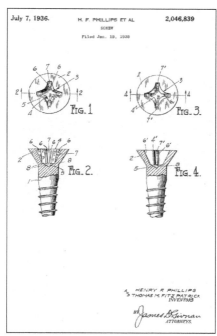

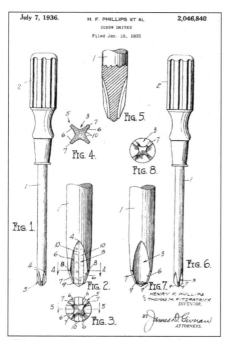

Figure 60. Henry Phillips's patent no. 2,046,838 of July 7, 1936, for a Phillips's screwdriver. Stanley received license no. 1 from Phillips to manufacture this screwdriver.

Figure 61. Phillips's patent no. 2,046, 839 for a screw was also issued on July 7, 1936.

Figure 62. Patent no. 2,046,840 for a screwdriver was also issued to Phillips on July 7, 1936.

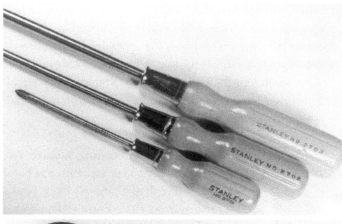

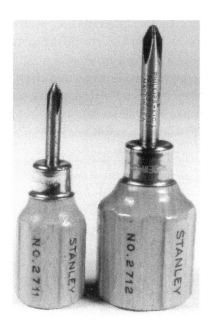

Figure 63 (left, top). Stanley's no. 2701, 2702, and 2703 Phillips-head screw drivers.

Figure 64 (left, bottom). A Stanley display showing seven sizes of Phillips screws.

Figure 65 (right). Stanley screwdriver model nos. 2711 and 2712.

Beginning around 1935, Stanley manufactured several models of screwdrivers using Stanloid handles. Stanley boasted in its 1939 catalog that, "Stanloid two-tone, amber-colored handles were made from the toughest non-metallic substance ever."[7] These plastic-handle screwdrivers were called Stanloid and were offered in standard, square-blade, and cabinet tips. Earlier models were numbered 1006, 1007,

and 1008. These screwdrivers had the usual blade lengths, ranging from 4 to 12 inches. Stubby screwdrivers were also made with 1-inch and 1¾-inch blade lengths with standard tips and were numbered 1009, 1012, and 1013.

At the same time, another line of plastic-handle screwdrivers was introduced with numbers starting with 2006 (Figure 71). This line was part of the Victor line and was a medium-priced screwdriver.

A third line of plastic screwdrivers was introduced under the Hercules name and consisted of standard, cabinet tip, stubby or close, quarter size, and pocket screwdrivers. They were available in a range of sizes and were numbered in the 3006

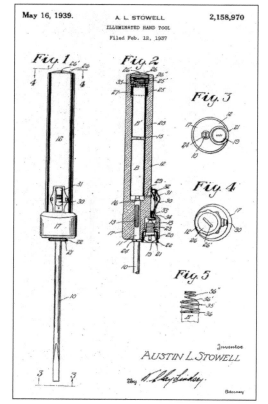

Figure 66 (left). Austin Stowell's patent for the "Flash-lite" screwdriver shown in Figure 67.

Figure 67 (below). Stanley's no. 1021 "Flash-lite" screwdriver.

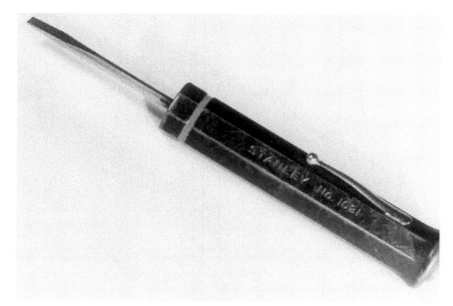

STANLEY SCREW DRIVERS
NEW! "FLASH-LITE" SCREW DRIVERS

Practical and novel. A handy screw driver and a flashlight combined into one attractive much needed tool. Ideal for auto mechanics, radio, refrigerator and oil burner service men, gas station attendants, piano tuners, car owners and others who need it for working and lighting in dark places.

The "Stanloid" black and amber composition handle holds two standard batteries and a flashlight bulb. The blade is made of the finest steel, tempered overall, highly polished and protected from rust with clear lacquer. The tip is machine cross ground to size and magnetized for picking up small objects.

Should the blade break a new one can be driven in. Extra blades $0.20 each. Furnished with a bulb, but with or without batteries. Nos. 1020 A and B packed six in a box with a display card; No. 1020 one in a box.

No.	Blade (Inches)	Bar (Inches)	Overall (Inches)	Packet	Price Each
1020 With Batteries	5	3/16	10½	1 only— ⅜ Lbs.	$2.05
1020A No Batteries	5	3/16	10½	6 only—1⅜ Lbs.	1.90
1020B With Batteries	5	3/16	10½	6 only—1¾ Lbs.	2.05

Figure 68. Page 109 of Stanley catalog no. 138 (1939) showing the no. 1020 "Flash-lite" screwdriver.

to 3027 range but not consecutively. All of the Hercules screwdrivers were budget-priced, low-end drivers.

By 1940 and through to the 1950s, the plastic-handle screwdriver gained in popularity and the offerings of models and sizes increased. Slowly the plastic-handle screwdrivers took over the line. By the 1970s, wood-handle screwdrivers were almost eliminated from the line, and by 1989, wood-handle screwdrivers no longer produced by Stanley.

Notes
1. Patent description for patent no. 671,039, April 2, 1901.
2. "I Drive Stanley Screwdrivers Handles," *Stanley Tool Talks*, no. 15. (1938): 3.
3. The radio had become so important in American life that ownership of household radio was one of the questions on the 1930 U.S. census (question no. 9, under "Home Data").
4. *Stanley Works*, catalog 129 (1929):124.
5. *Stanley Works Automotive Catalog*, no. 27 (1931).
6. "I Harden Stanley Screwdriver Blades," *Stanley Tool Talks* no. 16 (1939).
7. *Stanley Tools*, catalog no. 139 (1939): 109.

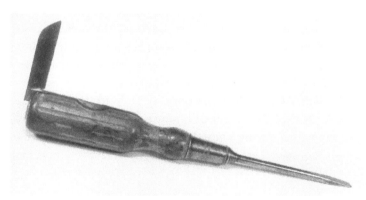

Figure 69 (above). Stanley's no. 1022 Jack Knife screwdriver which was made from 1939 until 1941.

Figure 70 (below). Stanley's no. 70 Jack Knife screwdriver with removable knife.

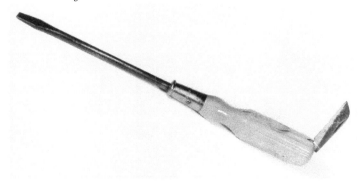

Figure 71 (above). Stanley's no. 2006, 8-inch screwdriver with the "Stanloid" handle.

Brace Up for a Bit of Stanley History

The Stanley Rule & Level Company, having been formed by the merger of A. Stanley & Company and Hall and Knapp, was, in 1857, a manufacturer of boxwood and ivory rules, levels, sliding T-bevels, and try squares. By 1859, marking and mortise gauges were added to the line. In 1862 the Stanley Rule & Level Company purchased the E. A. Stearns & Co. rule business of Brattleboro, Vermont, from Charles L. Mead. By the middle of the 1860s, Henry Stanley incorporated Augustus Stanley's tool-handle business into the Rule & Level Company. This change helped the Stanley Rule & Level Company through the disruption of the Civil War when the tool industry was hit with hard times. Mallets, hand screws, handles for planes, axes, picks, adzes, sledges, and hammers were made on a Blancard lathe during the war. In 1869, Stanley's purchase of Leonard Bailey's Boston, Massachusetts, plane business was a daring step since metallic planes had not yet been fully accepted in the marketplace. But this endeavor would prove, by 1900, to be Stanley's greatest acquisition, as it made Stanley the largest carpenter's hand tools company in America.

On November 20, 1869, Augustus Stanley—one of the original founders of A. Stanley—received a patent for a bit stock (Figure 1). This brace was made of cast iron and had a *lignum vitae* head (Figure 2). The bit was held in place with a latch or pawl. Stanley only offered it in 1870; apparently, it was not too successful. Stanley would not reenter the bit stock or brace business for thirty-three years, when the company purchased three brace manufacturers in the early 1900s. When the decision was made to enter a new tool field, management always felt that it was better to purchase an existing toolmaker's business with the following characteristics. The company to be acquired must have:

- *first hand knowledge of what users required of that particular kind of tool;*
- *experience in manufacturing the tool;*
- *a work force of skilled craftsmen in their particular techniques;*
- *specialized equipment required for the production of this kind of tool;*
- *patents on the article and patents or trade secrets on the methods of production; and finally,*
- *able management people and an established reputation with tool users.*

If Stanley could find a company that would possess as many of these characteristics as possible, then the company would have a high success rate with the tool. Stanley had long wanted to enter the bit brace business and, in 1903, the opportunity came up to purchase three companies that made quality braces. The companies were: Parmenter and Bullock, of Gananoque, Canada; Mason and Parker, of Winchendon, Massachusetts; and the Harry S. Bartholomew Co. of Bristol, Connecticut. With the purchase of these three companies, Stanley acquired the machinery and manufacturing know-how to offer a line of bit braces.

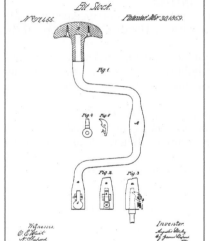

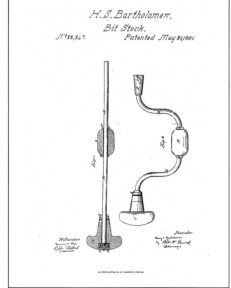

Figure 1 (left). 1869 bit stock patent.

Figure 2 (below). A brace made from the patent.

Figure 3 (right). Harry S. Bartholomew's 1861 bit brace patent.

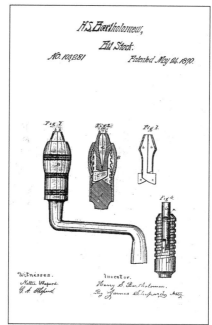

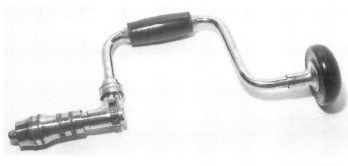

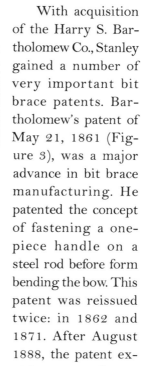

Figure 4 (left). The Bartholomew chuck patent for use on the no. 139 brace.

Figure 5 (above). The Bartholomew no. 139 brace.

Figure 6 (right). The no. 139 brace's distinctive thimble nut.

Figure 7 (below). An early Stanley no. 946 brace.

With acquisition of the Harry S. Bartholomew Co., Stanley gained a number of very important bit brace patents. Bartholomew's patent of May 21, 1861 (Figure 3), was a major advance in bit brace manufacturing. He patented the concept of fastening a one-piece handle on a steel rod before form bending the bow. This patent was reissued twice: in 1862 and 1871. After August 1888, the patent expired and most brace manufacturers used his patent. In May 1870, Bartholomew patented a chuck with adjustable automatic jaws (Figure 4). The chuck isshown on an H. S. Bartholomew no. 139 brace in Figures 5 and 6. Notice the distinctive thimble nut, or shell. Shown in Figure 7 is an early Stanley no. 946 brace, with Bartholomew's automatic jaws and chuck. This chuck was discontinued by 1907.

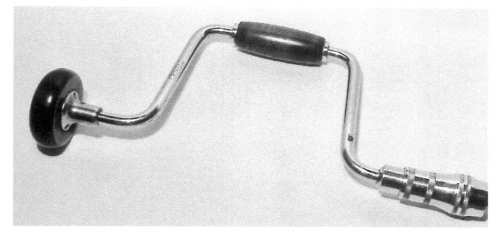

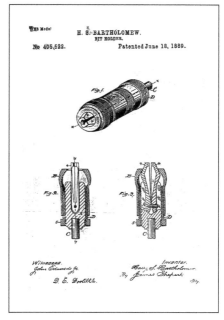

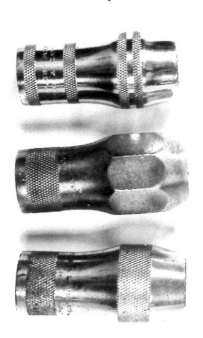

Figure 8 (left). Bartholomew's patent for a chuck with a differential thread bit holder.

Figures 9 (above) and 10 (right) show variations in the jaws and sleeves.

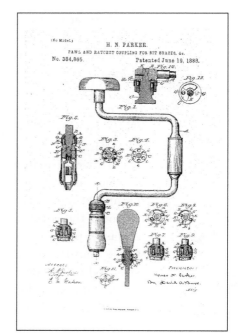

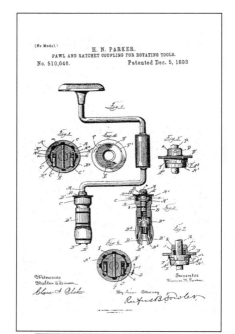

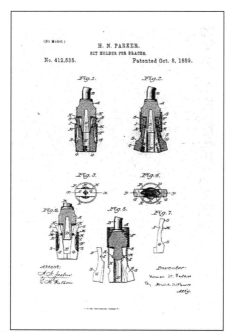

Figures 11, 12 and 13 (above). The three patents acquired by Stanley with the purchase of Mason and Parker. Figures 11 and 12 (above, left and middle) are the patents for bit braces and Figure 13 (above, right) shows the chuck patent.

Figure 14 (near right). Charles Mitchell's patent for a redesign of Homer Newtown Parker's concealed-ratchet patent.

Figure 15 (far right). Harris J. Cook's patent for a concealed ratchet with a clutch-roller system employed.

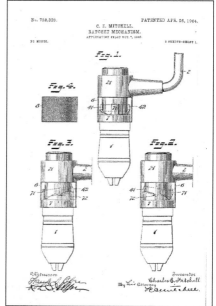

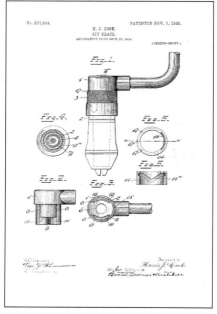

Mr. Bartholomew, in June 1889, received a patent on another chuck, called a differential thread bit holder (Figure 8). By the time Stanley acquired the Bartholomew company, the chuck was simplified to a one-piece shell, but retained the two-piece jaws (Figure 9). The first jaws were plain, followed by ones with teeth, called alligator jaws, as shown here.

The sleeves or shells were originally like the one on the top in Figure 10. Then an octagonal sleeve was available, like the one illustrated in the center of Figure 10; the type shown on the bottom was predominantly manufactured. With the purchase of Mason and Parker in 1903, Stanley acquired three patents. Two of them concerned pawls and ratchet mechanisms for bit braces (the patents of June 1888—illustrated in Figure 11—and December 1893—illustrated in Figure 12), and one was for an 1889 chuck (Figure 13). Stanley was especially interested in Homer Newtown Parker's concealed-ratchet patents. With the help of Stanley's Charles Mitchell, the

ratchet mechanism was redesigned, and a patent was filed on October 7, 1903. The patent was awarded April 26, 1904 (Figure 14). This patent was for an improvement in the tilt-pawl mechanism in the ratchet.

Harris J. Cook, another engineer at Stanley, devised another application to the concealed ratchet and filed in September 1904. This patent was received in November 1905 (Figure 15). This patent had a clutch-roller system employed rather than the tilt-pawl mechanism. Many patent designs were put into production shortly after the patent was filed in the Patent Office, but before the patent was officially granted. Joseph Bartholomew patented, in 1904, an improvement in bit brace jaws, which was used on Stanley medium-grade braces until 1908 (Figure 16). Hubert Richards of Stanley

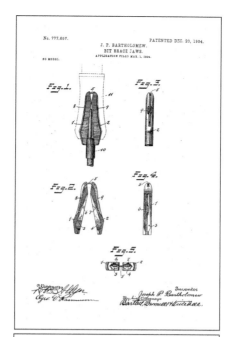

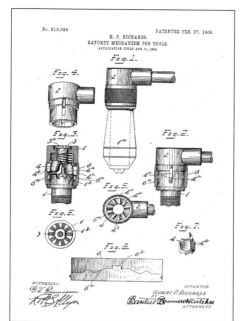

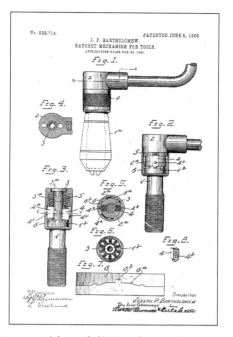

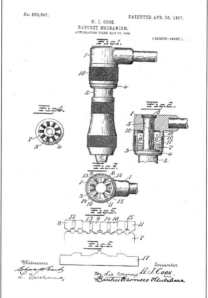

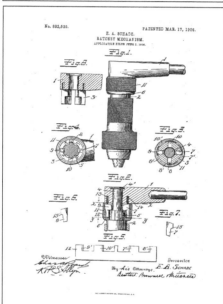

Figure 16 (above, left). Stanley used Joseph Bartholomew's improvement in bit brace jaws, on its medium-grade braces until 1908.

Figure 17 (above, middle). Hubert Richards's concealed-ratchet patent used a split pawl.

Figure 18 (above, right). Joseph Bartholomew's June 5, 1906, patent had two ratchet pawls energized by coil springs.

Figure 19 (far left). Harris Cook's improvement on Hubert Richards's concealed-ratchet design included a new configuration of the ratchet pawl.

Figure 20 (near left). Edmund Schade's improvement to Joseph Bartholomew's 1906 patent aligned the pawls and ratchets in a different direction.

further refined the concealed ratchet by using a split pawl, which would activate the ratchet direction by lifting one side or the other depending on direction desired. Richards filed his patent in April 1905, and received the patent in February 1906 (Figure 17). Joseph Bartholomew, in February 1905, thought up another arrangement whereby two ratchet pawls were energized by two coil springs (Figure 18). He received his patent in June 1906. Harris Cook, in May 1906, improved Hubert Richards's concealed-ratchet design by changing the configuration of the ratchet pawl. He received a patent on this invention in April, 1907 (Figure 19).

Edmund Schade changed Joseph Bartholomew's 1906 patent, where the configuration of the pawls and the ratchet is aligned in a different direction. This patent was granted to Schade in March 1908 (Figure 20). From 1905 to 1909, Stanley offered two models of its concealed ratchet braces, the no. 911 and the no. 921, and three models of its box-ratchet braces, nos. 913, 923, and 933.

Three models of sleeve braces— nos. 914, 924, and 934— with no ratchet were offered. Four models of its Victor ratchet braces and four models of the Victor sleeve braces were also offered.

After the Fray Purchase

In April 1909, Stanley purchased the old, established business of John S. Fray Co. of Bridgeport, Connecticut. With this acquisition a number of very early and significant brace patents were acquired. Nelson Spofford's patent of November 1859 (Figure 21) had been acquired by John Fray in 1866. Spofford's March 1880 (Figure 22)

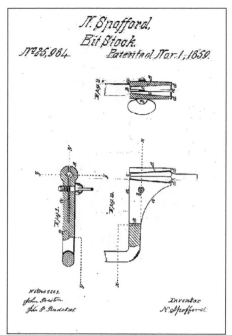

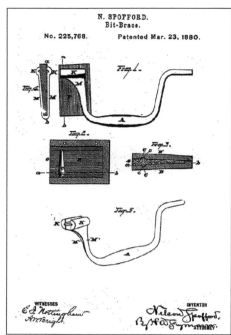

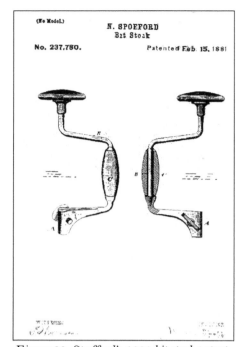

Figure 21. Spofford's 1859 patent for a clam-shell chuck bit stock.

Figure 22. Spofford's 1880 bit brace patent.

Figure 23. Spofford's 1881 bit stock patent.

and February 1881 (Figure 23) patents, also concerning the well known clam-shell chuck, were assigned to John Fray. The Spofford brace was thus manufactured by Fray and then by Stanley. An advertisement that appeared in the July 1890 issue of *Iron Age* magazine showed the Fray line of braces (Figure 24). The close-up shows the clam-shell chuck. Stanley/Fray made these Spofford bit braces in 7-, 8-, 10-, 12-, and 14-inch sweeps (Figure 25).

The Stanley/Fray no. 107 through no. 114 braces differ from the nos. 7 through 14 series in that they have cocobolo heads and handles (Figure 26). Another brace that Fray made is the no. 12 Spofford double crank, or whimble brace, for mill-wrights and ship carpenters (Figure 27). It is a take-off of Fray's May 11, 1869, patent (Figure 28), which was for a detachable brace extension.

The Stanley/Fray no. 12 whimble brace was discontinued in the late teens. Stanley reintroduced it in 1929 as a no. 12W, a modified version of the earlier no. 12 (Figure 29).

On July 14, 1888, John Fray filed a patent for a ratchet brace. (The patent was granted in January 1889). This patent would become the standard ratchet mechanism for most of the Victor line of bit braces often advertised as moderately price braces (Figure 30; see also Figure 24).

John Fray also received a patent on December 25,

1888, for a brace chuck (Figure 31), which had a spring connecting the jaws so that when the chuck was loosened the jaws would open. The jaws were produced either plain or with teeth, called alligator jaws.

Joseph Bartholomew, in November 1908, received a patent for an interlocking chuck (Figure 32). This chuck was used on the Fray nos. 66 through 166 ratchet braces and Stanley's nos. 917, 918, and 919 braces (Figure 33).

Figure 24 (above). Fray advertisement from Iron Age magazine, July 1890.

Figure 25 (below). No. 8 Stanley/Fray Spofford brace.

Figure 26. No. 108 Stanley/Fray Spofford brace.

Figure 27. No. 12 Stanley/Fray whimble brace.

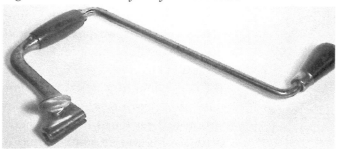

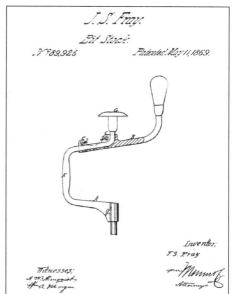

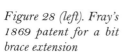

Figure 28 (left). Fray's 1869 patent for a bit brace extension

Figure 29 (above). Stanley's no. 12W whimble brace.

In July 1909, another patent was granted to Joseph Bartholomew for a ball bearing chuck (Figure 34). These chucks were used on the no. 811 and 813 braces after 1911. Early models used the Fray alligator jaws. John Fray and Hubert Richards were granted patents in 1910 for several ball bearing chucks (Figures 35 and 36).

The John Fray line of braces, when acquired by Stanley, consisted of ratchet braces and sleeve braces. The ratchet braces were made up of a bow connected to a chuck with the addition of a ratchet mechanism. This allowed the user to drill a hole in a restricted area where the bow could not be rotated a full 360 degrees. (A sleeve brace was merely a bow connected to a chuck. The user had to swing the brace a full 360 degrees to bore a hole as will be illustrated in Figure 40). Each of the ratchet

and the sleeve braces were offered in various grades, i.e., a ball bearing head with a steel-clad underside or a ball bearing head with a partial-clad underside.

Top grade braces used cocobolo heads and handles while lower grade braces used ebonized or mahogany-finished hardwood. Higher grade braces used drop-forged steel for the jaws; lower grade braces used plain cast-steel jaws. High grade braces were furnished with a closed ratchet where low grades had an open ratchet. Full nickel-plated metal parts were furnished on high grade tools versus plain polished parts on low grades.

The Fray numbering system consisted of several numbering patterns. The ratchet braces were graded nos. 1 through 9. The sweep size was then added to the left side of the number, so a grade 1 ball bearing, steel-clad head, ratchet bit brace in a 10-inch sweep would have a number of 101. The same brace with a 6-inch sweep would be a no. 61.

A no. 1 brace was the top of the line with the best sleeve chuck, forged-steel jaws with spring (see Figure 31), fully nickel-plated, and cocobolo head and handle. The no. 2 was a medium-finished ratchet brace with the same chuck, and would be designated no. 142 for a 14-inch sweep brace (Figure 37). The no. 3 braces would be plain polished ratchet braces. The nos. 1, 2, and 3 were the standard ratchet-sleeve chuck braces. The top grade was represented by no. 1; no. 3 was average grade. Fray's no. 4 braces were top-of-the-line ball bearing chucks. This was a different chuck and this line was made in 8-, 10-, 12-, 14-, and 16-inch sweeps, known as Fray's Dreadnought pattern.

No. 5 ratchet bit braces, having cast-steel alligator jaws, were the next lower grade

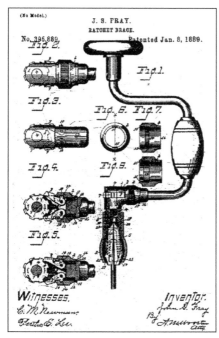

Figure 30. Fray's January 1889 patent for a ratchet brace.

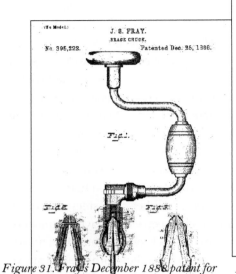

Figure 31. Fray's December 1888 patent for a brace chuck.

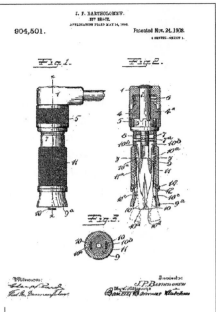

Figure 32. Bartholomew's 1908 interlocking bit brace chuck.

from no. 3 braces. These braces later would become Stanley's no. 945 and 955 braces (Figure 38). The Fray no. 5 series was discontinued October 31, 1927. However, the Stanley no. 945 braces were offered (same brace, different number) as early as 1909 and continued to be manufactured until 1963 with some improvements added.

Fray's no. 6 braces were made with the interlocking chuck design (see Figure 32). Here again, the sweep is designated in the number. For example, a 6-inch sweep would be no. 66 (see Figure 33).

Fray's numbering system did not include no. 7 and no. 8, but with the invention of Fray's ball bearing chuck in 1910 (see Figures 35 and 36), a no. 9 line of ratchet bit braces was established. These braces were manufactured in 10-, 12-, 14-, and 16-inch sweeps. Figure 39 shows a no. 109 brace.

Fray and Stanley also offered non-ratchet sleeve bit braces in various grades from nos. 2 through 6. The numbering system was just the opposite of the ratchet bit braces, in that a no. 2, in a 10-inch sweep, would be designated a no. 210.

A no. 2 series sleeve bit brace was the same as a no. 1 ratchet brace except it did not have a

Figure 33. Fray's no. 66 brace with interlocking chuck.

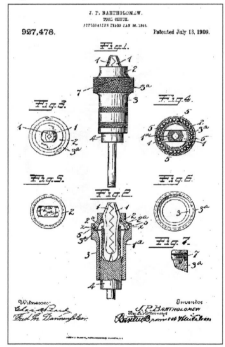

Figure 34. Bartholomew's 1909 ball bearing, bit brace chuck.

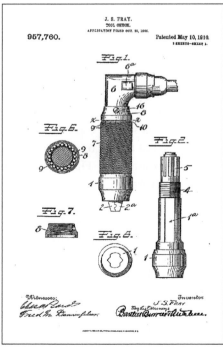

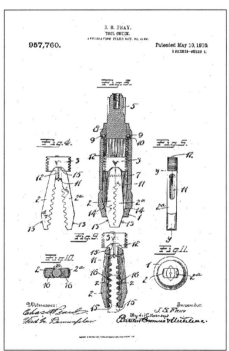

Figures 35 and 36. Fray's 1910 ball bearing chuck patents.

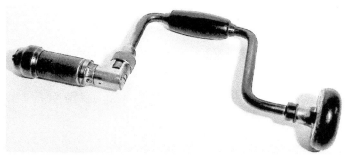

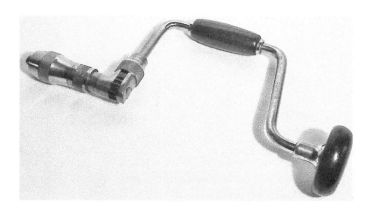

Figure 37 (left, top). 14-inch sweep brace, no. 142.

Figure 38 (left, bottom). Stanley no. 945, ratchet bit brace.

Figure 39 (above). No. 109 Stanley/Fray brace with ball bearing chuck.

Figure 40 (below). The no. 946 Stanley sleeve bit brace.

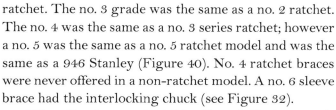

ratchet. The no. 3 grade was the same as a no. 2 ratchet. The no. 4 was the same as a no. 3 series ratchet; however a no. 5 was the same as a no. 5 ratchet model and was the same as a 946 Stanley (Figure 40). No. 4 ratchet braces were never offered in a non-ratchet model. A no. 6 sleeve brace had the interlocking chuck (see Figure 32).

When Stanley acquired John Fray & Co. in 1909, it kept Fray as a separate division and slowly phased the complete line over to the Stanley name. Stanley discon-

tinued most of the Fray model numbers by 1927.

The braces made in the Fray plant were labeled "Stanley" for the Stanley brace numbers offered in the Stanley tool catalogs of 1909 through 1927. The braces made with the Fray numbers were labeled "John S. Fray and Stanley Rule & Level Co." and were marketed through the John S. Fray catalog.

Stanley's brace numbering system did not include the brace's sweep size into the number, thus reducing the model numbers (Stanley's number 916 was a sleeve-type, non-ratchet bit brace offered in 6-inch, 8-inch, and 10-inch sweeps.) Only the Fray braces had the sweep size incorporated into the model number.

With the expanding brace line and its many improvements, Stanley found a large increase in the demand for bit brace heads and handles. Large enough, in fact, that in 1911 it purchased the controlling interest in the woodworking plant of Thayer and Harmon, located in Ashfield, Massachusetts. This plant was Stanley's source of supply for these parts through the 1930s.

But first, I'm going to step back a few years to 1910 when Stanley inventors were working on a universal

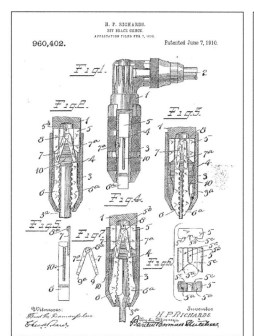

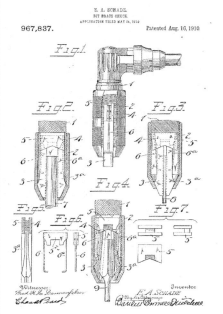

Figures 41 and 42 (above, left and right). H.P Richards (left) and Edmund Schade's (right) patents, which refined the chuck.

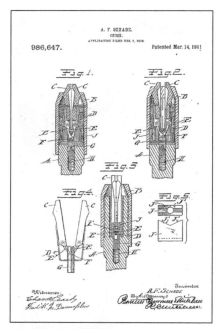

Figure 43. Albert Schade's chuck refinement.

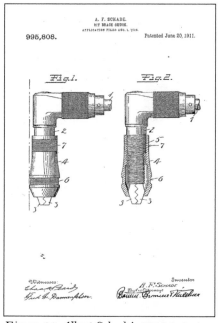

Figure 44. Albert Schade's 1911 patent.

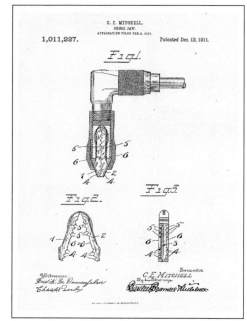

Figure 45. Charles Mitchell's patent on a new design for an unusual jaw.

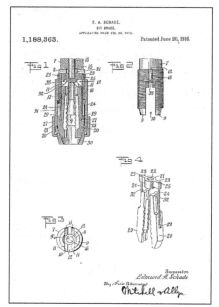

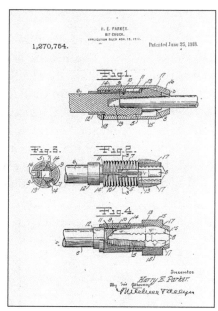

Figure 46 (above, left). Edmund Schade's universal chuck, which led to Harry Parker's 1918 patent.

Figure 47 (above, right). Harry Parker's 1918 patent.

Figure 48 (left). A close-up of the Parker chuck on a Stanley no. 811 ball bearing brace.

chuck and were consolidating many of its in-house chuck designs with improvements. H.P. Richards's chuck patent of June 7, 1910, and Edmund Schade's patent of August 16, 1910 (Figures 41 and 42), refined the chuck by placing a sliding carrier with springs to open and close the jaws. (See part no. 5 in both of the above mentioned patents.)

Albert Schade further refined the chuck in his March 14, 1911 (Figure 43), patent. But this design consisted of two springs: one to open the jaws and another to push the jaws forward. A. Schade, in his June 20, 1911, patent (Figure 44), changed the shape of the tubular rotatable controlling sleeve for a better grip when tightening. By December 1911 (Figure 45), Charles Mitchell received a patent on a new design, for an unusual jaw. This jaw had teeth at both ends and was straight in the center, making the jaws stronger at that point where breakage usually occurred. It also refined the jaws so that they could be used with a square-tapered shank as found on most auger bits, or the round shank found on machine drills. Edmund Schade went one step further in developing the universal chuck with his June 20, 1916, patent (Figure 46). In this patent E. Schade placed a thrust-receiving pin in the chuck body, which guided the jaw yoke (part no. 22), which in turn was

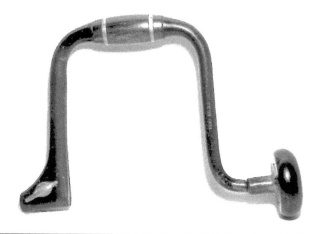

Figure 49 (left). A Spofford brace produced mainly for World War I.
Figure 50 (above). A Stanley Four-Square brace.

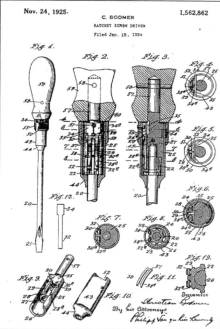

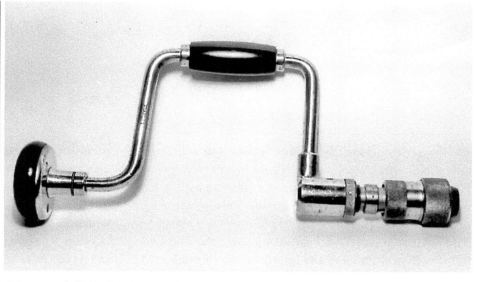

Figure 51 (left). Bodmer's patent for a ratchet screwdriver.
Figure 52 (above). Stanley advertised the no. 810 as "The Aristocrat of bit braces."

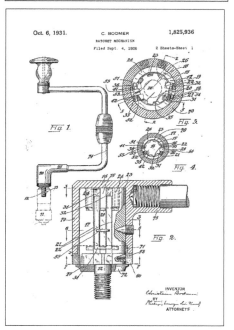

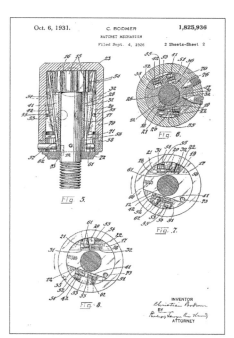

Figures 53 and 54. Christian Bodmer's second patent.

connected to the jaw. This arrangement led to Harry Parker's chuck of 1918 (Figure 47). Figure 48 shows a close-up of the Parker chuck on a Stanley no. 811 ball bearing brace.

Stanley, in 1916, purchased the bit brace business of the Lancaster Machine and Knife Company, Lancaster, N.Y.. The acquisition expanded Stanley's manufacturing base, added skilled labor to its workforce, and eliminated competition. By 1917 Stanley offered twenty-four different models of bit braces. Taking into account the fact that each model brace was available in various sweep sizes, the total number of different braces was eighty-two. This calculation does not include the Fray models, which were phased out by 1927. Likewise, the

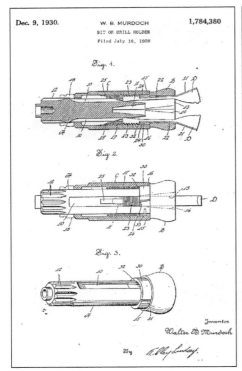

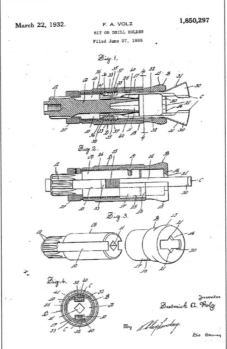

Figure 55 (far left). Murdoch's improved interlocking-jaw chuck.
Figure 56 (near left). Volz's patent, a refinement of the Murdoch patent.
Figure 57 (above). A close-up of Volz's refinement.

count does not include the Spofford braces (nos. 7 through 14 and Nos. 107 through 114). These braces were being manufactured in the teens but production was mainly for World War I military use (Figure 49). This is why a lot of Stanley Spofford braces are found marked "Ordnance Dept." After World War I ended in 1918, the Spofford braces with wood handles and pads (nos. 107 through 114) were available again in the Stanley catalogs.

In 1923, Stanley introduced the Four-Square line of tools (Figure 50). One of these tools was an 8-inch sweep, household-grade brace with a black-japanned head, handle, and chuck shell. About 1932, Stanley changed the sweep to 10 inches and numbered it the no. 1151.

In 1925, Christian Bodmer received a patent for a ratchet screwdriver (Figure 51), but screwdrivers were not the only thing on which Stanley used the patent. By 1927 the company applied this patent to a new style of concealed-ratchet, ball bearing bit brace. It was numbered the no. 810 and was advertised as "The Aristocrat of bit braces" (Figure 52). This would turn out to be the finest bit brace that Stanley would make. It had a cocobolo head and handle, forged universal jaws, a ratchet mechanism with sixteen divisions

permitting operation in small spaces, and a metal-clad, bronze-brushed, ball bearing head.

The concealed ratchet for the no. 810 was improved in 1926, when Christian Bodmer filed his second patent, which he received in 1931 (Figures 53 and 54). All the later no. 810 braces used this patent until they were discontinued in 1935.

Walter Murdoch filed a patent in July 1928 for an improved interlocking-jaw chuck (Figure 55). The patent was granted on December 9, 1930. Frederick Volz refined Murdoch's chuck with his patent granted in March 1932 (Figure 56). A close-up of this interlocking chuck on a no. 919 brace is shown in Figure 57. Stanley also used this chuck on its no. 919 and 982 braces. All braces with interlocking jaws were discontinued in 1942.

Figure 58. The 903A with aluminum head and handles.

Starting in 1926 Stanley made several braces with aluminum heads and handles. The 929 and 903A were made up until 1934. The 903A had a universal chuck (Figure 58), which was changed to an alligator-jaw type. These braces were mainly used by plumbers.

Austin Stowell, an engineer at Stanley, patented an improved form of Harry Parker's universal chuck (Figure 59) in October 1932. The patent eliminated the sliding ring that held the jaw spring wires to just one spring wire, as shown in Figure 60. Figure 61 illustrates Harris Cook's 1933 patent for fastening the chuck on the body with means to take up play. Figure 62 illustrates Austin Stowell's 1949 patent, showing his improved ratchet end. Figure 63 shows a Stanley no. 813 ball bearing brace with Harry Parker's chuck and Austin Stowell's improved ratchet end.

On May 1, 1946, Stanley purchased the North Brothers Manufacturing Company of Philadelphia. The North Brothers Company manufactured "Yankee" ratchet screwdrivers, hand drills, and braces. With this acquisition Stanley acquired one of the best braces manufactured: the models 2100 and 2101.

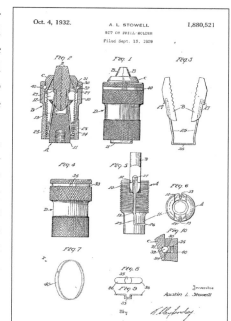

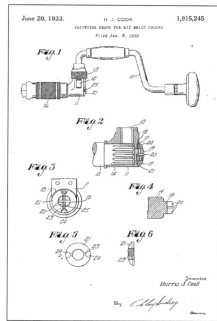

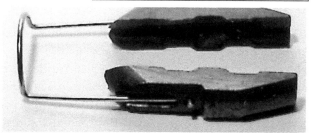

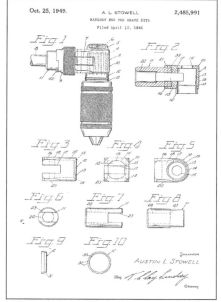

Figure 59 (top, left). Austin Stowell's improved form of Harry Parker's universal chuck.

Figure 60 (above). An example of the spring illustrated ("Fig. 3") in Austin Stowell's patent.

Figure 61 (top, right). Harris Cook's 1933 patent.

Figure 62 (right). Austin Stowell's patent showing his improved ratchet end.

Figure 63 (below). An example of the Stanley no. 813 ball bearing brace with Parker's chuck and Stowell's improved ratchet end.

They differed only in finish. They were originally patented by Thomas J. Fegley in four patents dating from November 1923 to July 1928. Two patents concerned the chuck. One was for the ratchet mechanism and the last concerned the head and handle. These braces were preferred for use by public utilities, telephone companies, and industrial plants because they were made of a super rugged construction that held up under adverse conditions.

By 1958 Stanley was making only 12 different models of braces in 21 different sweeps, as compared to the heyday of 1911 when it produced 40 models with 121 available sweeps.

Figure 1. Fray no. 3 hand drill.

Stanley Hand Drills

The Beginning: The Fray Line

The Stanley Rule & Level Co., New Britain, Connecticut, purchased the bit brace business of John S. Fray Co. of Bridgeport, Connecticut, in April 1909. With that acquisition, Stanley added breast drills and hand drills to their line. When Stanley acquired Fray, the company kept all the products manufactured by Fray as a separate division at the Fray manufacturing facility in Bridgeport, Connecticut. The Stanley Rule & Level Co.

called this line the Fray Division, which included braces and two hand drills.

The two hand drills, no. 3 (Figure 1) and no. 4 (Figure 2), used Herbert D. Lanfair's chuck patent of August 13, 1895 (Figure 3). The 1895 patent had been assigned to the Goodell-Pratt Company of Greenfield, Massachusetts. I believe that Fray had previously purchased from Goodell the rights to all the three-jaw chucks for its breast and hand drills.

As a division of Stanley in 1909 Fray continued to manu-

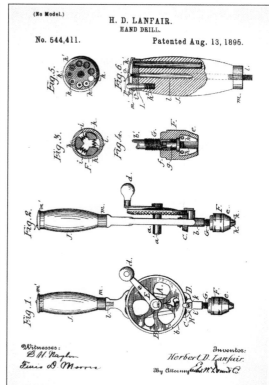

Figure 2 (far left). Page 22 of the Stanley Rule & Level Co. Fray Division Catalog, 1916. The S-spoke design in the gear wheels was used through the 1920s.

Figure 3 (left). Herbert Lanfair's August 13, 1895, U.S. patent for a hand drill. "Fig. 3" and "Fig. 4" in the patent drawing show the coil spring construction.

facture the two hand drills. The no. 3 had a chuck capacity of 0 to ⁵⁄₃₂ inch. The no. 4 had a capacity of 0 to ¼ inch and was an intermediate size between the no. 3 hand drill and the Fray breast drills. Notice the "S" spokes in the gear wheels, a design that would be carried through the 1920s (Figure 2).

The hand drills were made with one pinion on the main shaft, operated by the cast gear wheel. They were supplied with six drill bits ranging in size from ¹⁄₁₆ to ⁵⁄₆₄ inch.

The Lanfair chuck was made up of coil springs (see the patent illustrations no. 3 and no. 4 in Figure 3). The chuck could be taken apart by use of a hook spanner wrench. Figure 4 is a photo of the Lanfair patent chuck markings on the chuck base, illustrating the hook spanner holes.

Christian Bodmer, one of Stanley's top inventors and a longtime employee, filed a patent on September 4, 1914, for useful improvements to chucks. The patent, granted on March 23, 1915 (Figure 5), states that "…the

main object being to improve and simplify the construction, reducing the amount of friction generated in the operation of the chuck to a very substantial degree whereby the jaws may be effectively tightened upon the tool by a hand alone." Thus, Bodmer's patented chuck replaced the Lanfair chuck on the Fray hand drills. The Bodmer chuck used anti-friction balls against a washer, which pressed against the jaws, thereby reducing friction when closing the chuck.

Figure 6 shows a Stanley Fray no. 3 hand drill with a Bodmer no. 1 chuck attached. The no. 1 denoted size 0 to ⁵⁄₃₂ inch. "Fray No. 3" and "Stanley Rule & Level Co" is visible on the gear crank in Figure 7. This drill has the patent dates and size and Stanley logo marked on the chuck base (Figure 8). The Fray no. 3 had a cocobolo—a tropical hardwood—handle that was hollow and held six drill bits (Figure 9) and had a harp-shaped frame (Figure 10). The no. 3 and no. 4

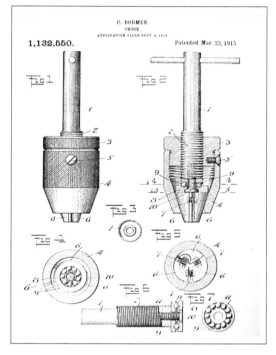

Figure 4 (above). Close-up of Fray's Lanfair hand drill chuck showing patent date.

Figure 5 (right). Christian Bodmer's March 23, 1915, patent for a drill chuck.

Figure 6 (below). Stanley/Fray no. 3 hand drill.

Figure 7. *Close-up of Stanley/Fray no. 3 hand drill crank handle showing inscription.*

Figure 8. *Close-up of chuck base showing Bodmer's patent no. 1-size chuck.*

hand drills continued to be manufactured in the Bridgeport, Connecticut, Fray Division plant until the early 1920s.

With the merger of the Stanley Rule & Level Co. and the Stanley Works in 1919, engineers in the Stanley model shop started working on a completely new line of hand drills. This resulted in many new drill models and the closing of the Fray facility in Bridgeport in the early 1920s.

The Early Twenties

When the Fray Division plant was relocated in May 1920 from Bridgeport to New Britain, Connecticut, Stanley began developing a completely new line of hand drills. (In 1923, however, probably in an effort to use up the

leftover inventory of the Fray drills, Stanley began offering the no. 3 hand drill in its no. 888 and no. 850 tool kits.) Two basic frame designs were developed for the new line. The first design type was the malleable, parallel-frame drills; the second design type utilized a steel frame.

The malleable, parallel-frame drills came in different models with different chuck capacities. They were available in single or double pinions. Initially, six drill bits were supplied with the drill; however, some models had hollow handles which, in later years, were used to store up to eight drill bits. Other models had extra-wide gear wheels for delicate hand operations. Each drill chuck spindle was provided with a keyway so a nail could be inserted to lock the spindle when closing or loosening the chuck.

The malleable, iron-frame hand drill line-up included ten different models numbered from 610 to 626. Because production lines were being set up, not all of the models were available in 1923. Initially, the nos. 610, 611, 614, 615, 621, and 624 were offered. These drills were all malleable, parallel-frame drills. By 1925, nos. 612, 613, 622, and 623 were added. Their differences will be addressed in numerical order.

All of the Stanley hand drills in this period had the speed gear cast in an open "S-spoke" design, a take-off from the Fray drills. The ³⁄₁₆- and ¼-inch chuck models had 3¼-inch speed gears, whereas the ³⁄₈-inch chuck models had 4-inch speed gears.

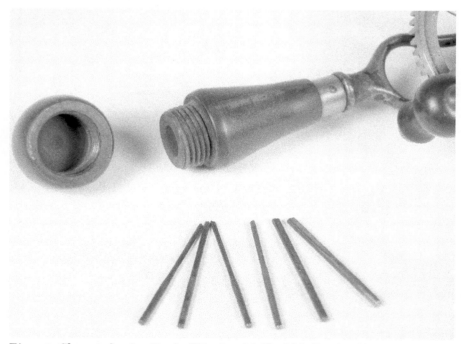

Figure 9. *Close-up showing Stanley/Fray hand drill with hollow handle and bits.*

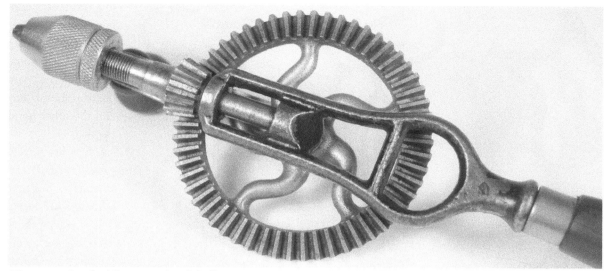

Figure 10. Stanley/Fray no. 3 hand drill, rear side, showing harp-shaped frame.

Christian Bodmer and Albert Langdon, two of Stanley's inventors, filed a patent on November 3, 1922, for a hand drill which incorporated a parallel frame and a pistol grip handle (Figure 11). The patent was granted on May 6, 1924. This hand drill became known as Stanley's no. 610 (Figures 12 and 13).

Offered first in early 1922 without a drill compartment, the model no. 610 was redesigned in 1923 with a parallel frame that could be used in Christian Bodmer's drill stand (Figures 14 and 15). When redesigned, a cast hole below the

handle enabled the drill to be attached to the lever of a drill stand, for which Christian Bodmer had filed two patents on December 9, 1922. The patents were granted on May 6, 1924, the same day as the patent for the model 610. The parallel frame of the hand drill would slide down between two slots (or ways) on the drill support stand (see Figures 16 and 17). Pulling on the lever, to which the drill was attached, would lower the drill as it was being turned by the crank on the the speed gear. It is interesting to note that I have never seen a catalog offering Christian Bodmer's drill pedestal or stand

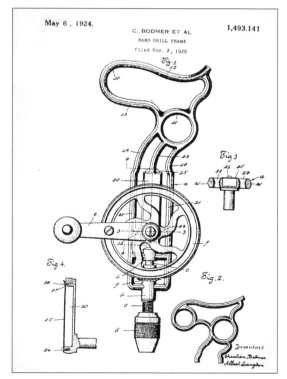

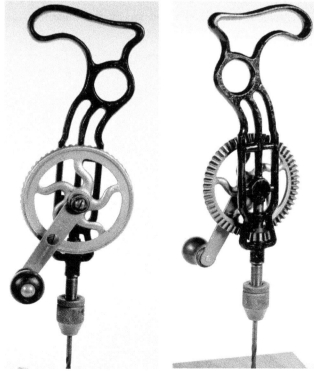

Figure 11 (above left). The Christian Bodmer and Albert Langdon patent—no. 1,493,141—for a hand drill.

Figure 12 (above middle). Stanley hand drill model no. 610 (early model) based on the Bodmer and Langdon patent.

Figure 13 (above, right). Reverse side of the model no. 610.

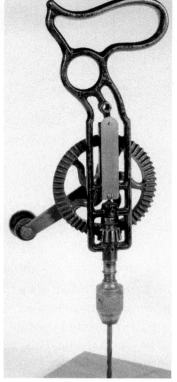

Figure 14 (detail above and near right) Stanley's second model no. 610; note the cast hole below the handle (see detail).

Figure 15 (far right). The other side of the 610 which shows the drill compartment. Compare the frame to the early model 610 shown in Figures 12 and 13.

use the tool, making it unnecessary to clamp the work. Bodmer's stand required that the work be clamped in such a way that the operator could use one hand on the lever and the other hand to crank the drill.

Stanley's no. 610 pistol grip hand drill initially used Christian Bodmer's chuck patented on March 23, 1915. The chuck on the Fray drills used the no. 1 chuck size, which accepted drills up t o a ⁹⁄₁₆-inch diameter. When the redesigned model 610 hand drill made its debut, Stanley changed the rear of Bodmer's chuck from a flat back (Figure 18) to a curved back (Figure 19) with the patent marked on the smooth part of the chuck shell just below the knurling. After 1915, the chuck capacity had been increased to ¼ inch.

even though all models of the parallel-frame type hand drills were made with a screw hole so the drill could be attached to the drill stand lever. Perhaps the reason Stanley never offered Bodmer's hand drill pedestal was because at the time, electric drills with drill pedestals were beginning to appear on the market. With an electric drill, only one hand was needed to

Stanley's no. 611 hand drill (Figures 20 and 21) was also added to its line. This drill had a parallel frame with one pinion, but instead of a pistol-grip handle it had a

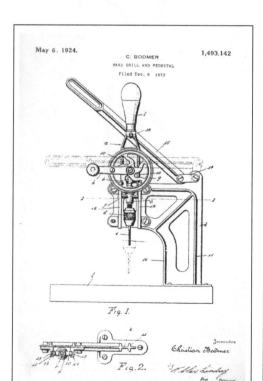

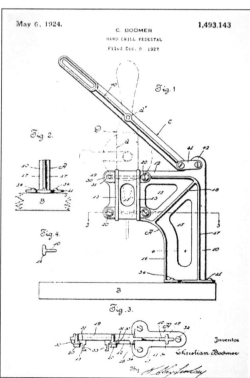

Figure 16 (far left). Christian Bodmer's patent no. 1,493,142 granted May 6, 1924, for a hand drill and stand.

Figure 17 (left). Bodmer's patent no. 1,493,143, also granted May 6, 1924, for a drill stand.

Figure 18 (above, left). Detail of Stanley's 1915 chuck patented by Christian Bodmer. Note the flat back of the chuck.

Figure 19 (above, right). Detail of Bodmer's chuck with curved back.

cocobolo handle with a screw-off top, which held six drill bits. This drill originally had a ⁹⁄₁₆-inch capacity chuck, but by 1925 the size was increased to ¼-inch. Eight drill bits were furnished with the drill, and a side knob was added. The total length of the early model, with or without the side knob, was 12 inches. By 1927, the hollow handle had been made longer, extending the length to almost 13 inches (Figure 22).

Stanley's no. 612 (Figure 23) hand drill also had a malleable-iron parallel frame with a ¼-inch capacity chuck. The 612 differed from the no. 611 in that it was a double pinion without a hollow handle and with an extra-wide flanged speed gear (Figure 24). This drill also had a side knob.

Stanley's no. 613 (Figure 25) was also a ¼-inch chuck capacity, malleable-iron, parallel-frame hand drill, but with a single pinion, no side knob, and a solid maple handle. This drill initially used Christian Bodmer's no. 2 (¼-inch) flat-back chuck (Figure 26) because, I suspect, Stanley was using up the older chucks. Later models (Figure 27) had the revised style chuck. The speed gears were the original 3¼-inch S-spoke style.

Stanley's no. 614 (Figure 28) malleable iron frame hand drill was similar to the no. 613 ¼-inch chuck capacity hand drill, but the no. 614 had double pinions, a hollow tropical hardwood handle with eight drill bits, and a side knob; it was 12 inches long (Figure 29).

Stanley's no. 615 (Figure 30) hand drill was exactly like its model no. 614, except that the 615 was equipped with an extra-wide, flanged gear wheel. This feature enabled the user to have more control over tricky drilling operations. The no. 615 was the last of Stanley's ¼-inch, early malleable-iron hand drill line.

In addition to these six

Figure 20 (top). Stanley no. 611 hand drill with parallel frame and one pinion.

Figure 21 (above). Stanley no. 611 hand drill showing reverse side. Note the addition of the side knob.

Figure 22 (below). Stanley no. 611 hand drill showing the later model with a long, hollow handle.

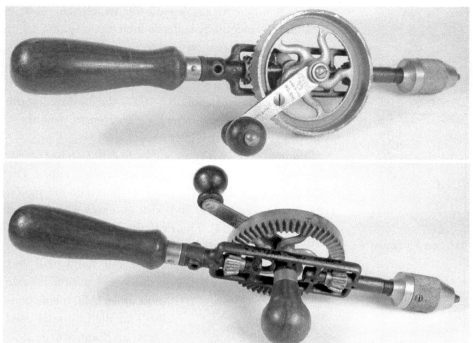

Figure 23 (left, top). Stanley's no. 612 hand drill. Unlike the no. 611, the 612 had double pinions, a solid handle, and a side knob.

Figure 24 (left, bottom). Stanley's no. 612 hand drill reverse side.

malleable-iron frame, ¼-inch hand drills, Stanley made four malleable-iron models with ⅜-inch capacity chucks. These drills were numbered 621, 622, 623, and 624. All had a 4-inch speed gear. The no. 621 also had a parallel malleable-iron frame with only one pinion. This drill had a side knob and a hollow handle that held eight drill bits and a total length of 14 inches (Figure 31).

Stanley's no. 622 (Figures 32 and 33) is a double-pinion, ⅜-inch drill with a solid tropical hardwood handle and side knob. The no. 623 (Figures 34 and 35) is a Stanley hand drill similar to the no. 622, except it has only one pinion and the handle and side knobs are hardwood (maple).

Completing the ⅜-inch hand drill line is the no. 624

CONTINUED PAGE 140

Figure 25 (far left). Stanley's no. 613 hand drill with a single pinion, solid handle and no side knob.

Figure 26 (left). The no. 613 hand drill reverse side.

Figure 27 (below). A later version of Stanley's no. 613 hand drill with the curved-back chuck.

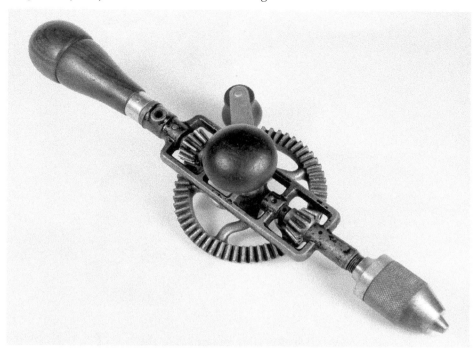

Figure 28 (left). Stanley's no. 614 hand drill with double pinions, side knob and hollow handle.

Figure 29 (below). The no. 614 hand drill showing reverse side.

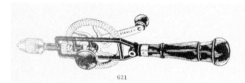

No. 621

Parallel Frame. Single Pinion. 4 in. Speed Gear. Cocobolo Handles and Side Knob. Chuck takes drills up to ¼ in. diameter. Complete with 6 Drill Bits carried in handle.

Weight 2¼ lbs.

621

Figure 30 (left). Stanley's no. 615 hand drill. This drill is similar to the no. 614 but has a flanged gear.

Figure 31 (above). A entry from the 1923 Stanley Works tool catalog no. 120 (page ix) illustrating the no. 621, ⅜-inch capacity hand drill.

Figure 32 (below, top). The no. 622 hand drill showing the double pinions, ⅜-inch chuck, solid handle, and side knob.

Figure 33 (below, bottom). The reverse side of the no. 622.

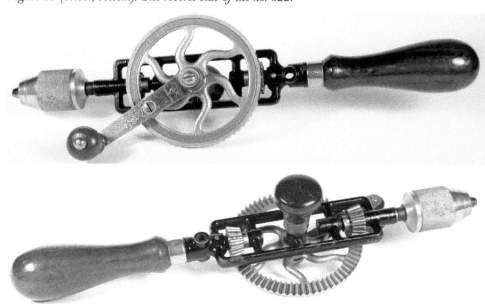

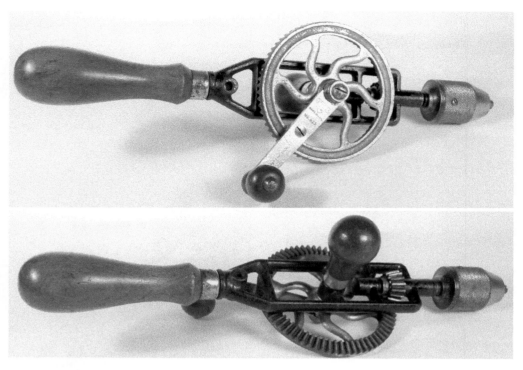

Figure 34 (left, top). Stanley's no. 623 hand drill, which is similar to the no. 622 but only has one pinion.

Figure 35 (left, bottom). The reverse side of the no. 623.

(Figures 36 and 37), which had double pinions like the no. 622 but had a hollow, tropical hardwood handle and a side knob. It was 14 inches in length.

Drill nos. 621 and 622 were, apparently, discontinued around 1926. The no. 623 continued until 1930. All of the ten malleable-iron hand drills remained in the Stanley hand drill line until about 1935, when major changes occurred.

Early Twenties Steel-Frame Drills

In 1923, Stanley introduced steel-frame hand drills in the "New Tools" insert bound into its no. 120 catalog (copyrighted in 1923). Initially, model nos. 616, 617, and 626 hand drills were offered.

Stanley's steel-frame hand drills were manufactured under a joint patent filed on November 9, 1925 (Figure 38). The patentees were Christian Bodmer and Harris J. Cook, both employees of the Stanley Works. This patent, no. 1,642,986,

Figure 36 (right, top). Stanley's no. 624 hand drill showing the double pinions.
Figure 37 (right, bottom). The reverse of the no. 624.

was granted on September 20, 1927, and consisted of a tool steel bar fitted with a chuck and pinion, a driving gear with crank, and a handle. The chuck used on these drills was Bodmer's patent of March 23, 1915 (no. 1,132,550).

The steel-frame drills using Bodmer's and Cook's patent were numbered 616 through 619. All of these hand drills were a basic design but with variations similar to the malleable-iron hand drill models. All of these models had the S-spoke speed gear.

The no. 616 was a ³⁄₁₆-inch chuck capacity hand drill featuring double pinions, a 3¼-inch cast iron speed gear, and six drill bits in a hollow cocobolo handle (Figure 39). There was no side knob on this model. This drill was manufactured from 1923 to 1925, after which the hollow handle was replaced with a hardwood handle, and the chuck was increased to a ¼-inch capacity (Figure 40).

Stanley's no. 617 hand drill initially was a ³⁄₁₆-inch chuck capacity drill similar to the no. 616 with a hollow cocobolo handle and six drill bits, but it had a side knob, double pinions, and a ½-inch-wide flanged speed gear (Figure 41). The

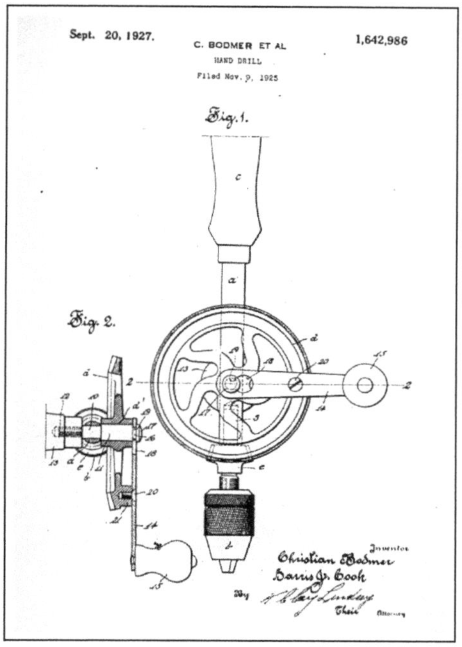

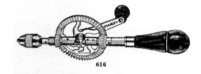

STANLEY HAND DRILLS

In the line of Hand Drills shown below the gears are machine cut, the teeth having a correct pitch so as to insure the Spindle running quietly and smoothly.

The Chucks are of steel and are fitted with hardened tool steel jaws. They are securely locked on the Spindle, consequently not likely to get mislaid or lost.

The Spindles are provided with a keyway, so that an ordinary nail can be used to prevent turning when inserting a drill in the Chuck.

Special attention is called to the finish of all parts of these tools.

No. 616

Steel Frame throughout. Double Pinions. 3¼ in. Speed Gear. Cocobolo Handles. Chuck takes up to ⅜ in. diameter. Six Drill Bits carried in handle.

Weight 1¼ lbs.

Figure 38 (left). Bodmer's and Cook's patent for a steel-frame hand drill.

Figure 39 (above). Page x of the "New Tools" insert in Stanley's 1923 catalog (no. 120) showing the no. 616 hand drill with hollow handle.

Figure 40 (right). Page xiii of Stanley's 1923 catalog "New Tools" insert illustrating a no. 616 hand drill with a solid handle.

Figure 41 (below). Page x of the 1923 catalog illustrating the no. 617 model hand drill with hollow handle.

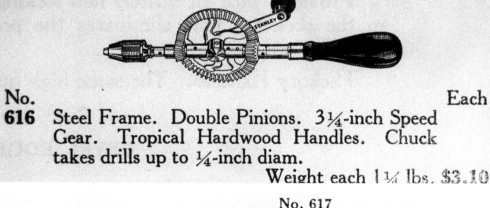

Steel Frames

No. 616   Each
Steel Frame. Double Pinions. 3¼-inch Speed Gear. Tropical Hardwood Handles. Chuck takes drills up to ¼-inch diam.

Weight each 1¼ lbs. $3.10

No. 617

Steel Frame throughout. Double Pinions. 3¼ in. extra wide flanged Speed Gear. Cocobolo Handles and Side Knob. Chuck takes up to ³⁄₁₆ in. diameter. Six Drill Bits carried in handle.

Weight 1¾ lbs.

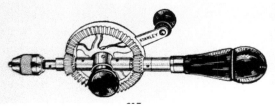

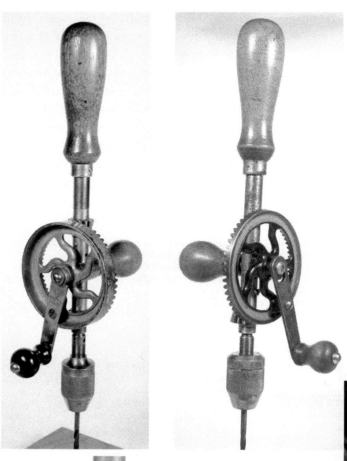

no. 617 was, likewise, changed in 1925 to a ¼-inch chuck capacity with a solid tropical hardwood handle (Figure 42). The double pinions and flanged speed gear made for a stronger drill. The operator could grasp the wider than normal flanged speed gear with his fingers, which allowed for greater control of the drill. He would turn the drill bit manually, without catching his fingers in the pinion gears.

The no. 618 Stanley hand drill (Figure 43) was a single pinion, ¼-inch capacity hand drill with a 3¼-inch speed gear, solid handle, and a side knob. First offered in 1925, the 618 was the least expensive of the steel frame models, with one exception—a variation of this model known as the no. 118.

The no. 118 (Figure 44) was a low-end hand drill

Figure 45 (right and above). Stanley's no. 118 "Defiance" model hand drill. The detail (right) of the crank shows the model name.

Figure 44 (above and right). Stanley's no. 118 "Victor" model hand drill. The crank (inset, right) was marked with the "Victor" name.

No.		Each
619	Steel Frame. Single Pinion. 3¼-inch Speed Gear. Hardwood Handle and Side Knobs. Eight drill bits included in the Handle. The chuck takes drills up to ¼-inch diam. The chuck is made of steel and fitted with hardened tool steel Jaws. It is securely locked on the spindle end, so that it is not likely to get mislaid or lost. All gears are machine cut, the teeth being pitched so as to insure the Spindle running quietly and smoothly.	
	Weight each 1¼ lb.	**$2.60**

Figure 46 (above). The "New Tools" insert (page xiii) of Stanley's no. 120 catalog, illustrating the no. 619 hand drill.

Figure 47 (below). Stanley hand drill no. 1616, which had a hollow handle.

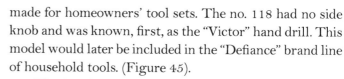

made for homeowners' tool sets. The no. 118 had no side knob and was known, first, as the "Victor" hand drill. This model would later be included in the "Defiance" brand line of household tools. (Figure 45).

The Stanley no. 619 (Figure 46) hand drill was the same as the no. 618, except it featured a hollow handle with eight drill bits. It also had a ¼-inch capacity chuck.

In 1929, Stanley introduced its no. 1616 (Figure 47) hand drill. This drill was the same hand drill as the 1923 model no. 616, except the no. 1616's hollow handle was longer and held eight drill bits.

Stanley's no. 626 was the company's entry into the ⅜-inch capacity hand drill line. This drill, first offered in 1923, had double pinions, a hollow co-cobolo handle with six drill bits, a side knob, and a four-inch S-spoke speed gear (Figure 48). By 1925, the hollow handle was replaced with a solid handle (Figure 49).

In 1929, Stanley introduced no. 1626. This drill was the same as the no. 626 but with a hollow handle and eight drill bits.

All of these steel-frame models were manufactured with the S-spoke speed gear wheels up to about 1934, when solid speed gear

No. 626

Steel Frame throughout. Double Pinion. 4 inch Speed Gear. Cocobolo Handles and Side Knob. Chuck takes up to ¼ in. diameter. Six Drill Bits carried in handle.

Weight 2 lbs.

Figure 48 (above). The no. 626 model illustrated in the "New Tools" insert (page x) in the Stanley Works catalog no. 120.

Figure 49 (below). Stanley no. 626 hand drill, which had a solid handle.

wheels began to replace the S-spoke models. Other changes also began to appear around 1930.

Solid Gear Wheels

The Roaring Twenties came to an end with the stock market crash in October 1929, but this financial crisis had little effect on the development of hand drills at The Stanley Works, where work on new models continued. Most significantly, in 1929, Stanley replaced its S-spoke gear wheel with a solid-flanged gear wheel and a gray-iron gear wheel. The solid-flanged gear wheel offered a stronger gear, which meant less chance of breakage, together with more control especially when using smaller drill bits. Stanley's no. 617 (Figure 50), a ¼-inch-chuck capacity, steel-frame hand drill, was the first in the line to use the new solid-flanged gear wheel. The no. 617, introduced in 1929, was the obvious choice for the design improvement since it was the only S-spoke hand drill that Stanley manufactured in

Figure 50 (above, left). Stanley's no. 617 drill showing the solid-flanged gear. The flanged gear replaced the earlier S-spoke models.

Figure 51 (above, middle). Stanley's no. 1617 drill was the same as the no. 617, except it had a hollow handle.

Figure 52 (above, right). Stanley no. 1626 drill with solid gray-iron gear wheel. It has a hollow handle that holds eight drill bits.

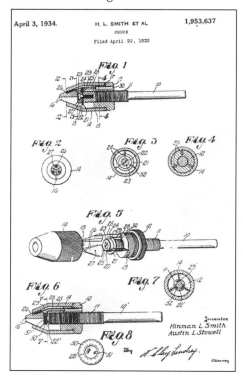

Figure 53 (far left). Hinman Smith's and Austin Stowell's April 3, 1934, patent chuck. The new patent eliminated the possibility of jamming the springs that had been a problem with the earlier chuck based on a Christian Bodmer patent.

Figure 54 (left). The Christian Bodmer chuck showing the springs that were often jammed.

Figure 55 (left, top). The Stanley no. 1617 hand drill was sold with the new Smith/Stowell chuck. The model also was improved with the use of an enlarged crank with handle.

Figure 56 (left, bottom). Stanley no. 616 hand drill with solid gray-iron gear wheel.

crank handle with turned knob, as had the earlier S-spoke models.

Stanley's ⅜-inch chuck models no. 626 and no. 1626 were its entry-level S-spoke drills, and in 1930 these models were replaced by a 4-inch, gray-iron, solid gear wheel. It was, however, not flanged (Figure 52). The no. 1626 had a hollow handle with eight drill bits.

During the Great Depression, tool sales plummeted, and Stanley discontinued all of the S-spoke hand drill models. Because of poor sales, however, many models remained in stock, and these models were carried in Stanley catalog no. 34 until 1934.

Hinman L. Smith and Austin L. Stowell, employees of the Stanley Works, applied for a patent on April 20, 1932, for an improvement of hand drill chucks. Patent no. 1,953,637 was granted on April 3, 1934 (Figure 53). The improvement to this patent chuck was that the new chuck had concealed jaw springs that hooked into the jaws in such a way that the drill point, when inserted, would not jam or bend the springs. This problem was a common fault of Christian Bodmer's earlier March 23, 1915, patented chuck (Figure 54). When an operator inserted the drill bit incorrectly, the spring would become jammed. This prevented the chuck from functioning properly. Although the Smith and Stowell chuck was an improvement, Stanley continued to use the Bodmer chuck with its lower grade model hand drills.

The no. 617 and no. 1617 hand drills, by 1932, were sold with the Smith/Stowell patent chuck. Also beginning that year, on the new versions of the no. 617 and no.

the 1920s that featured a flanged-gear wheel. Apparently, the flanged gear was popular and sold well.

Shortly thereafter, the no. 1617, ¼-inch hand drill with the flanged gear wheel was offered by the company (Figure 51). The no. 1617 was the same as the no. 617, but it had a hollow handle with eight drill bits inside. Both the no. 617 and the no. 1617 drills featured the straight

Figure 57 (left). A Stanley no. 619 hollow-handle hand drill with solid gray-iron gear wheel.

1617 hand drills, the handles on the crank were enlarged and were made with a heavier crank (Figure 55).

Stanley sold its model no. 616 (Figure 56) with the gray-iron, solid gear wheel and the Smith/Stowell chuck. This model was a popularly priced hand drill with a ¼-inch chuck capacity and with double pinions and a hardwood red-lacquered handle.

Stanley changed its hand drill no. 619 (Figure 57) from the old S-spoke to a solid gray-iron gear wheel

in 1934. This drill had the Bodmer chuck and a hollow, hardwood handle with eight drill bits.

Late in 1932, Stanley made a major change in the handle of its no. 617 hand drill (Figure 58). Stanley referred to the no. 617 as "a large frame handle which gives a more comfortable grip."[1] This design remained in the Stanley line into the 1960s. Shown in Figure 59 is a prototype no. 617 hand drill (tag dated "5/15/1940") with a tapered thread chuck design. To my knowledge, this type chuck was never placed into production.

In 1934, Stanley changed the no. 626, giving it a large-frame handle and long-crank handle (Figure 60). This drill had a ⅜-inch capacity Smith/Stowell drill chuck and double pinions.

The Stanley no. 624 was the only malleable-iron frame drill to continue in the hand drill line. Between 1929 and 1932 the S-spoke gear wheel had been replaced with the gray-iron gear wheel (Figure 61). This drill had a ⅜-inch capacity chuck and a hollow handle. All examples I have seen that were made before 1940 have a military finish (i.e. the black enamel and base metal parts are galvanized), with a narrow, rear double pinion (Figure 62). These drills were listed in any of the 1930s catalogs showing a solid gray-iron gear wheel, but were in all the dealer price lists with no catalog page numbers as a reference.

In 1940, a new version—no. 624 (Figure 63)—was introduced with a different handle and an orange-enameled, gray-iron gear wheel. These later drills (1940 and after) used the Smith/Stowell chuck. The pre-1940 model no. 624 used the Christian Bodmer chuck. The later models were available into the 1960s and were illustrated in the Stanley catalogs.

Figure 58 (top). A Stanley no. 617 hand drill with the new, large-frame handle.

Figure 59 (above). A Stanley' no. 617 model shop hand drill with tapered-thread chuck design.

Figure 60 (right). The Stanley no. 626 hand drill with large-frame handle and Smith/Stowell drill chuck.

Stanley's Popularly Priced
Model 620 and Later Variations

On November 4, 1936, the engineers in the Stanley Rule & Level Division's Model Shop finished designing a new, medium-priced, quality hand drill (Figure 64).[2] This drill (model shop no. 8853) featured double pinions, an all-steel frame, a 3½-inch solid speed gear, a three-jaw, coil-spring chuck, and a "jumbo" handle. The solid gear wheel was cast from gray iron and had machine-cut teeth.

In manufacturing, the solid gear gives extra strength and a high degree of accuracy because the gears can be milled to a uniform size and shape. The teeth are then machine cut and pitched. This provides for a very smooth operating drill when used with the solid steel pinion gears on a nickel-plated steel frame.

Stanley advertised the large handle as a "jumbo handle." The handle was made of the best grade Vermont rock maple and had a screw-on maple cap. The handle contained a set of eight drill bits, sizes ⁵⁄₆₄ inch to ¹¹⁄₆₄ inch in width. The size and shape of this new handle design gave the user more control when operating the drill.

This drill's cadmium-plated chuck design was based on Christian Bodmer's chuck patented March 23, 1915. Although Bodmer's chuck would occasionally have problems if the user was sloppy with inserting the drill bit, the chuck

Figure 64. The original model shop no. 8853, which would become the no. 620 hand drill. The tag is dated 11-4-1936 and reads "Original Model/low priced 2 pinon type/Design A."

Figure 65 (left). Stanley no. 620 hand drill with flanged gear.

Figure 66 (below). Close-up of the flanged gear wheel showing the edge decoration.

No. 1220 DEFIANCE HAND DRILL

New Design

Real quality at a Bargain Price — When sold will stay sold!

$1.50

Native Hardwood Handle with Large Screw Cap →

← *8 Drill Points* ⅛" to ¹¹⁄₆₄" in the Handle

← *Gear Ratio —* 3.7 for Power

Wide Flange Gear — pleasing appearance and serves as a finger grip to start small drills

← *Ferrule and Handle* Pinned to Frame—Will Not Pull Off

← *Long Life Gear and Pinions* Combination of fine textured, cast grey iron gear with machine cut teeth driving two steel pinions results in easy turning and lasting accuracy

← *Removable, Hardwood Knob* with Ferrule Screws on Frame

No. 1220

Beautifully finished—natural lacquered handles, red screw cap and gear, nickel plated frame, highly polished chuck. Packed one in a box with a selling tag.

Weight 1¼ lbs.

$1.50

Complete with 8 Drill Points

Full ¼" Capacity Chuck Designed with minimum outside diameter for drilling in tight places →

3 Hardened and Ground Steel Jaws for Long Wear and Tight Grip →

STANLEY TOOLS [STANLEY] NEW BRITAIN, CONN.

was overall very simple and serviceable. In addition, and perhaps most important for a lower-priced line, the drill's manufacturing costs were very reasonable.

The no. 620 hand drill was placed in production and was first offered as a new tool by April 15, 1937, according to Stanley's nos. 134 and 138 dealer price lists.

When first offered, the cast, gray-iron gear wheel was thin and not flanged. It had a red-enameled finish. The maple handle and knobs were also finished in a glossy red with the cap darker in color.

By April 1938, the solid gear wheel was replaced with a solid-flanged gear wheel that was stronger with less chance of breakage. This design provided more control when using smaller drill bits (Figure 65). The new gear wheel had a decorative design on the flange, which was surface dressed to highlight the design (Figure 66).

In February 1938, Stanley introduced the no. 1220 hand drill (Figure 67). This drill was the same as a Stanley no. 620 except the handles and knobs had a natural-finish handle

CONTINUED PAGE 150

Figure 67 (left). A Stanley advertisement introducing the Defiance no. 1220 hand drill.

Figure 68 (right). The Defiance line no. 1220 hand drill.

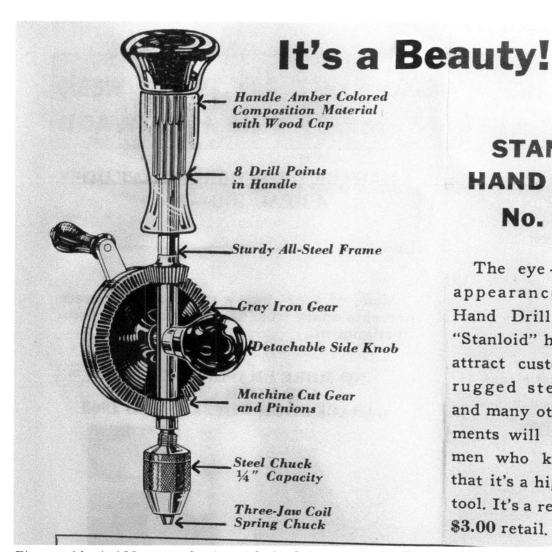

It's a Beauty!

Handle Amber Colored
Composition Material
with Wood Cap

8 Drill Points
in Handle

Sturdy All-Steel Frame

Gray Iron Gear

Detachable Side Knob

Machine Cut Gear
and Pinions

Steel Chuck
¼" Capacity

Three-Jaw Coil
Spring Chuck

STANLEY HAND DRILL No. 625

The eye-appealing appearance of this Hand Drill with its "Stanloid" handle will attract customers. Its rugged steel frame and many other refinements will convince men who know tools that it's a high quality tool. It's a real value at **$3.00** retail.

Figure 69 (above). A May 1940 advertisement for Stanley's no. 625 hand drill. The drill had an amber-colored composite (plastic) handle, which Stanley referred to as "Stanloid." The cap, however, was wood. When the United States entered the war, the 625 was discontinued.

Figure 70 (above). The 620 was sold in a special gift box for the 1940 Christmas season.

Figure 71 (right). Stanley's no. 620 hand drill with a clear-lacquer handle. It had a maple handle with a knob-shaped red cap.

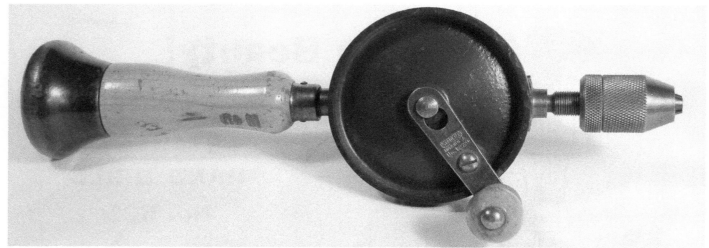

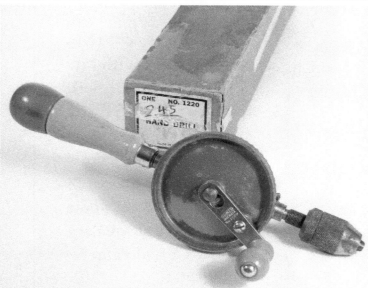

Figure 72 (top). The Stanley no. 1220 with the rust-brown gear wheel. This war-production Defiance model had a thinner (⅛ inch) pinion near the handle, probably due to war restrictions.

Figure 73 (above). War restrictions meant additional changes in design. The Defiance no. 1220 had a smaller handle during the war.

Figure 74 (right). Following the war, the "jumbo" handle returned. This drill also had a side handle.

with a red cap. The edge of the flanged gear wheel was not surface dressed (Figure 68) like the no. 620 (see Figure 71).

In May 1940, Stanley brought out its no. 625 hand drill (Figure 69). The no. 625 was similar to the no. 620 except for the handle, which was made of an amber-colored composite—a yellow plastic—with a red-lacquered wood cap. Stanley referred to the handle, which was made of a nitrocellulose plastic, as its "Stanloid" handle. In Stanley's no. 139 "Price List," dated December 21, 1942, however, the no. 625 was listed as "discontinued" due to the outbreak of World War II.

In October 1940, anticipating the upcoming holiday season, Stanley offered the no. 620 drill (labeled as no. X620) in

Christmas gift packages (Figure 70). The Stanley no. 620 hand drill, manufactured in 1941, had a clear-lacquered maple handle and knob with a red cap like the no. 1220 (Figure 71).

The war affected other hand drill manufacturing as well. In 1942, Stanley began a war-production model of the Defiance no. 1220 and continued to manufacture it throughout

CONTINUED PAGE 152

Figure 75 (left). The Stanley Defiance hand drill with a mid-size handle. During the period of 1951–1954, the company was gradually phasing out the Defiance line and replacing it with the Stanley Handyman. This handle is larger than the handle in the period from 1942–1950.

Figure 76 (below, left). The transition is also evident in this model, which does not have the side handle of the Defiance. The color scheme on this Defiance example was painted the red and gray of the later Handyman series.

Figure 77 (below, middle). The H1220, the Stanley Handyman. It had a hammered-gray gear wheel and a side handle.

Figure 78 (below, right). The Handyman no. 1220 with no side knob.

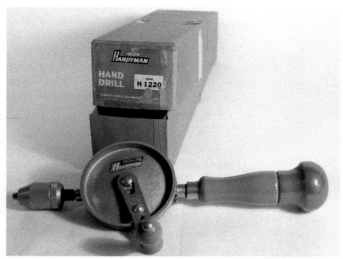

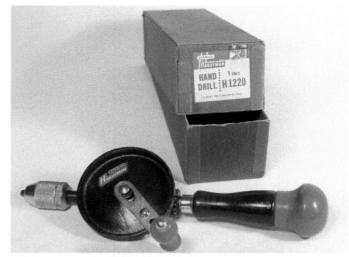

Figure 79 (above, left). In 1958, a Hy-Lo drive crank was added to the H1220. This feature allowed the user to move the crank in or out, increasing the speed of the drill.

Figure 80 (above, right). In 1965, the handle of the no. H1220, as well as the crank, were painted dark blue.

Figure 81 (below and detail, right). The no. H1220A, the Stanley Handyman. A close-up of the H1220A showing the hexagonal chuck that could be used with a wrench.

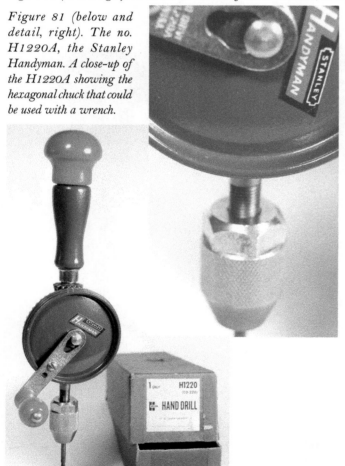

This configuration lasted at least until 1950. At that point, Stanley changed the no. 1220 once again, giving it a larger-sized handle (Figure 74).

The use of that model 1220 handle design was, however, brief. Starting in 1951 and through 1953, Stanley began to phase out most of the Defiance line. During that period the company again changed the no. 1220 handle profile (Figure 75), making it smaller than the original "jumbo handle" but larger than the war-time drill (shown in Figure 73).

The Stanley plan was to make a gradual transition by May 1954 from the Defiance line to a new line, called the Stanley Handyman. The Stanley Handyman line had a red and gray color scheme and was nicknamed the "Red and Gray Line."

During the transition, the no. 1220 Defiance hand drill gear wheel was changed to a hammered, gray color, and the side knob was deleted (Figure 76). The red cap on the handle was changed to the "Handyman Red" color.

When the Stanley Handyman line came into production, the new drills were marked as H1220, reflecting the "Handyman" line. The new H1220 had a hammered-gray gear wheel with a darker gray handle with crank knob, and—yes—the side handle again. The upper half of the handle cap was red (Figure 77). By April 1954, Stanley again removed the side handle (Figure 78) on the H1220 hand drill, but everything else, including the color, remained the same.

In 1958, a new Hy-Lo drive crank (Figure 79) was introduced. This feature enabled a person to move the crank in or out, thus increasing the speed of the drill. The Hy-Lo drive crank was created by simply making a double keyhole and two screw holes in the crank. Also that year,

the war. The war model had a rust-brown colored gear wheel. The pinion near the handle was only ⅛ inch thick (Figure 72). This thinner pinion may have been due to saving materials for the war effort. Shortly after 1942, the drill's hollow handle was smaller and had a different shape and the gear wheel was again made with red enamel (Figure 73).

Figure 82 (left). Defiance no. 118 hand drill.

Figure 83 (below). Close-up of the Defiance logo on crank of the no. 118 hand drill.

Figure 84 (right). Defiance no. 1218 hand drill with solid cast-iron gear wheel.

Under the Defiance Brand we offer a long line of dependable, practical and attractive tools priced for each sale to meet competitive conditions. These tools are made by a tool specialist—a manufacturer who has made and expertly designed woodworking tools since 1850. There are no better, low priced tools on the market.

The introduction of the Defiance line coincided with the Great Depression, which began with the stock market crash of October 1929. Fortuitously, Stanley created this line of inexpensive, quality tools for household and professional use just as the market bottomed out. Stanley advertised these lower-priced tools for the average homeowner's use, at the same time that many people were cutting back on spending and could no longer afford to hire someone to do work around the house. The Defiance line included a number of hand drills with different models reflecting a range of quality and price.

Introduced in 1929, the Defiance no. 118 was the earliest hand drill to be manufactured in the new household line (Figures 82 and 83). It featured a steel frame, black-japanned, S-spoke, cast-iron speed gear and a steel pinion, but with no side knob. The chuck was Christian Bodmer's March 23, 1915, patented chuck with a ¼-inch capacity. The 118 model number was replaced around 1932 with Defiance model no. 1218. Other than the number change, the drill remained the same.

In 1934, the Defiance no. 1218 hand drill (Figure 84) was changed from an S-spoke speed gear to a red-japanned, cast-iron solid speed gear with machine-cut teeth and a shorter crank. This hand drill also utilized Christian Bodmer's 1915 patented chuck. In fact, all the Defiance line drills made use of Bodmer's chuck design. The no. 1218 remained in the Defiance line until January 26, 1942.

Defiance model no. 1219, which had a unique handle, was also introduced around 1932 (Figure 85). This hand drill was the same as the no. 1218 but included a side knob

---

the gray paint was lighter than on earlier models. Then in 1965, the gray paint on the H1220's handle and crank became dark blue (Figure 80).

At the start of the 1970s, Stanley began to designate the model number as H1220A (Figure 81). The H1220A chuck had a hexagonal bottom so one could place a wrench on it. The speed gear was made of die-cast aluminum. By 1980, the number was changed to H1220B, which had the Hy-Lo feature but with a sliding bar and a different die-cast gear wheel. This drill was discontinued in 1988.

The no. 620 hand drill, which ultimately became the 1220, was produced the longest period of time, over a fifty-year span, from 1938 to 1988. It was quite a remarkable feat for a hand-operated piece of machinery to remain in production well into the electric and battery-operated ages!

Defiance Brand Hand Drills

The Defiance line of tools was made from the 1920s until the 1950s. The tools in this line were well-made and sold at an economical price. Marketed to the do-it-yourselfer, the line actually began as the Four-Square line in the 1920s.[3] But by the end of the 1920s, the Four-Square Household Tool line had been gradually phased out and this new line—Defiance—was introduced. Stanley advertised the tools as dependable, practical, and low priced. An internal Stanley memo (found in "Folder S36" dated March 1938) noted:

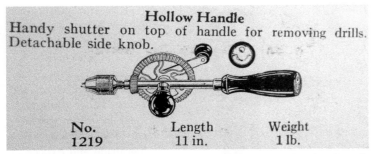

No. 1219	Length 11 in.	Weight 1 lb.

Figure 85 (above). Defiance no. 1219 catalog illustration showing S-spoke gear wheel, side knob, and hollow handle with shutter on the top of the handle to remove a drill.

Figure 86 (below). Catalog illustration of a later model no. 1219 with solid gear wheel.

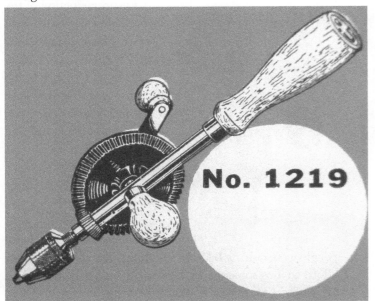

620 hand drill. The no. 1220, which became Stanley's most popular hand drill, was manufactured under the Defiance brand until 1953, when it began to be merged into the Stanley Handyman line. The no. 1220 remained in the line until 1988, when battery-powered drills replaced the hand drill market.

Stanley introduced, in August 1940, three new Defiance drills (Figure 88). They were numbers 1214, 1216, and 1217. These drills featured a steel hexagon frame and a die-cast, aluminum gear wheel and single pinions. The three-jaw steel chuck with a quarter-inch capacity used Bodmer's patent but had a hexagon base (Figure 89).

The Defiance no. 1214, (Figure 90) was a basic single-pinion drill with a natural beechwood handle that was flared out at the top. This handle would remain the general handle design of this new line of drills.

The Defiance no. 1216 was the same as the no. 1214, except the handle was hollow and fitted with a metal shutter top for drill bit storage. The no. 1216 had a side knob. No drills were supplied when purchased.

Defiance no. 1217 was also the same as the no. 1214 except it had a hollow handle with a screw cap and a side knob. The die-cast speed gear was bright red lacquered. Again, no drill bits were supplied with the no. 1217. By March 15, 1941, Defiance model no. 1216 was discontinued, and numbers 1214 and 1217

and a hollow handle for drill bit storage with a shutter on top for removing drill bits, but no drill bits were furnished. First manufactured with the S-spoke speed gear, Stanley soon after switched this drill to a red-japanned, solid-gear wheel (Figure 86).

The no. 1219 remained in the line until December 21, 1942, when it was temporarily discontinued due to World War II. Model numbers 1218 and 1219 were permanently discontinued in 1948.

Model numbers 1218 and 1219 were the only hand drills in the Defiance line until February 1938, when Stanley introduced the Defiance no. 1220 hand drill (Figure 87). This hand drill was a take-off of Stanley's no.

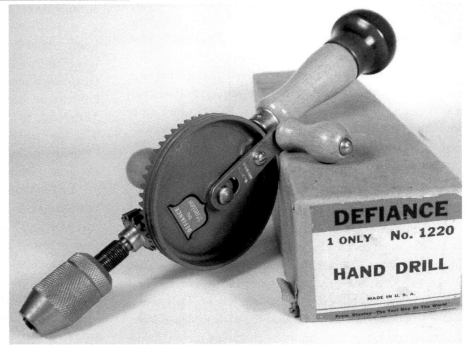

Figure 87. Defiance no. 1220 hand drill with wide-flange gear wheel.

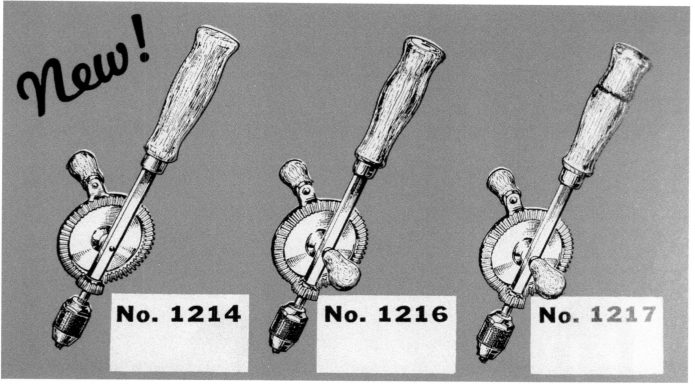

No. 1214   No. 1216   No. 1217

Figure 88 (above). An illustration from the August 1940 Stanley catalog showing the nos. 1214, 1216, and 1217 hand drills with hexagon steel frames.

Figure 89 (left). Christian Bodmer's patented steel chuck with hexagon base that was used on Defiance drills nos. 1214, 1216, and 1217.

had handle changes. Figure 91 shows the no. 1214 with the new handle design.

The Defiance no. 1217 (Figure 92) shows the new handle design with a dark-red-lacquered finish. The dark-red-lacquered finish was short lived. Later models (Figure 93) with a natural-color bottom and a black top seem to predominate.

By 1951, the Defiance no. 1214 hand drill gear wheel finish was changed from a red lacquer to a hammered-

gray-lacquer finish (Figure 94). This later merged into the Stanley Handyman line as model no. H1214.

In December 1942, Stanley introduced the Defiance no. 1221 (Figure 95) hand drill. This drill was the same as a no. 1220 except it had a solid handle and no side knob. It featured double pinions and a cast-iron, machine-cut, flanged gear wheel. In 1953, 1220 was merged into the Stanley Handyman line as the H1221.

Thus, the Defiance hand drill line was merged, in most models, into the Stanley Handyman Household Tools line. As the

CONTINUED PAGE 157

Figure 90 (right). Stanley's Defiance no. 1214 hand drill with a natural beechwood handle.

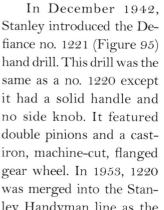

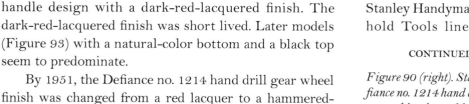

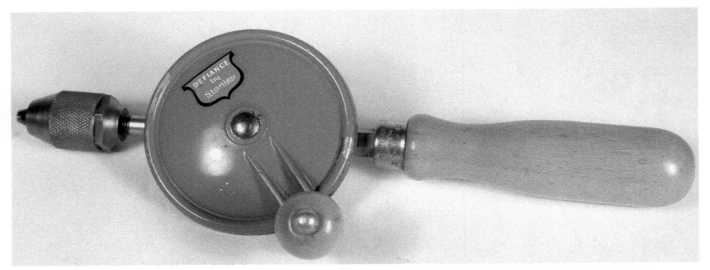

Figure 91 (above). A no. 1214 Defiance hand drill with the later style handle.

Figure 92 (left). Defiance no. 1217 with a dark-red-lacquered, hollow handle with screw top.

Figure 93 (above). Defiance no. 1217 with a two-color handle.

final half of the twentieth century drew to a close, hand drills were discontinued in favor of battery-operated drills. However, many craftsmen and homeowners prefer the control offered by a hand drill and seek the older models for their tool chests. Hand drills live on, a tradition begun centuries ago by early craftsmen.

Notes

1. "New Tools Section," Stanley Catalog No. 34 (July 1932): page f.
2. This was advertised as "A Popular Priced Hand Drill," meaning it wasn't low end nor was it top-of-the-line. The cost was $2.50 in 1937. A high-priced drill was $5.00.
3. Walter W. Jacob, "The History of Stanley Four-Square Household Tools," *The Chronicle* 59, no. 3 (2006).

Figure 94 (above). Defiance no. 1214 hand drill with hammered-gray-lacquer finish.
Figure 95 (below). Defiance no. 1221 hand drill.

Stanley Defiance Brand Breast Drills

After the Stanley Works and the Stanley Rule & Level Company merged on May 1, 1920, the new company almost immediately developed a line of tools for the do-it-yourself and household-use market called the Four-Square line. The Four-Square line remained popular, but it was slowly phased out starting in 1929 following the introduction of the Defiance line, which served the same markets. The Defiance brand was a line of dependable, practical, and attractive tools priced to meet competitive conditions. With the October 1929 U.S. stock market crash, followed by the Great Depression in the 1930s, Stanley's Defiance line served the average homeowner with quality, inexpensive tools.

Breast drills: the reader may ask "What are they?" They could be described as the "big brother" to hand drills. These drills are built stronger and heavier and are made to drill larger holes in wood and metal using more pressure.

Hence, the curved plate at the top of the drill. It fitted against the user's chest to provide the needed pressure.

Defiance drills were manufactured in three models. Model no. 1265 was the first Defiance drill introduced in 1929 (Figure 1). With a 0 to ½-inch capacity, three-jaw chuck, the drill was made to receive round, shank-twist drill bits. This model had a steel shank fitted with a cast, gray-iron gear and breast plate. The breast plate was adjustable to two positions to accommodate different uses. The gear had a 3-to-1 ratio and was fitted with a large offset crank handle. This offset crank protected the fingers of either hand, so they would not get caught between the gear and/or the shaft and to assure a freely turning drive gear. A side handle was also fitted to the drill opposite the drive gear to help in stabilization. The no. 1265 was discontinued in 1941.

Defiance model no. 1247½ (Figure 2) was introduced in 1934 and continued in production to 1960. This breast drill featured a two-speed, die-cast gear and had a ½-inch capacity, three-jaw chuck. The gear was manufactured with two sets of teeth (Figure 3), which provided two speeds. The outer set of teeth was made for a 3-to-1 gear ratio. The inner set made a 1.2-to-1 gear ratio or a slow speed. The speed change was made possible by unscrewing the side handle and sliding the gear housing down toward the chuck for a slow speed (Figure 4). This drill also had an adjustable breast plate, a steel shank and an offset crank handle.

In 1939, Stanley introduced their "Baby" Defiance no. 1255 breast drill (Figures 5 and 6). This drill featured a %₃₂-inch capacity, three-jaw chuck

Figure 1 (above, left). Model no. 1265, the first Defiance drill introduced in 1929.

Figure 2 (above, right). Defiance model no. 1247½ breast drill with a two-speed, die-cast gear.

and a cast, gray-iron gear with a 3-to-1 regular speed gear ratio. It was, for all practical purposes, a Defiance no. 1218 hand drill (Figure 7) fitted with a side handle similar to a regular hand drill and a cast, gray-iron, adjustable breast plate on a steel shank 9 inches in length. Also, the knob on the crank handle of the no. 1255 was increased in size. The no. 1255 is the rarest of the Defiance breast drills, having been made for only three years (1939 to 1941).

Defiance brand tools are an interesting part of Stanley's tool-making history.

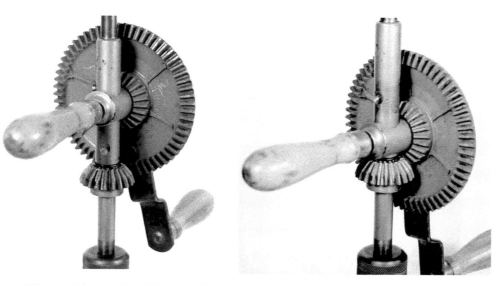

Figure 3 (above, left) and Figure 4 (above, right). The model no. 1247½ had two sets of teeth—one for a 3-to-1 gear ratio (Figure 3) and one for a 1.2-to-1 gear ratio (Figure 4). The speed change was made possible by unscrewing the side handle and sliding the gear housing down toward the chuck for a slow speed.

Figures 5, 6 (above, left and middle), and 7 (above, right). The "Baby" Defiance no. 1255 breast drill (Figures 5 and 6) was in actuality, a Defiance no. 1218 hand drill (Figure 7) that had been converted to a longer knob on the crank and fitted with a breast plate.

The History of Stanley Four-Square Household Tools

By the early-1920s, the Stanley company had been making high-quality tools for carpenters and mechanics for more than seventy years and had obtained a dominant position as a tool manufacturer. Stanley engineers recognized that the success of the business depended on developing new hand tools that could be used for unusual or special jobs, and they created tools for those purposes.

This drive to develop new products and markets led the Stanley Works, in late 1922, to manufacture a line of tools for householders. "This line," the company noted in one of its in-house sales publications, "is the growth of an insistent

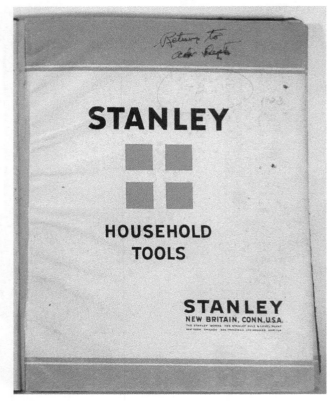

Figure 1 (top of page). Stanley Four-Square logo sign circa 1924 (15³/₈ x 18¹/₄ inches).
Figure 2 (above left). Cover of the booklet announcing the Four-Square tools at a January 1924 sales conference.
Figure 3 (above, right). Stanley catalog in 1923 (8 x 11 inches, 32 pages).

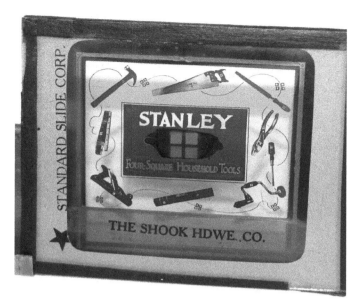

Figures 4 and 5 (above, left and right). Advertisement from the Saturday Evening Post (February 14, 1925) on left and The Literary Digest (January 21, 1924) on right.

Figure 6 (far right). A slide used as an advertisement for Four-Square tools at movie theaters.

and growing demand by householders for good tools."[1] Thus, "Four-Square Household Tools" were conceived, and Stanley created a line of twenty-one different classes of tools—"the best quality Stanley could make for the usage"[2]—strictly for household use. (See page 170 for a listing of the tools in the Four-Square line.)

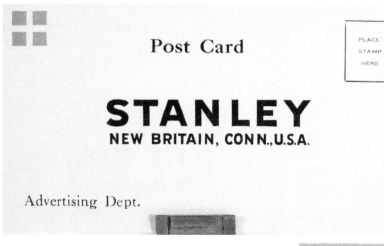

Figures 7a and 7b. A Stanley Four-Square postcard (above) and poster stamps circa 1924 (right).

The designation "Stanley Four-Square" and the accompanying mark consisting of four squares (Figure 1) were granted U.S. patent trademarks on May 15, May 29, and June 5, 1923. Stanley claimed use from October 20, 1922. These trademarks were carried on such goods as rules, levels, squares, marking gauges, bevels, vises, planes, hammers, and wrenches. Additionally, the trademark patent included drills for cutting holes, ice picks, and nail sets; hardware, such as hinges; bolts and latches for securing doors and windows; and handles for doors, drawers, boxes, chests, and similar articles, but to my knowledge none of these tools, except for the ice picks, were ever manufactured.

The whole focus of Four-Square tools was the "do-it-yourself" market that was beginning to evolve in the 1920s. This line was also designed to help the retailer by creating a product with a fast turnover at reasonable prices for hardware stores in residential areas. The ad

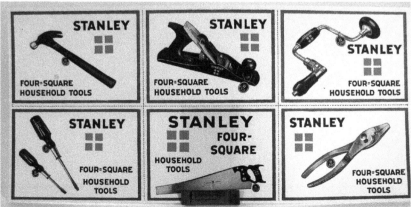

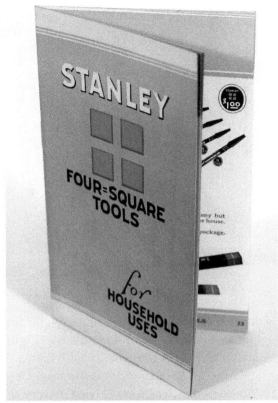

Figure 8. A Stanley Four-Square pocket catalog (3½ x 6 inches).

campaign was designed to promote sales in hardware items as well as tools. The company explained to retailers that this was to be a small and easy line of tools to handle with no "ponderous stocks to carry and tie up investments."[3] It was a very heavy merchandising and

advertising campaign, which, I think, was to be one of the greatest and most unique advertising campaigns ever created by a tool manufacturer.

"Telling the world about Stanley Four-Square" started with a sales conference on January 3, 4, and 5, 1924, at the Elks Club in New Britain, Connecticut (Figure 2). To kick off the merchandising campaign, such topics as reasons behind the household tool development, promotion plans, distinctive marking and packing, and the merchandising plan were disclosed to the Stanley salesmen.

Stanley claimed that "Eight out of every ten of the better families" would be reached by the Four-Square advertising."[4] The merchandising plan that acquainted the buying public with Four-Square was made up of an advertising booklet and catalog copyrighted in 1923 (Figure 3) that illustrated the Four-Square line of household tools with a list of material available free to hardware stores to help sales.

For those who leisurely scanned magazines, there were full- and double-page ads placed in the *Saturday Evening Post* and *The Literary Digest*, alternating every other week beginning in 1924 and continuing through 1925. These ads are interesting to collect and are neat when framed (Figures 4 and 5).

Other advertising was done using slides at theaters to catch the eye of the moviegoer (Figure 6). These glass slides are extremely rare and usually advertised the local hardware store where the tools could be purchased.

Postcards and poster stamps—an advertisement printed on a gummed stamp that was attached to letters, bills, and the back of envelopes—were provided so the

Figure 9. A Four-Square street car sign (11⅛ x 21 inches).

hardware merchant could send promotional material to prospective customers (Figure 7).

Small pocket catalogs promoting the line (Figure 8) were mailed to customers with their bills from the hardware store. There were newspaper advertisements to attract, as Stanley said, "the busiest of busy men." Street car cards were used to help answer where to fill your household needs (Figure 9).

Six colorful, lithographed, counter-top cards were used to promote impulse sales. These snappy, cut-out, lithographed figures included a lady holding a Four-Square screwdriver (Figure 10), a flapper using a Four-Square hammer to drive in a nail (Figure 11), a man using a pair of Four-Square pliers with a Four-Square household vise (Figure 12), a boy measuring his puppy with a Four-Square rule (Figure 13), a man sawing a board with a Four-Square saw (Figure 14), and a character boring a hole with a Four-Square brace and auger bit (Figure 15). These

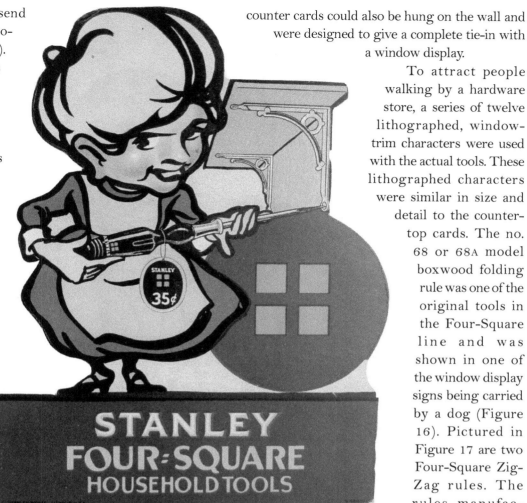

counter cards could also be hung on the wall and were designed to give a complete tie-in with a window display.

To attract people walking by a hardware store, a series of twelve lithographed, window-trim characters were used with the actual tools. These lithographed characters were similar in size and detail to the counter-top cards. The no. 68 or 68A model boxwood folding rule was one of the original tools in the Four-Square line and was shown in one of the window display signs being carried by a dog (Figure 16). Pictured in Figure 17 are two Four-Square Zig-Zag rules. The rules manufactured from 1924 through 1930 usually have a black Four-Square trademark printed on them (shown on top in Figure 17). These rules, of the deep yellow-orange color, were made until about 1929 and were four feet long. After 1929, the model no. 1156 rule became part of the line. The rule color was changed to a light yellow, and the no. 1156, the word "Four Square," and the trademark were

Figures 10 (above), 11 (below, left), and 12 (below, right). Stanley Four-Square counter display signs for screwdrivers (11⅛ x 12 inches), hammers (8⅜ x 10½ inches) and pliers and vises (9¾ x 13 inches).

printed in red. The later rules were 6 feet long and were discontinued in 1935. The 1156 is the rarer of the two.

Levels, shown with the window character in Figure 18, were made of cherry wood. The early examples, which were manufactured until about 1929, had a natural finish and a black-lacquered hand groove. They were 18 inches long. From 1929 to 1935, the levels were enameled gray and red and were 24 inches long with the plumb and level in the middle of the stock.

The Four-Square hammer had a black, polled head with a black-stained, hickory handle. It weighed 14½ounces and had the Sweetheart logo stamped on the head and a decal on the handle neck. The Four-Square hammer is shown with a matching display sign in Figure 19.

Early on, the Four-Square smooth plane was similar to a no. 5¼ but had a checkered lever cap ei-

ther with the Four-Square logo cast into it or with a plain, checkered lever cap with a Four-Square decal placed on the side (Figure 20). From about 1930 to 1932, the original smooth plane was discontinued, and no. 1104 and no. 1105 planes were introduced (Figure 21). These planes, a no. 4 and a no. 5 size, had gray-enamel beds with gray lever caps and red handle and knob, with the red, Four-Square logo cast into the smooth lever cap. These planes were discontinued in 1936.

The household Four-Square block plane, until 1930, was similar to a no. 220, but had the Four-Square logo cast into the lever cap (Figure 22). They were black japanned

Figures 13 (above), 14 (below, left), and 15 (below, right). Stanley Four-Square counter display signs for folding rules (13½ x 11½ inches), saws (10 x 12¼ inches), and brace and auger bits (10 x 12½ inches).

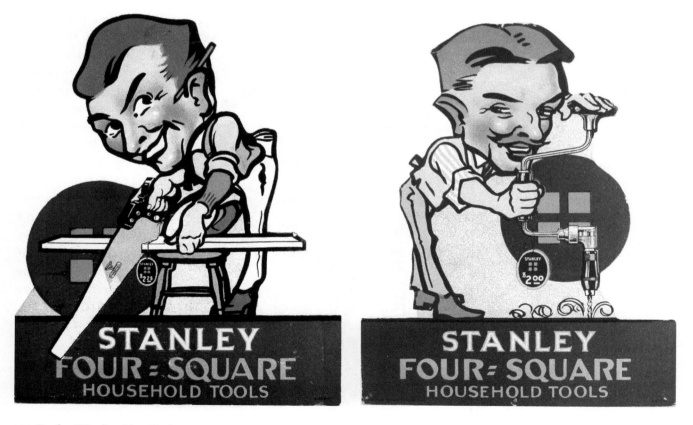

and adjustable. After 1930, the plane was made with no adjustment, had a gray-enamel finish, and was numbered 1120 (Figure 23).

A Four-Square axe was made up to 1930, and had the red Four-Square trademark embossed into the black head (Figure 24).

Advertising the Four-Square Line

The Four-Square advertising campaign in 1924 was one of the most extensive of any of the tool manufacturers. Advertisements in *The Saturday Evening Post* and *Literary Digest*, and in many other magazines, created great interest among all classes of people. Dealer counter-top displays and window-trim characters are some of the most colorful of display cards. Street car display signs, newspaper ads, movie slides, poster stamps, and postcards

CONTINUED PAGE 167

Figure 16 (above). Stanley Four-Square window display sign with a Four-Square folding rule (sign: 9⅝ x 6¼ inches).

Figure 17 (right). Stanley Four-Square Zig-Zag rules. The early model no. 1156 sits on a later model Four-Square rule.

Figure 18 (above). Stanley Four-Square counter-display sign with a Four-Square level (sign: 14¾ x 6⅛ inches).

Figure 19 (left). Stanley Four-Square counter-display sign with a Four-Square hammer (sign: 9¾ x 12½ inches).

Figure 20. Stanley Four-Square window display sign with bench plane (sign: 10 x 7⅛ inches).

Figure 21 (right). Stanley Four-Square no. 1105 bench plane.

Figure 22 (above). A Stanley Four-Square block plane.

Figure 23. Stanley Four-Square no. 1120 block plane (nonadjustable).

Figure 24. Stanley Four-Square catalog page showing the Four-Square axe.

Figure 25 (above). As part of the advertising campaign for Four-Square tools, customers were given a 5¢ piece to purchase The Saturday Evening Post so that they could then read the Stanley advertising in the magazine.

were used to advantage by hardware stores and dealers. One give-away that hardware dealers distributed to customers was a clever card (Figure 25) to which a 1924 buffalo nickel was attached and held in place by a brass clip. The card asked the customer to use the nickel to purchase the April

12, 1924, issue of the *Saturday Evening Post* to see the Four-Square advertisement. (This card is also discussed in "Get Your Nickel's Worth—Stanley's Use of Coins for Promotion" on pages 202-203).

A pipe wrench was part of the original twenty-one tool types (Figure 26) that was included in the original Four-Square line. This wrench had the Sweetheart mark and a black handle and was offered by Stanley until 1930. These wrenches are some of the rarer Four-Square tools. Another tool that is somewhat scarce today is the 15-inch Four-Square pry bar (Figure 27) offered until 1930. This bar exists in two forms—with the Stanley cut label forged into the head and with the Four-Square logo. The Four-Square file is another hard-to-find tool from the collection. They were offered in the mill file (Figure 28) and the slim taper file. Both had the Sweetheart stamped on the tang and a decal on a black handle.

No household tool set would have been complete without a handsaw, so Stanley included an eight-point, 24-inch crosscut saw with a black handle in its Four-Square line. Figure 29 shows a Four-Square saw with a window-display character. These saws were made for Stanley by Disston. Beginning in 1929, these saws were sold as model no. 1124.

Initially available in four sizes— ⅜-, ½-, ¾-, and 1-inch (Figure 30)—Stanley later added the ⅞- and 1¼-inch sizes to its set of socket chisels. The hickory handles were black and had the Four-Square decal as shown in Figure 31. Set no. 1150A of six chisels became available in 1935 in a canvas roll. These chisels had a clear, lacquered hickory handle with the decal.

A 10-inch-sweep bit brace was offered beginning in 1923 and had a black handle, pad, and chuck shell—the round metal piece that covers the jaws—with a Sweetheart mark. (Figure 32 shows the brace with window trim characters.) These braces were later marked as model no. 1151; they were discontinued in 1935. To go with the brace, Four-Square auger bits were offered in six sizes: ⁴⁄₁₆, ⁶⁄₁₆, ⁸⁄₁₆, ¹⁰⁄₁₆, ¹²⁄₁₆, and ¹⁶⁄₁₆ (Figure 33). These augers have black tangs with a red Four-Square decal on the shank and the Sweetheart mark. They were discontinued in 1930. Stanley

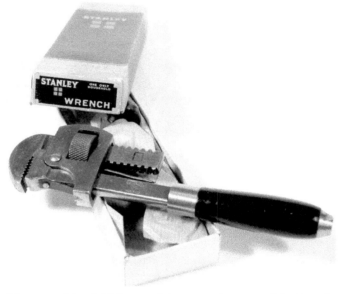

Figure 26 (above). This wrench is among the rarest of the Four-Square tools.

Figure 27 (below). The pry bar has the Four-Square and Stanley logos forged into the head.

Figure 28 (above, left). A Four-Square mill file. The file has the Sweetheart logo stamped on the tang and the Four-Square decal on the handle.

Figure 29. A Four-Square saw with window-display character. The saw was made by Disston.

designed a window-trim character (Figure 34) to help sell the auger bits.

Slip-joint pliers with a Sweetheart mark were available in a 6½-inch length until 1930. These pliers are hard to

find today (Figure 35). The Four-Square outfit also included a putty knife (Figure 36). The putty knife had a decal on its dark-stained handle. Stanley discontinued this Four-Square tool in 1930; today the putty knife is one of

CONTINUED PAGE 170

Figure 30 (left) and 31 (above). Four-Square socket chisels is shown at left, and above is a chisel with a window-display figure.
Figure 32 (below). A 10-inch-sweep brace shown with a double-character window display.

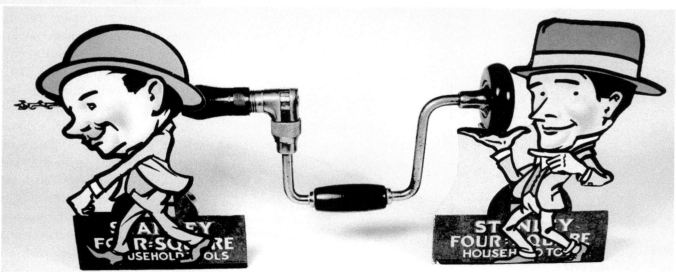

Figures 33 (above) and 34 (right). A set of bits (above) for the brace and a cardboard character posed with one of the bits (right).

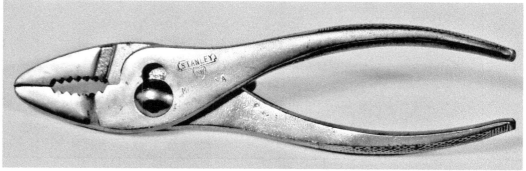

Figure 35. These slip-joint pliers are one of the less common Four-Square tools.

Figure 36. The putty knife is also a rare Four-Square tool.

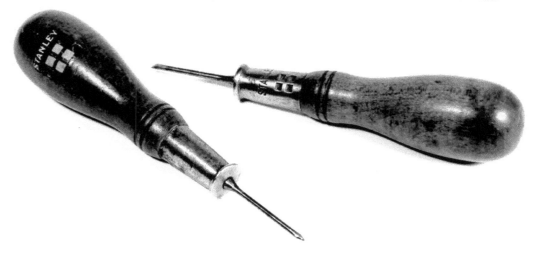

Figure 37 The Four-Square awl.

The Four-Square Line

From 1924 to 1930, Stanley produced twenty-one types of tools for the Four-Square line. Around 1930, Stanley began to phase out the original, non-numbered Four-Square tools and replace them with numbered tools. The Four-Square numbered tool series was completely phased-in by January 1932, except for the no. 3206 and no. 3306 Pull-Push rules, which were introduced in 1934. The numbered tools introduced January 1, 1932 were:

    1104, no. 4 bench plane
    1105, no. 5 bench plane
    1113, aluminum level
    1115, hammer—16 oz. claw
    1119, hand drill
    1120, block plane
    1124, saw—24-inch, 8-point
    1132, saw set
    1141, breast drill
    1145, vise
    1147, wood level
    1150, socket chisels—six sizes (the set sold as 1150A)
    1151, 10-inch sweep brace
    1156, 6-foot Zig-Zag rule
    1166, Pull-Push rule
    1170, screwdrivers—three sizes (4-, 5-, 6-inch)
    1175, ice pick

Two rules were introduced in 1934—the 3206 nickel-plated case, Pull-Push rule and the 3306 gun-blued case Pull-Push rule.

When Stanley introduced the numbered series in the Four-Square line, some of the tool types were changed or eliminated and other new tools were added. There were two bench planes of different lengths, instead of one, and an aluminum level. The Four-Square pliers, axe, wrench, pry bar, files, auger bits, and adjustable square were dropped from the line. New tools to the line were a saw-set, breast drill, hand drill, and three Pull-Push rules, making a total of nineteen numbered tools. All of these tools were dropped in 1935, with the exception of the Pull-Push rules, which continued to be available with the Four-Square logo but not marketed as such.

With the onset of the Depression, a less–expensive line of tools—Defiance tools—was introduced by Stanley in the mid-1930s, but that line is another story.

Figure 38. A Four-Square screwdriver with a female window-display character.

Figure 39. Two versions of the 7-inch try-and-miter square. The earlier version is seen with the advertising character.

the rarer Four-Square tools. A household awl (Figure 37) was also part of the Four-Square tool set. It has either a decal on the handle or Four-Square stamped on the ferrule.

Of course, any household tool kit would have to include screwdrivers. In the Four-Square line, screwdrivers were available in four sizes—1½ to 5 inches. Figure 38 shows a 2½-inch screwdriver with the natural finished handle, which has the Four-Square decal, being handled very delicately by a female window-trim character.

Stanley also manufactured a 7-inch try-and-miter square for the Four-Square line. The first models had a decal on the lock bolt housing and later, the logo was cast into the bottom part of the frame. Both variations (Figure 39) were discontinued around 1930. Stanley also made a small—2-inch width—jaw vise for the Four-Square line. It had the Sweetheart mark stamped on the jaw shank and a Four-Square decal on the side. The window display designed for the vise shows a very expressive and obviously upset little girl encountering the vise (Figure 40). About

1930, the jaw width was increased to 2½ inches, and it bore the model number 1145. It was discontinued in 1935.

From 1932 to 1935, a no. 1113 aluminum level with six vials was part of the Four-Square line. Beginning in 1932, a hand drill (no. 1119) with a hollow handle and ¼-inch capacity chuck and a breast drill (no. 1141) with ½-inch chuck

were introduced, but they were quickly discontinued and off the market by 1935. Shown in Figure 41 is the no. 1141 breast drill, which was later part of Stanley's Defiance line with the model number 1147½.

Also introduced in 1932 was a saw set, no. 1132. These saw sets were painted red and gray and seldom had the decal on them. In 1934, and only for that one year, a cast iron model was sold known as no. 1142 (Figure 42).

In 1932 when Stanley brought out its line of Stanley tape measures, the no. 1166 Pull-Push rule (Figure 43) was added to the Four-Square line. Shown in Figure 44 is an advertisement for Four-Square tapes. Although Four-Square tools were officially discontinued in 1935, the tapes were offered as Four-Square up to 1950.

Two 6-foot tape rules, the no. 3206 nickel-plated case and 3306 gun-blued case, were offered in 1934 only (Figures 45a and b). In 1934-35, two tapes—the 3-foot no. 7363 and 6-foot no. 7366—were introduced with the Four-Square logo (Figure 46. These were carried in the line until 1950).

The Four-Square tool line began in 1922 and was the start of the "do-it-yourself" movement. Between 1922 and 1935, Stanley met the needs of ordinary men and women by producing this line of tools for use in the home. These were lower grade tools which Stanley made for this new market, used by the do-it-yourself user/homeowner. The colorful and extensive advertising campaign encouraged the average householder to purchase good quality tools at a

Figure 40. The jaw vise illustrated was small, only 2 inches wide, but obviously could still pack a pinch.

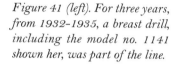

Figure 41 (left). For three years, from 1932-1935, a breast drill, including the model no. 1141 shown her, was part of the line.

Figure 42 (above). For one year, 1934, Stanley sold a cast-iron saw set.

Figures 43 a (left) and b (right). A no. 1166 Stanley Pull-Push tape measure (left) and a Four-Square tape measure (right).

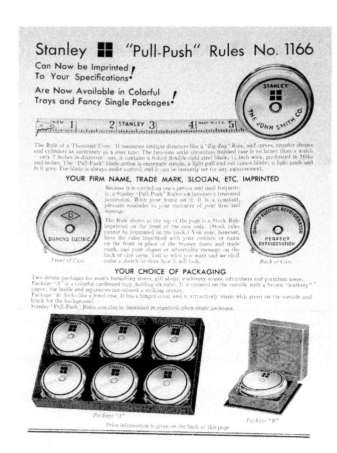

Figure 44 (left). An advertisement presenting the Four-Square tape measure.

Figures 45a and b (above). Two photographs showing each side of the Four-Square tapes model no. 3206 with a nickel-plated case, and no. 3306 with a gun-metal blue case. The tapes were offered only in 1934.

moderate price—even during the Great Depression years! There were more than twenty-one tools, as well as several tool sets and a workbench, included in the line in its heyday. In the past twenty years, the colorful Four-Square tools and their advertisements have become highly collectible.

I close this history with a picture of the Four-Square window-display doggie (Figure 47) with the quote made by Stanley in a historical sketch in 1935, which said: "There it stands, four square toward the future." This one little set of tools and the advertising campaign that accompanied it revolutionized home tools.

Figure 46 (above). In 1934 Stanley's nos. 7363 and 7366 were added to the Four-Square line.

Figure 47 (left). This dog is one of the display cards that advertised the Four-Square line.

Notes

1. *Stanley Household Tools, a New Forceful Idea for the Hardware Store* (Stanley Works, four-page dealer brochure, circa 1923), 1.
2. From various late-1923 Stanley Four-Square dealer advertising circulars.
3. From late-1923, Stanley Four-Square dealer advertising circulars.
4. Stanley Tools Dealer Promotion fold-out, 25- x 19-inch broadside, no. S200, 1924.

Stanley Non-Sparking Beryllium Copper Tools

The Stanley Works, in 1936, introduced a new line of non-sparking tools made of an alloy of copper containing 2 to 2½ percent beryllium. Beryllium is an element (atomic element number 4) that was discovered around 1848. It is found in a series of complex minerals, usually in silicates. Stanley stated in its advertising that the presence of beryllium in this new alloy imparted remarkable qualities in that it could be formed and machined in a soft condition and, after heat treating, resulted in a tough, hard material of high tensile strength, similar to spring-tempered steel.

Most beryllium tools were made from casting and then were heat treated to give them hardness. Stanley's beryllium copper tools exclusively were wrought from

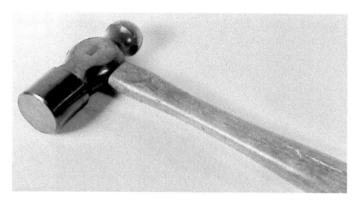

Figure 1 (above). A no. B3 ball peen hammer.

Figure 2 (below). The no. B7, a 1-pound scaling hammer.

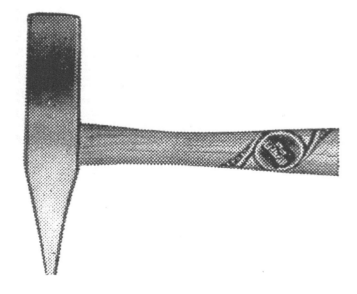

beryllium bars that had been found, through laboratory tests, and actual experience to have the best physical properties, especially in toughness and tensile strength. The quality level of this material resulted in a greater manufacturing expense.

Sales literature gave examples of the strength and hardness of Stanley wrought-beryllium copper tools: "A Stanley Beryllium copper cold chisel cut off the heads of 3¼ in. steel rivets [with] no damage to [the] edge of [the] chisel; sheared off [a] section of ⅛ in. thick cold-rolled steel 3 in. long [with] no damage to [the] edge of the chisel; using [the] corner of [the] chisel edge [it] scored a groove one in. long in [the] surface of wrought iron pipe ... ; using [an] undamaged chisel edge [it was driven] end-wise splitting [the] wall of 1 in. wrought iron pipe down a distance of 1½ in. Pipe wall [was] approximately .140 inch in thickness. No damage [was done] to chisel edge."[1]

Wrought-beryllium copper tools were almost as durable as similarly designed steel tools, but were non-sparking and non-magnetic. Stanley's wrought-beryllium copper tools were manufactured for use in industrial plants where flammable liquids or gases were used. A spark from a conventional tool could set off an explosion or fire. Lacquering plants, processors of cellulose nitrate, oil companies, and public utilities were among the companies where these tools were used.

In May 1936, Stanley issued a twelve-page pocket catalog illustrating its non-sparking tools.[2] This catalog had twenty-five wrought-beryllium copper tools, followed by a brief description of each.

The no. B3 ball peen hammer shown in Figure 1 was at the top of the list. This hammer was 24 ounces, and sold for $13.80 in April 1937 (compared to $1.20 for the top-of-the-line, drop-forged steel no. 312 ball peen hammer). The cost of the beryllium hammer was eleven-and-a-half times more expensive than a regular, forged ball peen hammer. Stanley also made a 32-ounce (2 pounds) ball peen (no. B4) priced at $18.60, which was thirteen-and-a-quarter times costlier than a drop-forged hammer.

Besides the two ball peens, a 1-pound scaling hammer, no. B7, (Figure 2) or boiler pick, and a 10½-pound handled sledge (no. B10) were offered.

A hand cold chisel (no. B15) with a ⅞-inch bit made out of ¾-inch octagon beryllium was manufactured. Also

Figure 3. A no. B31 standard blade screwdriver. The handle was painted green rubber.

produced was a diamond point chisel (no. B 18) with a ½-inch point.

Two screwdrivers with green-painted, rubber handles and standard-style blades were offered in 6-inch (no. B30) and 8-inch (no. B31) blade lengths. Figure 3 illustrates a no. B31 standard blade screwdriver with an overall length of 13 inches.

A series of scraper and spatulas were also manufactured. The scrapers included two hand scrapers, three floor scrapers, and a deck scraper. The hand scrapers had 3-inch wide blades. One of them had a flexible blade (no. B38) and the other had a stiff blade (no. B39). Both had tropical hardwood handles. The floor scrapers were socket types to be fitted to a wood handle (nos. B45 and B46) or one with a ½-inch standard brass pipe handle (no. B43). The no. B45 floor scraper had a square-edge, 6-inch-wide blade (Figure 4), and the no. B46 had a rounded-edge, 6-inch-wide blade for scraping rounded surfaces in tanks and barrels. Floor scraper no. B43 used a ½-inch standard brass pipe handle of any length and had a 3¾-inch blade width.

A no. B42 deck scraper was also offered (see Figure 5), which was 16¾ inches overall and had a 4-inch triangular blade, which was a ¼ inch thick.

Three spatulas were also in the beryllium copper tool line. They had blade lengths of 3 inches (no. B50), 6 inches (no. B51), and 12 inches (no. B52), available with tropical hardwood handles and fastened with non-sparking rivets.

A 1½- x 6-inch flanged wedge (no. B56) with a ¼-inch taper was offered with an ⅛-inch thick bit and was used for set-up work.

Beryllium fork tips (no. B66) were also manufactured to be attached to the prongs of standard forks for handling such things as celluloid scrap and gun cotton. These tips were attached to the prongs of a fork by soft solder or by

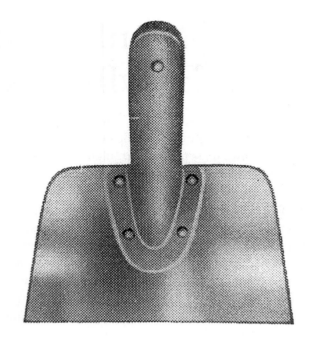

Figure 4 (above). The B45 floor scraper. It was a socket-type scraper meant to be fitted with a handle.
Figure 5 (below). The B42 deck scraper. The 4-inch triangular blade was ¼ inch thick.

drilling and fastening with brass rivets.

A straight drift pin (no. B67) 7½ inches in length and ¹³⁄₁₆ inches in diameter was offered for lining up holes.

Two pry bars made of ¾-inch octagon stock, 18 inches long, were manufactured with or without a claw. The no. B68 without claw was used for opening manhole covers on tanks and tank cars and for lining up holes. The no. B70 pry bar had a fork in the end, making it a very useful tool for certain kinds of work.

Another interesting beryllium tool that Stanley manufactured was a railroad or clay pick (no. B69) with a special eyeless pattern head which was permanently fastened to an Everdur bronze head. This head is a bronz,e

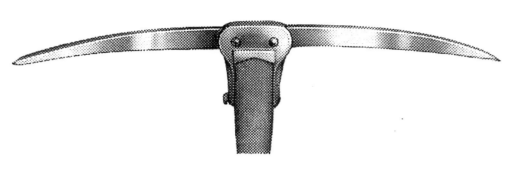

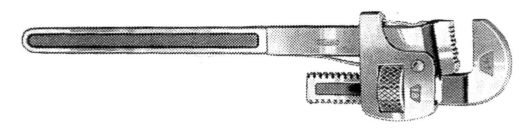

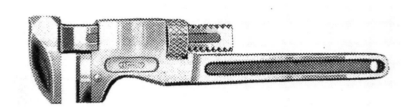

Figure 6 (left, top). Railroad or clay pick. The head was bolted to the handle with Everdur bronze bolts.

Figure 7 (left, middle). The B80 Stillson pattern pipe wrench (length: 18 inches).

Figure 8 (left, bottom). The B81 monkey wrench (length: 12 inches).

eyeless, glove-like fixture to which the handle was bolted by Everdur bronze bolts (see Figure 6). The pick is 27¾ inches in length and has a 30-inch wood handle.

To complete the line, two wrenches were offered. First designated as no. B80 was a heavy-duty, 18-inch Stillson pattern pipe wrench (Figure 7). This wrench had a capacity of ¼ to 2 inches

Last, but not least, what tool kit would be complete without a monkey wrench? Stanley's monkey wrench no. B81 (Figure 8) was a heavy-duty, 12-inch wrench of a special design that permitted more leverage as the size of the nut increased. The capacity was 2¼ inches.

Stanley's non-sparking wrought-beryllium copper tools were first introduced in 1936, with a twelve-page pocket catalog printed in May of that year. These tools were illustrated in the December 28, 1936, retail price list for catalog 134. The beryllium tools were also listed in the April 15, 1937, retail price list. Subsequent lists do not show any of the non-sparking Stanley tools. These tools were probably only offered for one year. The enormous production and high retail costs resulted in Stanley dropping the line.

Notes
1. *Reduce Explosion and Fire Hazard with Stanley Nonsparking Tools Made from Wrought Beryllium Copper.* New Britain, Conn.: Stanley Tools, May 1936. Not paginated.
2. Ibid.

Figure 1. A circa 1931 Stanley garden tools advertisement.

Stanley Garden Tools

Early Stanley garden tools were a product that rose out of the economic straits of the Great Depression of the 1930s. By mid-1930, building construction was at a standstill, and sales of building hardware were off. To offset the decline of hardware sales, Stanley began developing other products, including garden tools.

Stanley had poised its product line to meet these difficulties. In July of 1926, the company had acquired the business of the American Tube and Stamping Company of Bridgeport, Connecticut. The Hardware Division of the Stanley Works,

in the late 1920s, was seeing the ever increasing demand for building hardware. The acquisition of the American Tube and Stamping Company strengthened Stanley's ability to produce hot-rolled steel and stampings, a technique that was needed to produce this new line of tools. By mid-1931, Stanley launched a line of garden tools manufactured with all-steel tube handles and stampings. They made eight short-handled and seven long-handled tools (Figure 1).

The short-handled tools, when first introduced, were enameled with bright orange-colored handles with a black cap. Soon thereafter, the colors were changed to an assortment of bright orange with a black cap, red with a gold cap, blue with a yellow cap, and green with an orange cap (Figure 2). Each type tool was stamped and had a tubular handle. It was fitted with an end cap, which was spot welded on the handle end. Each tool was marked with the late-period (1930-1935) Sweetheart mark on the top of the handle about half way down (Figure 3). Eight different tools were available. No. 7041 (Figure 4) was a full-sized trowel with a width of 3 inches and a total length of 11⅝ inches. No. 7042 was a four-tined spading fork (Figure 5) with a width of 3 inches and a length of 11 inches. Each tine was 3 inches long and was used for digging around plants and shrubs.

No. 7043 was a cultivator (Figure 6) with five angular fingers for tough weeds. It was 10⅞ inches long and 3 inches wide. No. 7044, which

Figure 2 (above). The short-handled garden tools came in a variety of color combinations.
Figure 3 (left). Stanley's Sweetheart logo on a short-handled garden tool.

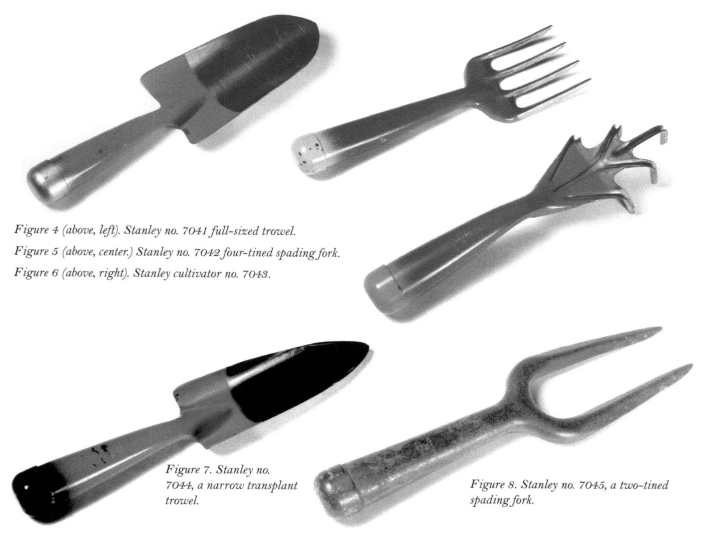

Figure 4 (above, left). Stanley no. 7041 full-sized trowel.

Figure 5 (above, center.) Stanley no. 7042 four-tined spading fork.

Figure 6 (above, right). Stanley cultivator no. 7043.

Figure 7. Stanley no. 7044, a narrow transplant trowel.

Figure 8. Stanley no. 7045, a two-tined spading fork.

Stanley advertised as also being useful as a lawn weeder, was a narrow-blade transplant trowel (Figure 7) 2 inches wide and of 11⅝ inches long.

No. 7045 was a two-tined spading fork (Figure 8) with a length of 10⅞ inches, a width of 2¾ inches, and 5-inch tines. Stanley advertised that this tool wouldn't clog with dirt and could penetrate hard soil. Garden tool no. 7046 was a two-tined cultivator (Figure 9) similar to no. 7045 but with the tines turned at a right angle, making stubby no-clog prongs. No. 7047, a dibble (Figure 10) used to rapidly punch a hole for seedlings or bulbs, had a curved tubular handle without a cap and was 10½ inches long. And finally, in Stanley's short-handled garden tool line was a hand weed cutter, no. 7048 (Figure 11). It had a flat, coarse, saw tooth-type blade.

Figure 9. Stanley no. 7046, two-tined cultivator.

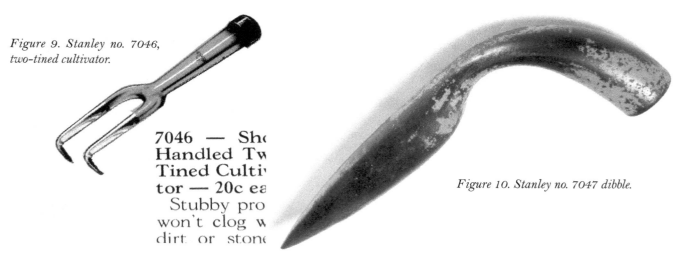

7046 — Sh〈
Handled Tw
Tined Culti〉
tor — 20c ea
Stubby pro
won't clog w
dirt or stone

Figure 10. Stanley no. 7047 dibble.

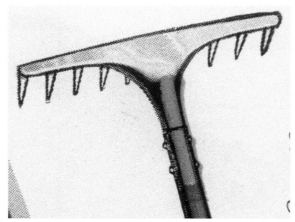

Figure 11 (above). An illustration of a hand weed cutter, Stanley no. 7048, from a catalog.

Figure 12 (below, right). The decal used on Stanley's long-handled garden tools.

Stanley offered a set of four of the most used short handle tools as set no. 7040 in an attractive box (Figure 2). This set consisted of the 7041 full-size trowel, no. 7043 short-handled cultivator, no. 7044 thin blade transplant trowel, and no. 7045 two-tined spading fork.

Stanley also offered seven long-handled garden tools. Each tool had a total length of 40 inches, with a $1\frac{1}{16}$-inch diameter tubular handle with a $\frac{3}{4}$-inch end cap. The tube handles were enameled in green with an orange-enameled cap and tool head. These tools were not stamped with the Sweetheart but usually had an earlier period Stanley decal affixed to the tubular handle about one-third up from

Figure 13. Stanley no. 7051 rake.

the bottom (Figure 12). First in this line-up was the no. 7051 rake (Figure 13) which had ten tines and was small enough to get between garden plants and to rake out piles of leaves and grass but large enough to be useful.

Stanley advertised its no. 7052 (Figure 14), a 4-inch wide spading fork, as "comfortable to step on and to keep the soil loosened." The back of the fork was reinforced by a $\frac{1}{4}$-inch-by-$\frac{1}{2}$-inch bar pinned into the handle (Figure 14, inset). No. 7053 (Figure 15) was a four-tined cultivator used for "shallow or deep cultivating work." This tool had a tine length of 3 inches and was 3 inches wide. Stanley's no. 7054 was an oval hoe (Figure 16), which was advertised as being "especially useful for working the ground underneath low-growing shrubs." The $5\frac{5}{8}$-inch-wide hoe was fastened to a curved $\frac{7}{16}$-inch bar that was inserted into the tubular handle (Figure 17).

Stanley also made a heart-shaped hoe, no. 7055 (Figure 18), used for making troughs for seeding and,

Figure 14. Stanley no. 7052 spading fork and the back of the same fork (inset) showing the reinforced back.

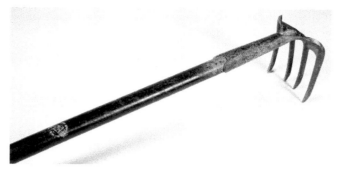

Figure 15. Stanley's four-tined cultivator, no. 7053.

Figure 16 (above). Stanley no. 7054 oval hoe.

Figure 17 (right). Close-up of oval hoe showing construction.

as advertised, "working the ground between crowded plants." The line-up of long-handled garden tools also included a two-tined cultivator, no. 7056 (Figure 19), used "for rooting out garden weeds without getting down on hands and knees." The width of this tool was 2⅝ inches.

Of course, any set of garden tools should have a spade or shovel. Stanley no. 7057 (Figure 20) was just such a tool. The spade blade had a total length of 6 inches and a width of 4 inches. It was reinforced in the back with an internal bar (Figure 21). Stanley also offered the most useful "long" garden tools in a long-handled set, no. 7050. This set consisted of the no. 7052 spading fork, the no. 7053 four-tined cultivator, the no. 7054 oval hoe, and the no. 7057 spade.

To compliment the long- and short-handled garden tools, Stanley also manufactured the no. 7058 garden markers (Figure 22). They had a gray metal top on which one could write, with a pencil, what was planted in that area. To finish out the line, Stanley produced no. 7060 solid steel garden stakes for supporting tall plants (Figure 23). These

Figure 18. No. 7055, Stanley's heart-shaped hoe as illustrated in the company's catalog.

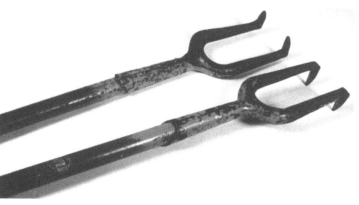

Figure 19. Stanley no. 7056, the two-tined cultivator showing the front and back sides.

Figure 20. Stanley no. 7057 spade or shovel.

Figure 21. The same spade (no. 7057) showing reverse side end reinforced bar.

stakes were available in 30-, 45-, and 60-inch lengths. Also, Stanley offered a fifteen-piece set which had one of each of both the long- and short-handled garden tools. One dozen garden markers were thrown in as a bonus.

About February 1939, Stanley offered a deluxe version of its garden tools that were chromium plated (rather than enameled) with red-enamel caps. A short-handled set of four was offered, numbered 7040CM. These sets were the same as the no. 7040 sets except for the chromium-plated finish (Figure 24).

Stanley's garden tools were displayed on a special stand made to hold one example of each tool. Shown in Figure 25 is one of the merchandising stands with many of the tools mentioned in this article. The entire line of Stanley garden tools was nicely made and has a wonderful feel. They aren't heavy and are a joy to work with.

Stanley began producing garden tools in mid-1931 and continued manufacturing them until about 1949, when the line was dropped. Stanley did not make garden tools again until 1958, when the line was completely changed, continuing through 1975. In 1998, Stanley once again began to produce a line of garden tools. Whether Stanley succeeds in a climate with a larger number of competitors is a story, however, for a future historian to tell.

Figure 22 (right). Stanley's garden markers (no. 7058).

Figure 23 (below). No. 7060, solid-steel garden stakes in 30-, 45-, and 60-inch lengths.

7058 — Garden Markers 60c dozen
For identifying plants. Penciled description written on the grey metal will last all through the season.

7060 GARDEN STAKES

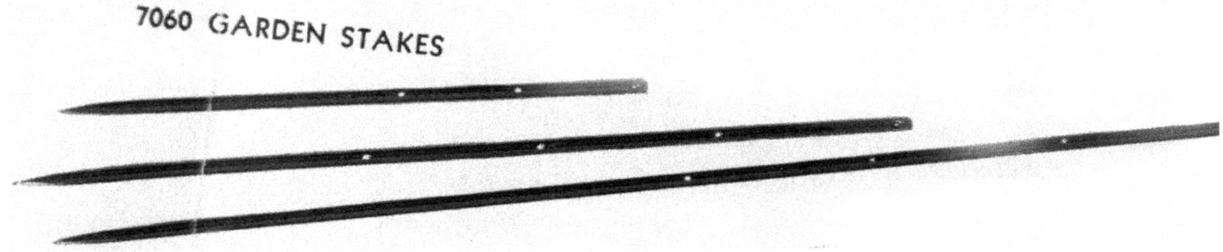

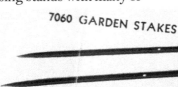

Figure 24 (above). Stanley's deluxe, chromium-plated garden tools.

Figure 25 (right). Stanley merchandising stand for garden tools.

Stanley Plumb Bobs

In 1873, the Stanley Rule & Level Company, with its line of rules, levels, squares, and planes, wanted to expand and diversify its line of carpenter's tools. Since many carpenters used a plumb line and level in their work, Stanley recognized its potential as a product.

A plumb line is basically a string with a weight on one end, which is used like a level to determine verticality, which is a line directed to the center of gravity of the earth. Justus Traut, one of Stanley's contractor/inventors, filed a patent application on April 28, 1874, for a plumb bob with an improvement of a friction wheel to hold the cord. The friction on the spool was made by an internal coil spring that would be adjusted by turning the screw that went through the reel. This allowed the user to adjust the length of the plumb line with ease. On June 2, 1874, Justus Traut received the patent and assigned it to the Stanley Rule & Level Co. (Figure 1).

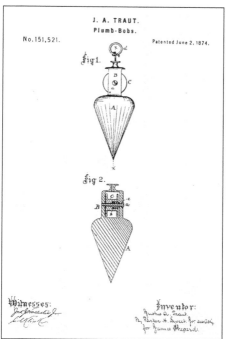

Figure 1. Justus Traut's 1874 plumb bob patent that was assigned to Stanley. Earlier versions of the patent are seen in Figures 2-5.

This patent ultimately led to Stanley's nos. 1, 2, and 5 plumb bobs. However, two plumb bobs that came from Stanley's Model Shop and are attributed to Justus Traut have surfaced. These preliminary designs show that in its early stages the Traut's patent had a slightly different look. The first (Figure 2) was a plumb bob 4¼ inches long that had a round ball attached to Traut's adjustable reel. Instead of a spiral spring, as shown in the patent, a leaf spring was used for the friction of the reel. This plumb bob was constructed in three parts, consisting of a 1⅜₆-inch point that had an extension screw that went through the 1¹¹⁄₁₆ inch-diameter ball and screwed into the spool holder (Figure 3). The point and ball were tool steel and the spool holder was bronze metal. The plumb line was threaded through a hole in the top and onto the spool that had a friction spring applied to it so that it could be adjusted to let the plumb line out for any length, as needed.

The second model (Figure 4) was an all bronze, 5-inch-long plumb bob.

Figures 2 (above) and 3 (right). A plumb bob attributed to Justus Traut from Stanley's Model Shop, c. 1873. It, along with the example in Figure 4, appears to be a preliminary design for Traut's patent. Figure 3 shows the plumb bob taken apart.

Figures 4 (above) and 5 (right). Another early version of Traut's patent, shown as a whole (above) and taken apart (right). Notice the leaf spring in the reel.

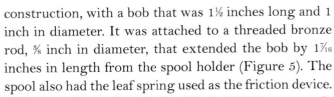

Adjustable Plumb Bobs.

These Plumb Bobs are constructed with a reel at the upper end, upon which the line may be kept; and by dropping the bob with a slight jerk, while the ring is held in the hand, any desired length of line may be reeled off. A spring, which has its bearing on the reel, will check and hold the bob firmly at any point on the line. The pressure of the spring may be increased, or decreased, by means of the screw which passes through the reel. A suitable length of line comes already reeled on each Plumb Bob.

No.		PRICES.			Each.
1.	(Small) Bronze Metal, with Steel Point.....			...$1 50
2.	(Large) " " "		.."	.... 2 00
5.	(Large) Iron " " "			.... 1 00

Figure 6 (above). Catalog (1874-1877) illustration of Stanley's plumb bobs, nos. 1, 2, and 5, shown below in Figures 7, 8, and 9.

construction, with a bob that was 1½ inches long and 1 inch in diameter. It was attached to a threaded bronze rod, ⅜ inch in diameter, that extended the bob by 1⁷⁄₁₆ inches in length from the spool holder (Figure 5). The spool also had the leaf spring used as the friction device.

Both of these model plumb bobs, I feel, were made prior to the final patent application. Apparently, in use, it was found that a spiral (coil) spring achieved a better friction control on the spool than the leaf spring.

Stanley's 1874 catalog, the first to show this new and adjustable plumb bob, notes that it was made in three sizes (Figure 6). The no. 1 was an 8-ounce bronze metal bob with steel point, 3½ inches long (Figure 7). The no. 2 was the same but larger, weighing 12 ounces and 4¼ inches long (Figure 8). The no. 5 was a nickel-plated, cast-iron bob with a steel point. It weighed 12 ounces

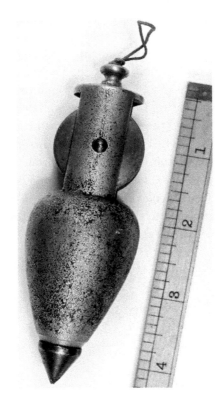

It was also of a three-part

Figures 7, 8, and 9 (above left to right). Stanley's plumb bobs, model nos. 1, 2, and 5.

Figure 10 (left). An 1874 Stanley no. 2 first production, adjustable plumb bob in its original decorated box.

and measured 4¼ inches in length (Figure 9).

The bobs were made in one piece with a steel point and were shipped in a colorful blue-and-white decorated, paper-covered telescoping box with a green label (Figure 10). By the 1880s, the boxes were solid green with no design.

The no. 3 cast-iron plumb bob remained in Stanley's product line until 1935, when it was discontinued. Two years later, in 1937, both of the remaining bronze plumb bobs (nos. 1 and 2) were discontinued.

In the late 1920s, Stanley experimented with two additional plumb bobs made of cast iron and finished in

Figure 11 (left). Two mysteries. Little is known about these cast-iron, two- and four-pound plumb bobs circa late-1920s. Were these millwright's bobs?

Figure 12 (right). Insert from Stanley's catalog no. 160 (1962) illustrating the new plumb bobs.

Figure 13 (below). Stanley plumb bobs, model nos. 170, 171, 172. The one on the far left is the earliest model in red enamel with a black top. The bob in the center is all red with a steel tip, and the one on the right, the latest model, is yellow with a steel tip.

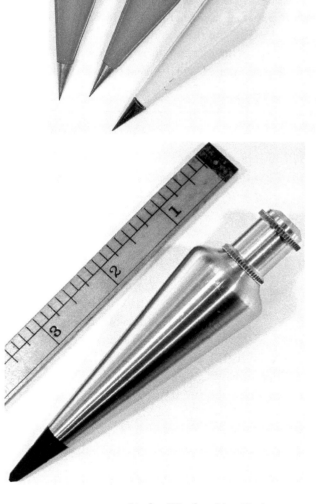

orange enamel. Little information is available on these two- and four-pound plumb bobs that came from the Stanley Model Shop. One theory is that they were millwright's bobs with unique spools and cord holders cast into the tops (Figure 11). Whether these plumb bobs were part of a production run or whether they were a special order for a customer remains a mystery (and in either case, how many were produced?). Further, it's unknown if smaller sizes were made or even if the model was ever patented. Perhaps in the future, more information will surface that will shed light on these particular plumb bobs' stories and their intended use.

After the discontinuance of the nos. 1, 2, and 5 plumb bobs in 1935 and 1937, Stanley did not offer plumb bobs again until 1962, when they were reintroduced in Stanley's *Catalog No. 160* on the new items for sale insert (Figure 12). This new line of plumb bobs, model nos. 170, 171, and 172, were one-piece, bright-red enamel, with die-cast bodies and black-enamel tops and replaceable nickel-plated hardened steel tips. They were made in three sizes: 5, 8, and 12 ounces (Figure 13). Shortly after their introduction, the black-enamel top was changed to red enamel. In 1984, the red enamel was changed to Stanley yellow enamel. That color remained in production until 2000, when a new, all-brass plumb bob with a hardened-steel tip was introduced (Figure 14) in 4-, 8- and 16-ounce sizes.

Figure 14 (right). Stanley's all brass plumb bobs were introduced in 2000 in three sizes.

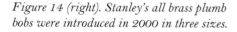

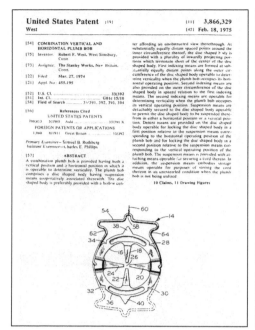

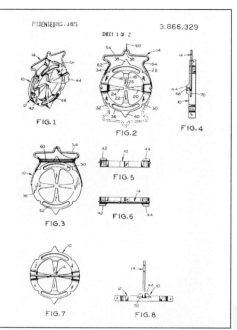

Figure 15 (above). Robert West's 1975 patent for a combination vertical and horizontal plumb bob.

In 1974, Robert West of Stanley Tools filed a patent for a combination vertical and horizontal plumb bob, receiving the patent on February 18, 1975 (Figure 15). This plumb bob was manufactured in the United States for one year. Production was then shifted to Stanley's Sheffield, England, plant, and the plumb bob was labeled no. 47-173 (Figure 16). This plumb bob is red-enamel, die cast and according to Stanley, "can be used to mark vertically from

overhead points by positioning the wheel in the horizontal position."

From 1873 to 1937 and from 1962 to the present, Stanley has carried a plumb bob in its line of tools and levels. The basic colors and weights may have changed, but a need for the simple tool, such as the plumb bob, remains, assuring its place as a staple in the Stanley line.

Figure 16 (right). A photograph of a Stanley catalog page showing a West patent plumb bob.

Dating the Markings

The first production models of Stanley's plumb bobs were stamped "PATD APR 28 1874" on the bob, just below the spool housing. (Figure 17 is a detail of a model no.

Figure 17.

2, shown as Figure 8 in the main article.) By 1890, the patent date stamped on the side was removed because patents expired sixteen years after being granted. For a brief period in the 1890s, some plumb bobs had no marks at all. When in 1891 a new federal law was enacted that stated that "all products exported or imported had to have the country of origin on the product," Stanley began placing the inscription "THE STANLEY RULE & LEVEL CO, NEW BRITAIN, CONN, USA" on the side of the cord reel (Figure 18, right, top).

In 1920, the three models of plumb bobs were marked on the reel "STANLEY – MADE IN USA." This was because another federal law, intended for exports and imports, stated that all products had to to be marked "Made in [country of origin]" (Figure 19, right, bottom).

Figures 18 (above) and 19 (left).

The Advertising Signs of the Stanley Rule & Level Co.— Script Logo Period (1910-1920)

The only advertising signs the Stanley Rule & Level Company had developed up to 1909 that are presently known are an 1860s broadside

Figure 1 (above). Stanley 9-x-18-inch, baked-enamel tin sign, circa 1910. Note the L-shaped bend on the left edge of the sign to allow it to be fastened to a wall.

Figure 2 (right). Stanley script logo 7-x-12³⁄₄-inch, embossed poster board sign, circa 1912.

showing rules, levels, and the Stanley factory, and two variations of paper broadsides issued as fold-up catalogs in the late 1880s.[1]

Stanley began offering signs to hardware stores, so each store could let the public know it carried Stanley tools. Around 1910, Stanley had the New York Metal Ceiling Company produce a 9-x-18-inch, baked-enamel tin sign to advertise Stanley planes (Figure 1). This unique sign showed Stanley's new script logo and was illustrated with a bench plane with a wood shaving shooting up to the Stanley name. It advertises Stanley planes without spelling out the word "plane." Made with an L- shaped bend on one end, the sign could be fastened to a wall

outside of the store or used inside the store. The white Stanley lettering was set on a green rectangle with cut-out corners and an orange background. The graphics are lithographed on both sides so the message could be read from either side.

Around 1912, Stanley began issuing a 7-x-12³⁄₄-inch heavy poster board sign (Figure 2) with the script logo advertising "Stanley Tools." This sign was, likewise, very colorful with the same color scheme as the tin sign, but with the notched rectangle and the script logo embossed or raised to give a 3-D effect. This sign had a brown hang string attached through holes in the center top so that the hardware merchant could hang it on a wall or from a hook in the ceiling.

Since hanging signs from the ceiling or in a display window was fashionable in the early 1900s, Stanley issued a series of 8³⁄₄-x-11¹⁄₄-inch, poster board signs around 1915.

Figure 3 shows the first of the series, which was obviously meant for a display window, stating "Come in" and get the current Stanley catalog—no. 34. This sign had the script logo or trademark and a greenish/gray background with a white hang string.

"'Bailey' Iron Planes" (Figure 4) were the subject of another sign in the series. Having the script logo and the gray background, this sign illustrated Bailey's no. 3, 4, 5, 6, and 7c planes with airbrush shading in the background.

To compliment the Bailey iron plane, another sign featured Native Americans and a Bailey plane (Figure 5), with a photograph of "An Interested Group of Native Americans and An Interesting Tool." The plane at which the Indians are looking is a Bailey no. 7 or no. 8 jointer plane. The facial expressions of the people in the photo tell their own stories.

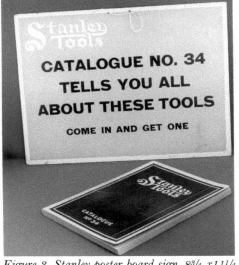

Figure 3. Stanley poster board sign, 8³⁄₄ x11¹⁄₄ inches, with a no. 34 catalog.

Figure 4 (left). Stanley poster board sign, 8¾ x 11¼ inches, circa 1915 featuring Bailey iron planes.

Figure 5 (below). Stanley poster board sign, 8¾ x 11¼ inches, circa 1915, showing the rather curious juxtaposition of Native Americans and Bailey joiner planes.

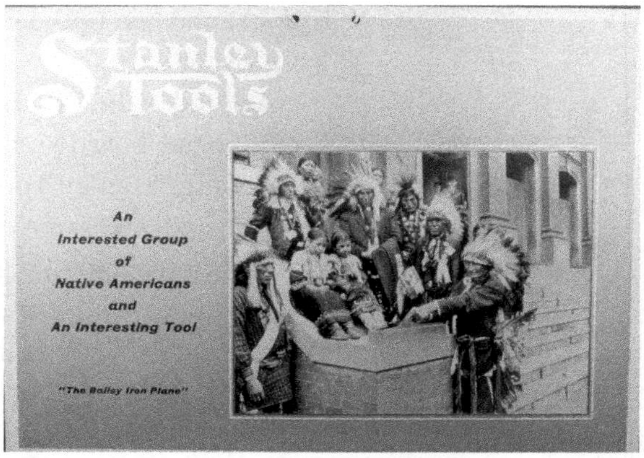

just about any molding he wished with the no. 55. The plane was unique among combination planes, and a craftsman could do more operations with it than with any other plane manufactured. It was advertised as "A Planing Mill Within Itself."

Another script logo sign advertised Stanley's line of scrapers and scraper planes (Figure 8). Used to finish wood to a super-smooth surface, scrapers could remove an onion-skin-thin wood shaving off of even fancy grained wood. On the other hand, some were merely used to scrape paint. This sign illustrated eight Stanley scrapers: nos. 12, 12½, 80, 81, 82, 83, 85, and 112. Also illustrated were a hand scraper and toothing irons. Toothing irons were used in a scraper to roughen the surface between glue joints or for veneer application.

Stanley advertised its elite bench planes with another sign in the series, which promoted the "Bed Rock" planes (Figure 6). This sign illustrated the construction of Bed Rock nos. 603, 604, 605, 606-c, and 607 and how the throat could be adjusted without removing the cutter.

Of course, Stanley needed to have another sign to promote its supreme combination plane, the no. 55 (Figure 7). Illustrated with two views of the plane and the ninety-three cutters that were available, this sign illustrated how a craftsman could make

Once the craftsman had the moldings made with the no. 55 (Figure 7), a miter box was needed to cut the special joints. To promote miter boxes, another sign—with the words "accuracy, strength, durability"—illustrated Stanley's no. 358 miter box (Figure 9), one of many sizes available.

Figure 6 (top, left). Stanley poster board sign, 8¾ x 11¼ inches, circa 1915, illustrating "Bed Rock" planes.

Figure 7 (top, right). Stanley poster board sign, 8¾ x 11¼ inches, circa 1915, illustrating the no. 55, "A Planing Mill Within Itself."

Figure 8 (bottom, left). Stanley poster board sign, 8¾ x 11¼ inches, circa 1915, advertising scrapers and scraper planes.

Figure 9 (bottom, right). Miter boxes are the subject of this 8¾-x-11¼-inch poster board sign, circa 1915.

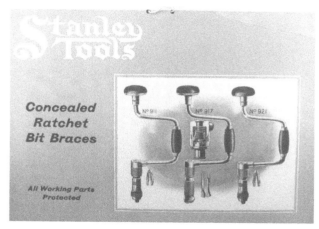
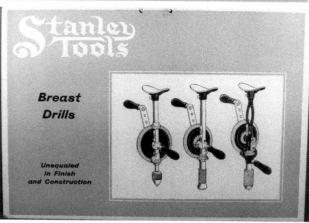
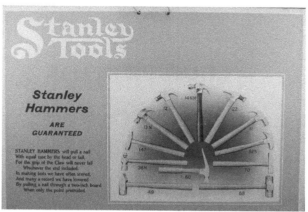

Figure 10 (top left). A group of Stanley 8¾-x-11¼-inch, poster board signs dating from circa 1915. This 8¾-x-11¼-inch, poster board sign claimed that Stanley plumbs and levels had "Superior Finish/Blackened Chamfers/Improved Adjustments/All Distinctive Stanley Features."

Figure 11 (top, right). Concealed-ratchet bit braces—"All Working Parts Protected"—were advertised in this 8¾-x-11¼-inch, poster board sign.

Figure 12 (bottom, left). Stanley claimed its breast drills were "Unequaled in Finish and Construction."

Figure 13 (bottom, right). This Stanley poster board sign claimed that "Stanley hammers will pull a nail with equal ease by the head or tail, for the grip of the claw will never fail, whichever the end included."

Plumbs and levels were other tools in the Stanley line of carpenter tools that Stanley promoted with a sign (Figure 10). Shown with the script logo were no. 0, 3, 9, 102 and 104 levels with a cut-away showing the adjustment features. This was a very small percentage of all the levels Stanley manufactured, but the sign got the message out that levels were available.

Every carpenter needs to bore holes, and Stanley manufactured an extensive line of bit braces in every price range. Figure 11 shows another sign with three of Stanley's top-of-the-line, concealed-ratchet bit braces with a cut-away illustrating how the braces worked and the style of jaws available.

Figure 12 illustrates another sign in this series that promoted Stanley's breast drills. Shown are the no. 711 steel frame drill with a three-jaw chuck, no. 723 steel-frame two-speed with interlocking jaws, and the no. 733 cast-iron frame, two-speed with universal chuck.

Stanley not only made tools for carpenters but for other mechanics as well. Hammers were used by many trades and the script logo sign shown in Figure 13 shows a variety of claw, ball peen, farrier's, tinsmith's, brick, and sledge hammers. The sign also included the catch phrase: "Stanley hammers will pull a nail with equal ease by the head or tail, for the grip of the claw will never fail, whichever the end included."

Stanley also made screwdrivers. Figure 14 illustrates eighteen Hurwood (Stanley's top-of-the-line screwdriver) screwdrivers with one of them cut in half to show the construction. The screwdrivers in the photograph were, of course, only a small portion of what was available, but the sign let the public know that Stanley manufactured screwdrivers as well as other carpenter tools.

In 1911, Stanley acquired Philip J. Leavens's "Jersey" vise business. The next sign (Figure 15) promoted the variety of vises with the phrase "A Necessary Addition to the Tool Kit of Every Mechanic, Amateur and House-

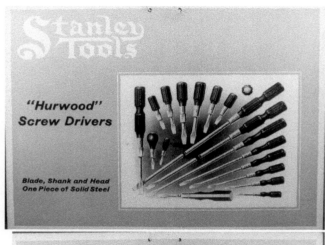

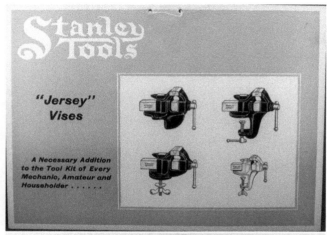

Figure 14 (top, left). Stanley poster board sign for "Hurwood" screwdrivers noted that the "Blade, Shank and Head/One Piece of Solid Steel."

Figure 15 (top, right). Stanley claimed its "Jersey" vises were "A Necessary Addition to the Tool Kit of Every Mechanic, Amateur and Householder."

Figure 16 (bottom, left). This sign's message was simple, "Look for the tools you need in your kit."

Figure 17 (bottom, right). The members of this "up-to-date" family from the Isle of Maarken, Holland, appear to each have a favorite Stanley tool. The sign also illustrates Stanley's export business.

builder." To motivate the public to purchase Stanley tools, one of the signs encouraged the potential buyer to "look for the tools you need in your kit" (Figure 16).

Figure 17, the last script logo sign in the series, introduced "an up-to-date family" from the Isle of Maarken, Holland. The photo is very interesting with each family member in wooden clogs holding a Stanley tool. I wonder what each person was thinking about when the photo was taken. This sign also told the public that Stanley's export business had made it to Holland.

All of these signs show the type of advertising promoted by hardware merchants of the early 1900s. In the 1920s, the variety of signs increased and became more colorful.

Notes
1. See pages 204–214, "Stanley Shirt-Pocket Catalogs" for more on Stanley's advertising campaigns.

A Sampling of Stanley Sweetheart–Era Hardware Store Displays

The Stanley brothers, Frederick and William, had been actively manufacturing hardware since 1843 when they organized The Stanley Works as a joint stock corporation on July 1, 1852, in New Britain, Connecticut. After the 1852 incorporation, the company hired William H. Hart, a clerk working at the local railway station. Mr. Hart was soon elected to the board of directors, serving the dual role of secretary and treasurer.[1] After he patented numerous inventions for the company and created cost cutting manufacturing ideas, he became president and treasurer of The Stanley Works in 1884. In appreciation of Mr. Hart's contributions to the company, Stanley introduced a new trademark in 1893, with the letters "S.W." within a heart (Figure 1). The "S.W." stood for Stanley Works; the heart-shape of the logo was a play on Mr. Hart's name. The logo was known as the "Sweetheart."[2] The early logo used only "S.W." in the heart and served from 1893 to 1920. It has two meanings—"Stanley Works" and "Service and Worth." The later logo, used when the Stanley Works and The Stanley Rule & Level merged in 1920, is the cut label with the "Sweetheart" under the "Stanley" name. This was used until 1936.

This article features only a small number of the type of sample boards and counter displays offered by Stanley to hardware merchants, but it does represent the different types of hardware Stanley manufactured. There are many other sample boards and counter displays. Each one is a unique and original working model. I have confined all the illustrations to a period in which Stanley used the Sweetheart logo.

By the 1890s, manufacturing companies began creating product displays for use in retail stores. Stanley was no exception. One of its earlier counter displays (Figures 2 and 3) was a

Figure 1. Stanley trademark shown on the side of the hinge display case.

Figure 2 (above). Stanley counter display showing no. 1774 garage door holder with no. 1456 garage door hinges.

Figure 3 (below). The reverse side of Stanley counter display showing no. 1774 garage door holder.

Figure 4 (right). Stanley featured the hardware on the cover of its catalog.

Figure 5 (above). Stanley display cabinet showing ornamental hinges. In the upper left and right corners are corrugated "butterfly" pattern hinges and between them are two sizes of the "clover leaf" pattern. Below them are the "shell" pattern (on the left) and the "lotus" pattern (on the right). At the bottom, to the right of center, is the "Greek Key" design.

Figure 6 (below). Stanley display showing a no. BB239A ball bearing hinge.

small model, roughly 3 x 6 inches, showing in miniature the use of a no. 1774 garage door holder with no. 1456 garage hinges. This display was a working model that could be shown to a customer. It demonstrated how the door opened and closed on the special hinges. It was finished in "Antique Copper" and displays the early Sweetheart trademark. The same hardware on the display was found on the cover of a Stanley catalog (Figure 4).

Small cabinet hinges were displayed on a chestnut counter cabinet (Figure 5), measuring 19½ inches high x 16¼ inches wide. The cabinet held four different panels, and the display panel could be changed by removing the

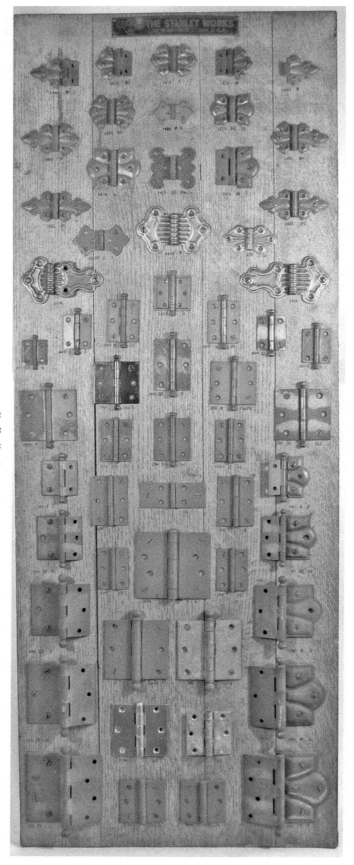

Figure 7. Sample board (18 x 48 inches) showing fifty-seven different hinges.

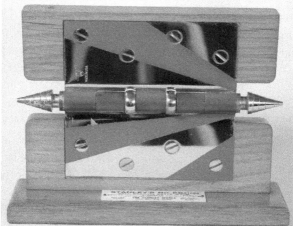

Figure 8 (far left). Stanley display showing samples of finishes for hardware.

Figure 9 (left, top). Stanley display showing no. BB 153A ball bearing friction hinge.

Figure 10 (left, bottom). Stanley no. BB21180 Art Deco ball bearing hinge.

Figure 11 (below). Stanley display showing no. 152 half-surface screen door hinge.

top of the cabinet. The panel shown in the cabinet in Figure 5 displayed ornamental cabinet hinges. On the upper left and right in Figure 5 are examples of corrugated "butterfly" pattern hinges. The center top shows two sizes of the "clover leaf" pattern. Below them are the "shell" pattern (on the left) and the "lotus" pattern (on the right). The "lotus" pattern is across the center and on the diagonal to the bottom. At the bottom, to the right of center, is the "Greek Key" design.

The Stanley Works was one of the pioneers of ball bearing hinges. Figure 6 shows a counter top display with Stanley's patented non-rising, loose-pin, wrought-steel, ball bearing butt hinge that could be opened or closed by a customer before purchasing.

Standard sample boards were a common item in early hardware stores. The Stanley 18-x-48-inch, oak sample board shown in Figure 7 had a well balanced line of fifty-seven stock hinges, which made it easier for the customer to see the types of hinges that were available.

Figure 12 (above, left). Two Stanley displays showing the no. 150J fast-pin, full-surface screen door hinge (left) and the no. 151J full surface screen door hinge with removable hinge (right).

Figure 13 (above, right). Stanley display showing the no. 1769J cellar window set.

Hinges were available in a variety of finishes, and Figure 8 shows a 9½-x-30-inch sample board with examples of available finishes, each designated by a letter code. For example, if a customer wanted a hinge with "Antique Copper" finish the merchant would add the finish letter code

Figure 14 (above). Stanley display showing no. 2705 wardrobe hardware (front view).

Figure 15 (below). Stanley display showing no. 2705 wardrobe hardware (rear view).

"D2" to the hinge product number. So, if the customer ordered a no. 1475 hinge in size 1½ in Antique Copper finish, the number would be no. 1475-D2 1½ inch.

Working counter displays of hinges not only included standard and ball bearing hinges but also featured samples of specialty hinges such as the extra-heavy, ball bearing, friction butt hinge (Figure 9) that was designed to be used on doors where quiet is essential, such as hotels and hospitals. The friction could be adjusted so the door would not slam. A model of an Art Deco ball bearing hinge with a unique finial and finish is shown in the Figure 10 display.

Stanley made hinge displays for most styles of butt door hinges with a similar make-up; the hinge would be mounted either horizontally or vertically and was fully workable. Screen door hinges—both the full-surface mount and half-surface mount types—were also made.[3] The tension on the Stanley adjustable, half-surface, screen door hinge no. 152 shown in Figure 11 was fully adjustable. The full-surface screen door hinge displays in Figure 12, show Stanley's no. 150 and no. 151 hinges. The no. 150 had a fast pin and the no. 151 has a loose pin with ball finial. The loose pin allowed removal of the pin so the door could be taken off its hinges without unscrewing the entire hinge unit. The customer could test the tension of the hinges on both of these displays.

Cellar window sets were also represented in the display line. Figure 13 shows a no. 1769J set, which included one of a pair of friction hinges, a handle, and a turn button mounted so that the friction hinge could be tried by an interested customer.

Stanley made hardware for school wardrobes, and Figure 14 and Figure 15 illustrate a fully functional display fitted with Stanley's no. 2705 wardrobe hard-

CONTINUED PAGE 194

Figure 16 (left). Stanley display that demonstrated its no. 1057J foot bolt.

Figure 17 (above, top). This display featured Stanley's no. 329 and no. 381 surface bolts.

Figure 18 (above, middle). A Stanley display showing a no. 386 lever flush door bolt.

Figure 19 (above, bottom). A display featuring Stanley's no. 369 Cremone bolt.

Figure 20 (far left). A working model of Stanley's no. 453 friction-roller door holder.

Figure 21 (left). Stanley display showing the various parts of its no. 1248 thumb latch set.

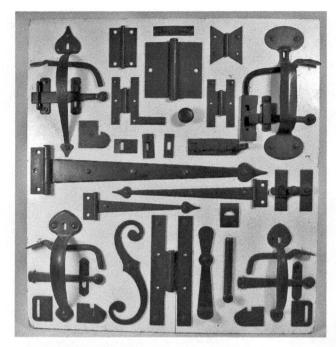

Figure 22 (far left). A sample board of Stanley thumb latches and matching hinges.

Figure 23 (left). Stand-up workable display of Stanley's no. 1289 mortise thumb latch

ware. The display demonstrated how the doors work in unison with the pull of only one door handle. The 2705 was sold as an entire package of top and bottom hinges, top and bottom guides, top track and bottom rail, and door pull.

Displays also demonstrated foot bolts. The display in Figure 16 featured Stanley's no. 1057J 6-inch foot bolt. Surface bolts designed for French doors were the subject of a workable display shown in Figure 17.

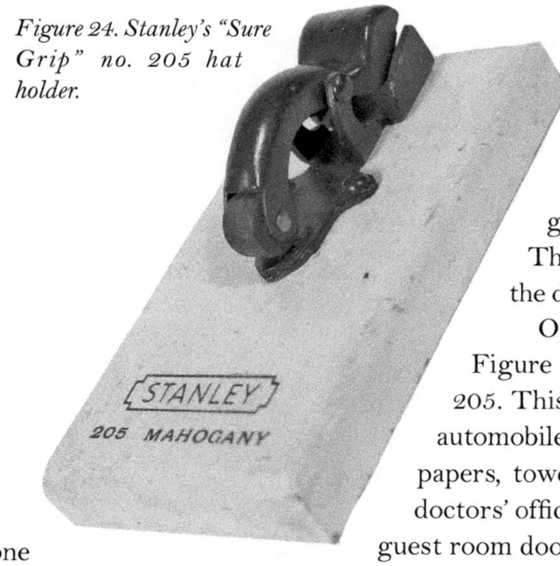

Shown in Figure 18 is a display model of a no. 386 wrought-bronze lever flush bolt that was fully functional and has a cut-away on the side to show the internal mechanism.

The workable display shown in Figure 19 is a Stanley no. 369 Cremone bolt for doors and casements. A twist of the knob extended the bolt in both directions.

Stanley's friction-roller door holders were designed to be used in schools, hospitals, and institutions where a quiet atmosphere was required. The company's no. 453 was featured in the display in Figure 20.

Using a hardware board, customers could see all the parts of various latch sets. Stanley's no. 1248 ornamental thumb latch set was for use in interior doors (Figure 21). A larger (18 inches wide by 20 inches high) hardware sample board (Figure 22) showed a large variety of thumb latches

Figure 24. Stanley's "Sure Grip" no. 205 hat holder.

with matching hinges, cupboard latches, and shutter tie backs. Figure 23 illustrates a display of a fully functional mortise thumb latch, Stanley no. 1289. Designed for use in industrial buildings, greenhouses, garages, and residences, this counter display allowed the customer to get a hands-on feel of this door latch. The latch was made to be mortised into the door.

One last counter display, shown in Figure 24, is a "Sure Grip" hat holder no. 205. This could be used in closets, churches, automobiles, etc. It was also adapted for holding papers, towels, newspapers, patients' charts in doctors' offices or in hospitals, and cards on hotel guest room doors. I end this article by hanging my hat up in a Stanley "Sure Grip" hat holder.

Notes

1. The Stanley Works, in the 1850s, had approximately fourteen employees.
2. A more complete history of William H. Hart, "The Man Who Turned The Stanley Works Around: The Story of William H. Hart," was published in *The Chronicle* 58, no. 4 (2005): 162-168, republished in this book on pages 6-12.
3. On a full-surface mount, two sides of a mounting platform would be visible. On a half-surface mount, one surface is on the door and the other surface is on the jamb/frame.

"A Christmas present worth having" Stanley Christmas Promotions

Many companies, including tool manufacturers, have understood the importance of promoting their products at Christmastime, and Stanley is no exception. The earliest Stanley Christmas advertisement that has surfaced to date was used by Stanley in 1911, and it promoted its 16-ounce claw hammer no. 14NM (Figure 1). This hammer had a nickel-plated octagon poll head with a full claw and a hickory handle that was available in natural finish or "mahoganized" (as shown in Figure 2). In this early advertisement, Stanley noted that "the custom of giving useful presents for Christmas is growing every year," which seems to indicate that the claw hammer was Stanley's entry into the Christmas market. The hammer continued to be advertised as the perfect holiday gift— one "that will last a long time and will serve as a continual reminder of the giver"—until about 1922.

As the 1920s progressed, Stanley began offering tool assortments to its line of tools, which led to a major change in its advertising emphasis. Now the company began promoting not only single tools as Christmas gifts, but a variety of tools made up in sets with a wide price range. In 1922, Stanley printed a four-color Christmas gift catalog touting its tool sets as the "Ideal Christmas Gift" (Figure 3). The sets ranged in price from $2.15 to $95.00 and contained from four to forty-eight tools per set. Stanley's set no. 910, for example, contained four Stanley Four-Square tools (Figure 4). The importance of Christmas sales for Stanley is reflected in the company's full-page, two-color, front cover advertisement in *Hardware Age* magazine in the November 30, 1922, edition (Figure 5). The *Hardware Age* advertisement pushed the tool assortments as a Christmas profit item for hardware stores: "Display your stock of Stanley Tool assortments and thereby reap the sales that are so easily coaxed through visual appeal. To see them means to buy them."

The promotion of tool sets was good business, and Stanley repeated the promotion in 1923 with another advertisement on *Hardware Age* magazine's front page on December 6, 1923 (Figure 6). Sets continued to be popular through the 1920s.

One of the eighteen tool sets offered in Stanley's catalog was the no. 888 tool

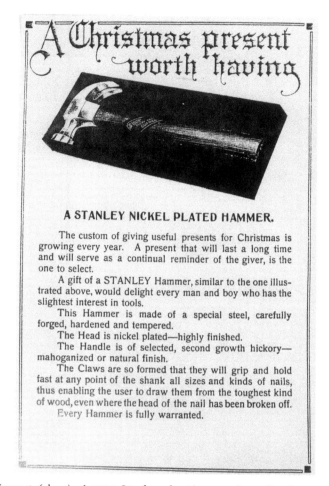

A STANLEY NICKEL PLATED HAMMER.

The custom of giving useful presents for Christmas is growing every year. A present that will last a long time and will serve as a continual reminder of the giver, is the one to select.

A gift of a STANLEY Hammer, similar to the one illustrated above, would delight every man and boy who has the slightest interest in tools.

This Hammer is made of a special steel, carefully forged, hardened and tempered.

The Head is nickel plated—highly finished.

The Handle is of selected, second growth hickory— mahoganized or natural finish.

The Claws are so formed that they will grip and hold fast at any point of the shank all sizes and kinds of nails, thus enabling the user to draw them from the toughest kind of wood, even where the head of the nail has been broken off.

Every Hammer is fully warranted.

Figure 1 (above). A 1911 Stanley advertisement, the earliest known Christmas promotion. It touts Stanley's no. 14NM nickel-plated hammer.

Figure 2 (below). The claw hammer (no. 14NM) illustrated in the advertisement with its "mahoganized" hickory handle.

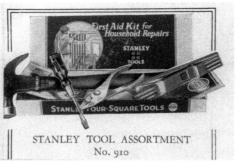

Figure 3 (left). The cover of Stanley's four-color 1922 Christmas gift catalog featuring tool sets.

Figure 4 (above). The Stanley Four-Square Christmas set, no. 910, was one of those featured in the catalog.

kit. The purchaser could choose one of four different tool assortments to complete the tool kit. Figure 7 illustrates a no. 888 assortment "D" tool kit containing twelve tools, which retailed for $15.00.

The Christmas market was good, and Stanley introduced different marketing techniques to make its product more attractive. In 1926, Stanley began promoting newly introduced tools in special, single, "gift wrap" boxes. Harris J. Cook's patented socket chisel no. 440, offered in an attractive box printed with holly paper, appears to be the first time Stanley offered gift-wrap boxes (Figure 8).

In its 1933 Christmas promotion, Stanley offered one of its new 100 Plus hammers in a special, chromium-plated model with a multi-colored, brush-finished hickory handle (Figure 9). It was the only year the unique handle was offered.

Figure 5 (above, left). Stanley's Christmas advertisement on the front cover of the November 30, 1922, issue of Hardware Age *promoting its tool assortments.*

Figure 6 (above, right). Stanley's Christmas advertisement on the front cover of Hardware Age's *December 6, 1923, issue.*

Figure 7. Stanley's no. 888 tool kit assortment **D.** *The set sold for $15.00.*

Tool sets continued to be promoted in the 1930s, but the company's emphasis turned to individual tools in gift wrap boxes. In 1936, some of the individual tools in the gift boxes were the 220 block plane, Pull-Push rules, screwdrivers, and the 100 Plus hammers. The boxes were decorated with stars and with stylized trees with stars (Figures 10 and 11).

Beginning in 1937, Stanley added the prefix "X" before the standard model number to indicate that it was a Christmas selection with a special gift box. The

Figure 8 (above). Stanley's 1926 Christmas gift box with Harris J. Cook's patent no. 440 chisel.

Figure 9 (left). In 1933, Stanley's Christmas promotion was the 100 Plus chromium-plated hammer with multi-colored hickory handle.

Figure 10 (above). A Stanley screwdriver offered in 1936 in a gift box with star "wrapping."

Figure 11 (right). A no. 9½ block plane was offered in 1936 in a gift box decorated with trees and stars.

Figure 12 (below). Stanley's 1937 gift boxes with the clear cellophane window.

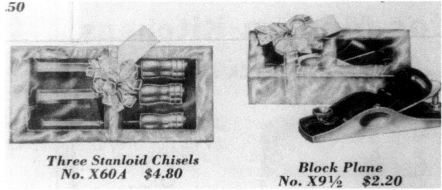

Three Stanloid Chisels
No. X60A $4.80

Block Plane
No. X9½ $2.20

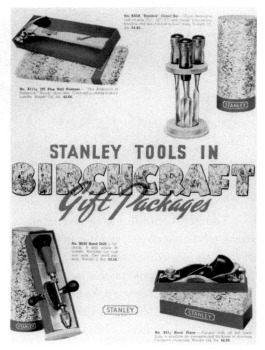

boxes were printed in green and had a simulated, wavy fabric look with a clear cellophane window (Figure 12). A variety of tools were sold in the Christmas packaging, including a hand drill, block plane, chisels, hammer, level, square, and a Pull-Push rule (Figure 13).

"Birchcraft" gift boxes were introduced in the 1940 Christmas line. An advertising brochure of the time illustrates the various available tools (Figure 14). A no. 4 bench plane and a Yankee screwdriver are examples of two of the

Figure 14 (right). A 1940 Stanley Christmas promotional brochure illustrating the "Birchcraft" gift boxes and the featured tools.

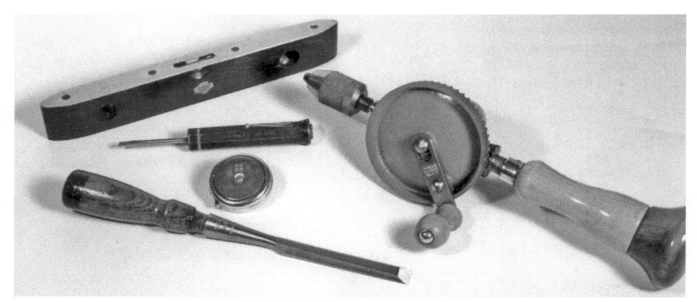

Figure 13. A selection of Stanley tools that were offered in the 1937 gift boxes. Clockwise from top are a no. 261 level, a no. 620 hand drill, a no. 750 chisel, a no. 7366, Four-Square tape rule, and a no. 1021 flashlight screwdriver.

Figure 15 (above). Two examples of the tools and gift boxes, circa 1946-1949. Shown are a no. X4 bench plane (on left) and a no. X133H Yankee screwdriver (on right).

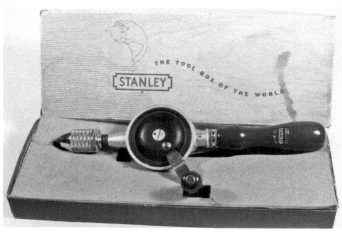

Throughout the 1950s, Stanley experimented with different packaging ideas. Figure 16 (above) shows the gift box scheme for 1950 with a no. 610 Stanley 100 Plus hand drill. Figure 17 (below) shows a variation on the 1950 design; this box is from 1951 and held a no. 133H Yankee screwdriver.

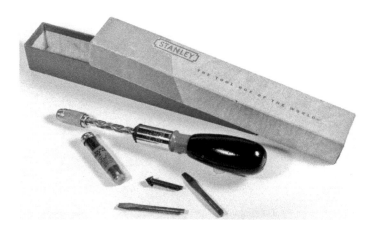

tools that were offered in Birchcraft boxes (Figure 15). The Birchcraft gift boxes were popular and apparently were used during and after the Second World War and until to 1949.

In the 1950s, no package design took hold and Stanley experimented with different gift boxes. By 1950, the Birchcraft look was over, and the new gift box was a wood grain design with green stripes and a globe with the words, "Stanley–The Tool Box of the World" on the lid of the box and a red bottom. Stanley's 100 Plus hand drill no. 610 was one of the tools offered in a gift box (Figure 16). That gift box changed a little in the 1951 Christmas season. The globe was removed and the left side of the lid had a green diagonal swath with the red Stanley logo and the "Tool Box of the World" motto printed in red. The Stanley Yankee screwdriver was among the tools available

Figure 18 (far left). The Stanley 1952 gift box and the assortment of tools that were available in the special packaging.

Figure 19 (left). In 1953, the red design was replaced by a Christmas tree paper.

Figure 20. A Stanley no. x4 bench plane and a no. x220 block plane in the 1953 Christmas tree gift box.

Figure 21. The Stanley 1954 Christmas promotion offered this range of tools with a red box and gold snowflakes.

Figure 22. A busy housewife could save time by buying a Stanley tool already wrapped.

in the box (Figure 17). The announcement flyer in 1952 shows that once again the design of the gift box changed. It was a red paper with the legend "Season's Greetings" in the center of the lid (Figure 18). Fifteen high-selling tools were offered in these boxes, which were, the flyer noted, "selected by popular vote." The flyer indicates that the gift box was simply a special sleeve that went over a stock box.

The next year (1953) the number of tools offered in holiday wrap increased to twenty-one. That season also introduced another new, attractive gift box with a green, Christmas tree decoration (Figure 19). The flyer distributed to dealers noted that the "attractive gift cover (with small identification sticker) fits over regular stock box." Dealers

Figure 23 (above, left). Stanley's promotional brochure for dealers in 1956 showing the Christmas stocking.

Figure 24 (above, right). A company used this Stanley promotional flyer enticing customers to "Give the best."

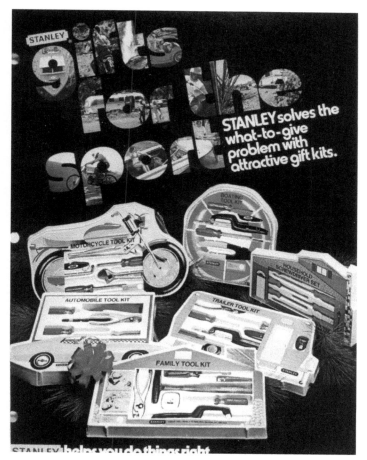

Figure 25. The Christmas gift box was replaced by other promotions such as these "Tool Kits" packed in shaped boxes.

would not need to worry about being stuck with excess Christmas-wrapped tools at the end of the shopping season. Tools included for the first time as special Christmas features were a no. 5 bench plane and the new "Featherlite" tape rule. The no. x4 bench plane and the no. x220 block plane were among the tools offered in the 1953 gift wrap (Figure 20).

A red box with gold snowflakes replaced the Christmas trees in 1954 (Figure 21). Eighteen tools were offered, and a company advertisement that year was no doubt meant to appeal to the busy housewife who could save time wrapping gifts (Figure 22).

The Christmas promotion for 1956 took a different tack. That year's gift packaging was a polyethylene stocking that would hold the gift tool, except, as the flyer notes, "Colorful Santa Claus gift display cards are included with four tools, too heavy for stockings." The store display included a giant 44-inch stocking filled with an assortment of sixteen tools. Each was offered in a giant polyethylene stocking (Figures 23 and 24).

Stanley continued to promote tools for the Christmas season into the 1960s and beyond, but the Christmas boxes gave way to other promotions such as the 1973 "Gifts for the sport" promotion with "tool kits" packed in shaped, themed boxes, such as the "Motorcycle Tool Kit" in a motorcycle-shaped box and the "Trailer Tool Kit" in a box shaped like an RV (Figure 25).

In 1911, the idea of giving "useful presents" took off. Over the years Christmas gift promotions increased in popularity and have continued to the present.

Get Your Nickel's Worth—
Stanley's Use of Coins for Promotion

This article was a collaboration between Walter Jacob and his wife, Suzanne Fellman Jacob, who is also an occasional contributor to The Chronicle.

The Four-Square Promotional

Over the years, the articles I have written for this column have concentrated on particular products that the Stanley Works manufactured, describing the evolution of the various tools from inventor to improvements and new models. I thought that in this column, with help from my wife Sue, I would deviate from that topic with two stories of Stanley Works product promotion using circulating coinage.

Story number one begins when Stanley decided to manufacture tools for the "do-it-yourself" or household tool market in the 1920s. This line of household tools, named Stanley Four-Square Household Tools, consisted of thirty-two tools.[1] To promote this new line, Stanley had an extensive merchandising campaign. Part of the campaign consisted of Four-Square advertisements in many magazines, including the *The Literary Digest* and *The Saturday Evening Post*. The advertisement in *The Saturday Evening Post* appeared every other week through 1924 and 1925.[2] The nickel promotion, however, was only used in conjunction with the *The Saturday Evening Post*.

In 1924, Stanley made up a 3-x-5-inch poster board card that had been punched out to hold a U. S. five-cent piece—the Buffalo nickel (Figures 1 and 2). One side was blank, and the other side stated "Use this [nickel] to buy the next *Saturday Evening Post*—out April 12th and look on page 102."[3]

The Four-Square advertisement for April 12, 1924 stated that the tools were a new product line and that the four red squares would be the line's new mark. The nineteen different types of tools that were sold under the Four-Square mark were illustrated in the ad (Figure 3). The tools were manufactured and sold both in the United States and in Canada. In the lower left corner of the ad is the statement "prices slightly higher in Canada."

Stanley manufactured Four-Square tools in New Britain, Connecticut, and other plants in the United States and at the Stanley Tool Company of Canada facility located at Roxton Pond, Quebec, Canada.

The size of the card was perfect for mailing; either Stanley or the hardware dealer could place it in an envelope and mail it to a prospective customer. Customer appreciation was gained when the patron could secure a "free" *Saturday Evening Post* and see the advertisement and have some leisure reading after a hard day at work.

Story two is told by Sue.

Figures 1 and 2 (above and left). The front and verso of a 1924 Stanley promotional for its new Four-Square line of household tools. With the nickel, customers could buy a copy of the latest Saturday Evening Post *and read the Stanley advertisement.*

Figure 3 (above, right). A Stanley Four-Square advertisement from the April 12, 1924 (page 102), edition of the Saturday Evening Post.

Figure 4 (left). A Stanley Steel Company advertising card with two Canadian five-cent pieces, which were made with Stanley cold-rolled strip steel.

Figure 5 (above). The Stanley Steel Company in Hamilton, Ontario.

And Now to Canada

What a find! Walt went to a tool show and auction and found something for me. I collect Canadian coins. The "treat" he brought home was an advertising piece by Stanley of Canada with two Canadian five-cent pieces in it (Figure 4). The cardboard advertising piece required a bit of research.[4]

The Hamilton, Ontario, plant of Stanley Works of Canada (Figure 5) was also known as the Stanley Steel Company, a subsidiary of Stanley Works of Canada. The facility manufactured sheet and roll steel. When the Canadian government decided to depart from the use of nickel for its five-cent coins and go to steel, Stanley Steel Company became the main supplier. In fact, the "Stanley Steel Company, Ltd. . . . was the largest producer of cold rolled strip steel."[5]

Stanley, Canada, created and distributed the presentation cards. My version is a deep, royal blue and came with two new 1951 Canadian five-cent coins in the two holes. This allowed the obverse (with King George VI's profile) and the reverse (with a beaver) to be viewed by the card owner. The card measures 2½ by 3⅞ inches wide. According to Henry Nienhus, Stanley, Canada, produced the cards from 1944 to 1954 as gifts for employees and plant visitors.[6]

The original five-cent Canadian coin was sterling (.925 fine) but was debased to .800 fine in 1920.[7] The Canadian five-cent coin became pure nickel in 1922, as Canada was providing a huge volume of raw nickel to the world. During both World War II and the Korean War, nickel was diverted to the war efforts, and the five-cent coins were made of tombac, a copper-zinc alloy (1942–1943), and plated steel (1944–1945 and 1951–1954). After the war, the coins were again pure nickel. In 1982, the five-cent coins became .75 copper and .25 nickel. This was cupro-nickel.[8] In 2000, the Royal Canadian Mint changed the composition, and today the coins are a multi-plated steel composite of .945 steel, .035 copper, and .02 nickel.[9]

Beginning in 1942, the coins were twelve-sided, a unique design that lasted until 1963, when the edge became round again.

Because Stanley Steel was used to make the Canadian coin, these five-cent coins are "Stanley"; Stanley was not involved in the manufacture of the five-cent coin in the 1924 Four-Square ad. My piece has a "doubly valuable" coin; it's Canadian and Stanley. What a combination!

We are aware of only the two instances of Stanley using circulating coins within its advertising, and we hope that numismatists and tool collectors will enjoy this account of unique marketing in the twentieth century.

Notes

1. The full story of Stanley Four-Square Household Tools was related in *The Chronicle* 59, no. 3 (September 2006): 114–119 and no. 4 (December 2006):155–160, and is found on pages 160–172. A listing of the full line of Four-Square tools is found on page 170.
2. The alternate weeks of the advertisement were in *The Literary Digest*. Most of the ads were different.
3. *The Saturday Evening Post* cost 5 cents in 1924.
4. The research was helped by the publication of a three-part series on the Canadian five-cent coins of 1951 in *Canadian Numismatic Journal (Le Journal canadien de numismatique)*, the official publication of the Royal Canadian Numismatic Association: Henry Nienhuis's "Canadian 1951 5 Cents–Part I," *Canadian Numismatic Journal* 54, no. 4 (May 2009): 200 - 205; "Canadian 1951 5 Cents–Part II," 54, no. 5 (June 2009): 274–281; and "Canadian 1951 5 Cents–Part III," 54, no. 6 (July/August 2009): 338–341. Special thanks to the Royal Canadian Numismatic Association for permission to quote from the articles.
5. Nienhuis, "...Part II," 274.
6. Nienhuis, "...Part II," 275.
7. "Nickel (Canadian coin)," Wikepedia; http://en.wikipedia.org/wiki/Nickel_(Canadian_coin) accessed July 30, 2009.
8. W. K. Cross, *A Charlton Standard Catalogue Canadian Coins*, 63rd ed., (Toronto: The Charlton Press, 2009), 71.
9. Cross, 72.

Stanley Shirt-Pocket Catalogs

The Stanley Rule & Level Company, in the late 1860s, began concentrating its product line on carpenter's tools. With its acquisition of Leonard Bailey's plane business in 1869, Stanley wasted no time in promoting the new plane line. Besides advertising in its general catalog, Stanley also promoted the carpenter's plane line through a small, fold-out, shirt-pocket size catalog. These small catalogs were 3¼ x 5¾ inches folded and 5¾ high x 16 wide inches unfolded, for a total of ten pages when both sides were counted. The pocket catalog idea was a typical advertising format at the time and was used by Leonard Bailey before Stanley acquired his business. These pocket catalogs did not cover the full Stanley line but basically concentrated on the carpenter's plane line with testimonials of the planes' acceptance.

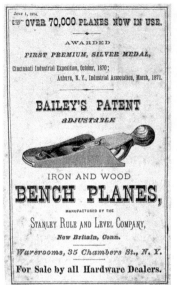 

Figures 2 (left) and 3 (right). Two years after it issued its first pocket catalog, Stanley was still using the same Bailey block plane to illustrate the cover. The following year, the plane in the illustration was changed to a bench plane (Figure 3).

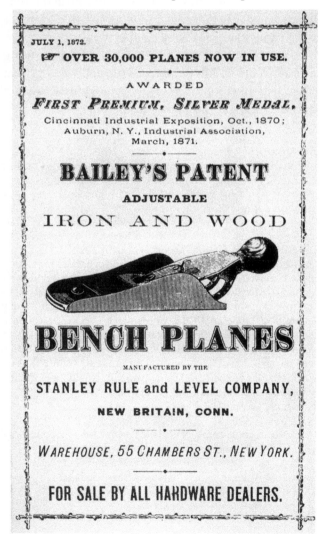

Figure 1. Stanley's July 1, 1872, catalog. The illustration is Bailey's no. 9³/₄ block plane (shown actual size).

With the publication of its January 1870 catalog, Stanley began promoting the carpenter's plane line. The next year, in January 1871, in the pocket catalog, Stanley included for the first time a claim about the popularity of its planes, stating that "6,500 planes were now in use." By the time of the publication of its August 15, 1871, catalog, sales of the Bailey planes had increased to 15,000. All three of these early pocket catalogs featured Bailey's patent adjustable no. 9¾ block plane on the cover.

The July 1, 1872, pocket catalog (Figure 1) also illustrated Bailey's no. 9¾ block plane and boasted of Stanley's latest awards at various industrial expositions. This catalog also noted that 30,000 planes were in use at that point. Checking the sales claims on the cover of the pocket catalogs is one of the best ways of dating them, especially after 1888 when publication dates were no longer printed on the catalogs. Another method of dating an early catalog is the address number of Stanley's New York City warehouse. The catalog in Figure 1 bears a "55 Chambers Street" address. This number changed four times by 1898. The differences don't necessarily indicate a change in the warehouse location, but more likely a change in the street numbers. Between the October 1872 catalog and the January 1, 1874, catalog, the New York warehouse address number changed from 55 Chambers Street to 35 Chambers Street, and the artwork also changed on the front cover or title page. The July 1,

CONTINUED PAGE 206

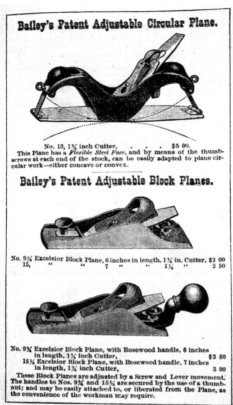
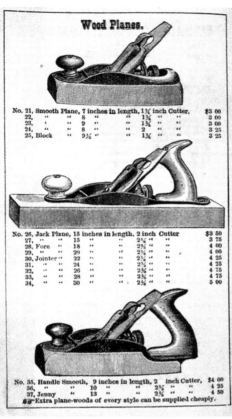

Figure 4. The same catalog shown in Figure 3, unfolded. The testimonial at the top of the first panel reads, "These tools meet with universal approbation from the best Mechanics. For beauty of style and finish they are unequaled, and the great convenience in operating, renders them the cheapest Planes in use; they are self-adjusting in every respect, and each part being made interchangeable, can be replaced at a trifling expense."

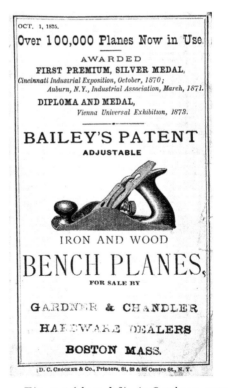

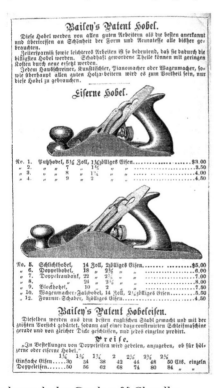

Figure 5 (above, left). An October 1, 1875, catalog imprinted with the name of a Boston hardware dealer, Gardner & Chandler.

Figure 6 (above, center). A German language version of a catalog from 1876, the same as the example in Figure 5.

Figure 7 (above, right). Interior pages of the German language catalog. Compare to left panel in Figure 4.

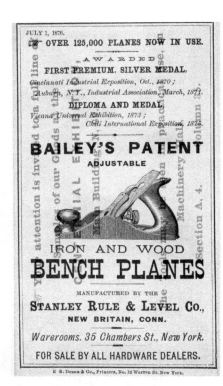

Figures 8a (left) & b (above turned 90 degrees for easier reading). For the 1876 U.S. Centennial Exhibition Stanley had its catalog overprinted with information about its location at the hall. The overprinting reads: "Your attention is invited to a full line of samples of our Goods at the CENTENNIAL EXHIBITION Main Building N, 69. The Tools may be seen in practical use in Machinery Hall, Section A, 4, Column 35."

1874, pocket catalog (Figure 2) used the same cover format as its predecessors, except that it boasted a new figure regarding the number of Bailey planes in use—70,000.

The April 1, 1875, catalog (Figure 3), with twelve pages folded out, boasted 90,000 planes in use. The Bailey plane featured on the title page was also changed from a block plane to a bench plane. Figure 4 shows the 1875 catalog folded out with Bailey's patent plane listed and with testimonials from users.

Sales of Bailey's planes continued to soar, reaching 100,000 planes in use by the publication of the October 1, 1875, catalog. The example shown in Figure 5 bears the imprint of a Boston, Massachusetts, hardware dealer. Stanley not only

Figure 9. A January 1, 1881, catalog showing the 29 Chambers Street address.

promoted its Bailey planes in America but also promoted them abroad. A January 1876 pocket catalog (Figure 6) with the inside panels was printed in German. Figure 7 shows Bailey's patent planes in the German-language catalog.

The United States Centennial Exposition in Philadelphia in 1876 attracted millions of visitors, many from all over the world. Stanley's July 1, 1876, pocket catalog (Figure 8), which boasted over 125,000 planes in use, had on the title page a light blue overprint stating where its exhibit was located in Machinery Hall at the exhibition.

In January 1878, the street address number of the New York warehouse changed again, this time to 29 Chambers Street. There were now 150,000 planes in use.

By January 1, 1881 (Figure 9), Stanley had 250,000 planes in use. It is interesting to note that sales in the ten years since Bailey planes were first introduced went from zero to a quarter million planes. Also, beginning with this catalog, Stanley discontinued placing the "number of planes sold" on the front cover and instead printed it above the plane listings on the second page inside the catalog. In addition, in this 1881 catalog, the back cover described Stanley's first product—boxwood and ivory rules (Figure 10).

Sales continued to grow and by January 1, 1884, Stanley claimed the total number of planes in use was 450,000. One year later, in Stanley's January 1, 1885, pocket catalog (Figure 11), the company noted that 600,000 planes were in use. In four years, 350,000 planes had been sold. Amazing!

According to its January 1886 catalog (Figure 12), Stanley

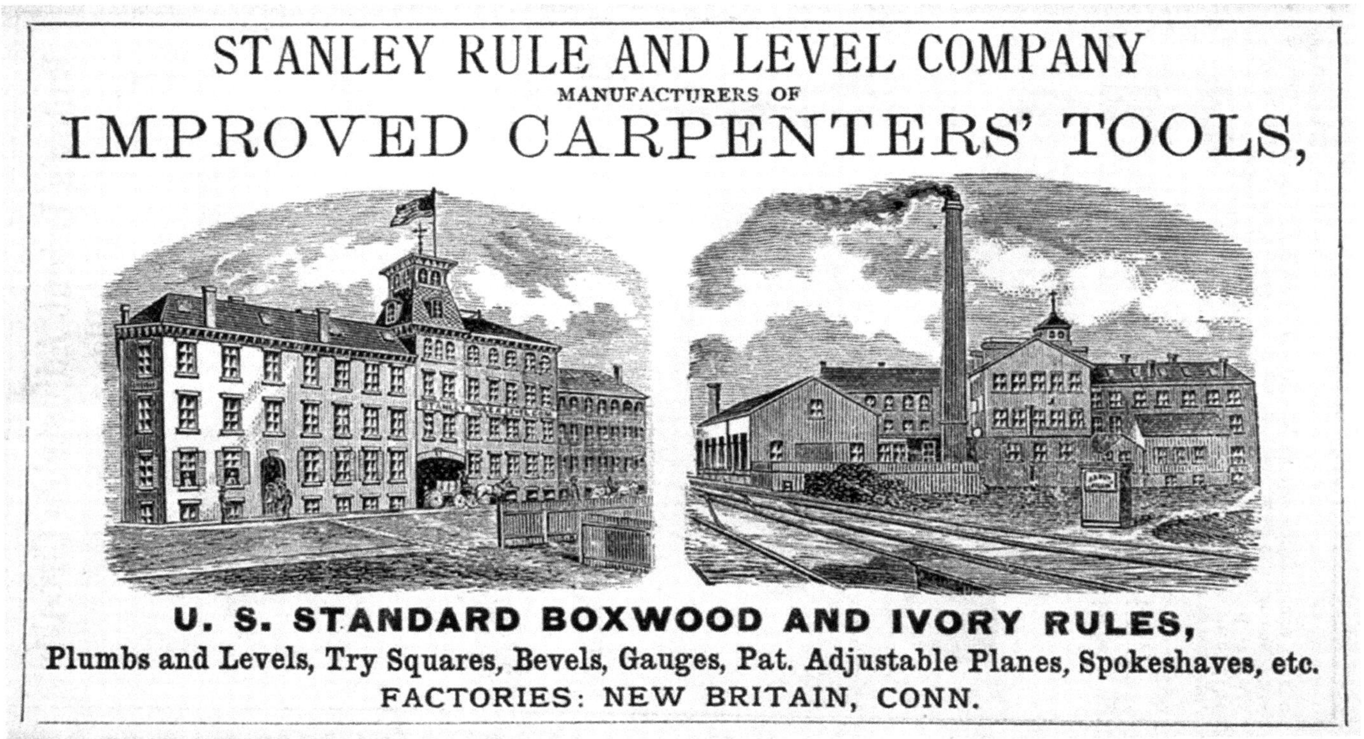

Figure 10. The back cover of the catalog shown in Figure 9 illustrates Stanley's factories in New Britain, Connecticut.

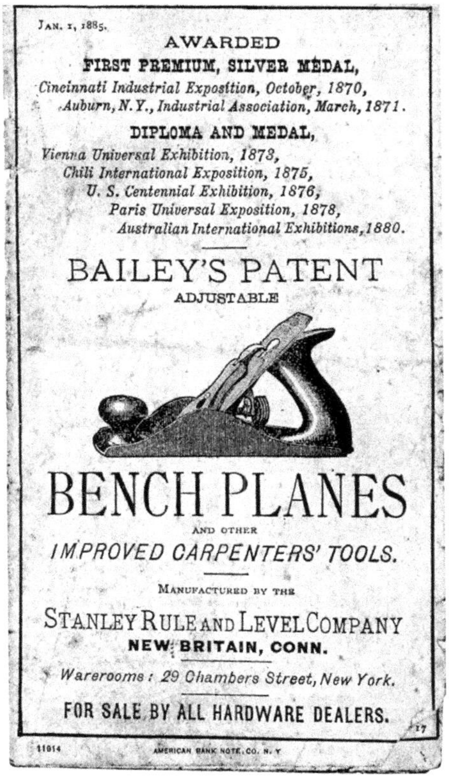

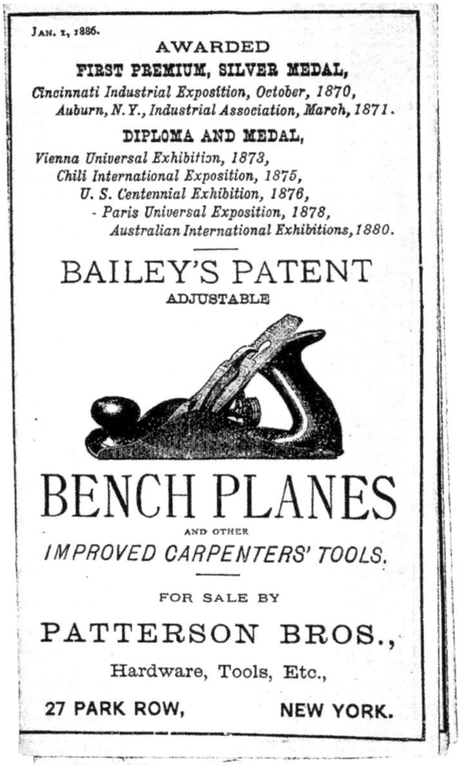

Figure 11 (above, left). The January 1, 1885, pocket catalog. Stanley noted in the catalog that "600,000 planes now in use."

Figure 12 (above, right). An 1886 catalog imprinted "For Sale by Patterson Bros., Hardware, Tools, Etc., 27 Park Row, New York." In this catalog, Stanley claimed 700,000 were in use.

had achieved the remarkable feat of selling 100,000 in one year's time—1885 to 1886. The company claimed on the cover of that catalog that 700,000 planes were in use. The back cover also showed an illustration of its tool factory in New Britain, Connecticut (Figure 13). Also, the number of pages in this catalog was increased to fourteen pages. Evidently, the company had repeated its 1886 sales performance in the following year, since it claimed in its January 1, 1887, catalog (Figures 14 and 15) that 800,000 planes were in use. Stanley used a different border around the engraving of the factory on the back cover of this catalog, and the catalog was increased to sixteen pages in a fold out 12½ inches wide x 11½ inches high.

The only exceptions to the shirt-pocket catalog were published in 1885 and 1886, when Stanley printed a catalog that folded up like a pocket catalog but was really a broadside, entitled "Woodworker's Companion." When unfolded, the catalog had all the advertising on one side of a 14 x 22-inch sheet of paper with the following words on the reverse: "Hang above your workbench." This pocket catalog

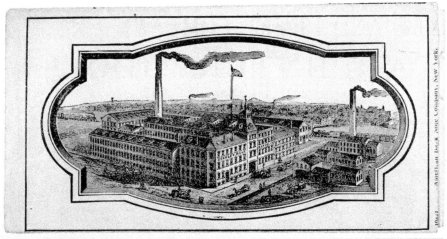

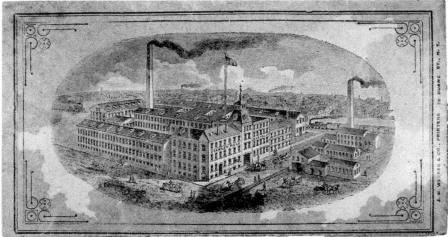

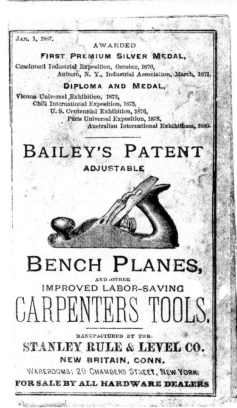

Figure 13 (top). The Stanley factory was illustrated on the back cover of the January 1, 1886 catalog.

Figure 14 (middle). A year later the back cover featured the same scene with a different border.

Figure 15 (left). The front cover of the January 1, 1887, catalog.

showed all of the Stanley planes around a center engraving of the company's factory (Figure 16).

In Comes the Imp

By 1888, Stanley had discontinued dating its pocket catalogs but continued to print in the catalog the number of planes sold, which has given today's collector and historian of tools an accurate way to date the catalogs. In the 1888 catalog (in which it was noted that 900,000 planes were in use), Stanley began illustrating the cover with an elf-like man riding a Bailey no. 9½ block plane (Figure 17). This character, created by F. A. Johnson, an artist about whom nothing is known to date, was used on the title page of catalogs from 1888 to 1902.

The character is known as "The Imp" by Stanley collectors, a monicker given him by Alvin Sellens in his 1975 book, *The Stanley Plane.*[1] Sellens referred to the rider on the plane as the "Imp trademark." However, Warren Roberts notes that at the turn of the twentieth century, popular cartoon characters, known as "Brownies," appeared in children's books. One such brownie was named "Duke." He "…was the snobbish and effete Englishman on whom the other brownies were always playing tricks, like putting him on a wild horse and turning him loose. Hence, the stance shown in the Stanley imp picture. The plane is running away with him."[2]

Roger Smith, in a 1977 article in the *British–American Rankological Society Newsletter*, pointed out that "…the Imp symbolizes the speed by which the iron plane overtook its wooden counterpart during the last quarter of the nineteenth century."[3] "The Imp" was also mentioned in an April 1953 issue of *Stanley News*:

In 1869, Stanley invested in a most unusual article—The "Bailey" plane. It was the first successful iron plane and was handier and sturdier than the old wood-bodied planes. The unique design and utility of the "Bailey" Plane plus the fine material and workmanship that went into this tool soon made it a by-word.

CONTINUED PAGE **210**

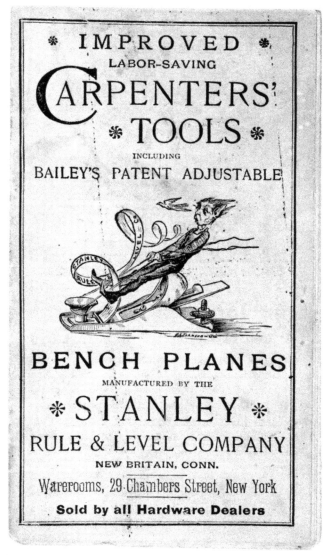

Figure 16 (above). Stanley's 1885 broadside catalog was meant to be hung over the workbench.

Figure 17 (right). "The Imp" first appeared on a Stanley catalog in 1888. For his debut, he rode a Bailey 9½ bench plane. The wording on the shaving reads "Stanley Rule & Level Company." The character remained on the cover of the pocket catalogs until 1900.

Figures 18 and 19 (below). There were two editions of the 1888 catalog. The first (below, left) had a back cover introducing the Odd-Jobs combination tool. Figure 19 shows five uses of the same tool.

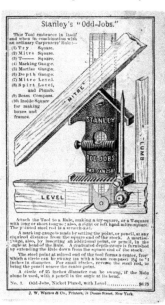

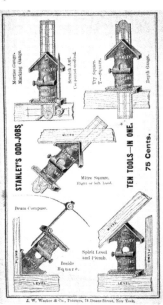

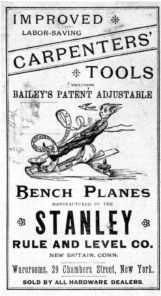

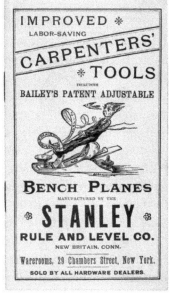

Figures 20 and 21 (above). The 1890 and 1892 catalogs appear the same. However, the 1890 (on left) was the last of the fold-out catalogs, and the 1892 is an actual bound booklet, held together by two staples.

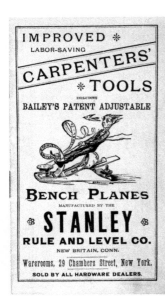
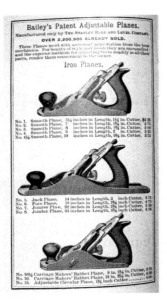

Figures 22 and 23 (above). The front cover of the 1895 catalog and an inside page (on right) which shows that the number of planes sold to that date was 2.2 million.

Figure 24 (above left). The first edition of the 1898 catalog. The plane on which "The Imp" is riding has cross hatches on the side.

Figure 25 (above, right). The second edition of the 1898 catalog has a new address for the Stanley warerooms in New York.

The speed with which it could be used was recognized by Stanley and a caricature began to appear on the early catalogs and folders. It depicted an elfin-like creature riding a "Bailey" Plane—attempting to hold back on the reins (or hold on for dear life) as the plane sped along with the flight of a bird on the wing. In fact, as you can see in the illustration, this plane is leading the bird![4]

Four variations of Johnson's imp character have been discovered on Stanley catalogs. The first, shown in Figure 17, has the plane with clear sides and "Stanley Rule & Level Co." written on the shaving coming from the plane. On the verso (when folded) of that catalog (Figure 18), Stanley introduced its "No. 1 Odd-Jobs Combination Tool." Apparently, Stanley issued two 1888 pocket catalogs. In the second edition (Figure 19), the front was the same, but the verso was not. It illustrated five different uses of the "ten tools in one" Odd-Jobs combination tool.

The 1890 pocket catalog (Figure 20) was essentially the same as the 1888 catalog. The layouts were identical and the only difference was the statement describing the "number of planes sold," which had increased to 1.2 million. Although the 1892 catalog (Figure 21) shared the same front and back cover designs as the 1890, there was a major format change. From its inception, the pocket catalog had used a design that folded up, with a finished size of 3¼ x 5¾ inches. The 1892 catalog was an actual fourteen-page booklet, 3⅜ x 6¼ inches, held together with staples. The number of planes sold was listed as 1.5 million.

The 1893 pocket catalog indicated an increase—to 1.8 million—in the number of planes sold and had the same front and rear covers as the previous year. In the 1895

catalog (Figures 22 and 23), the "planes sold" number increased to 2.2 million. The 1897 issue showed no change except for the number planes sold—2.8 million.

Three editions of the 1898 catalog were published. In the first edition, in addition to stating the "number of planes sold" had increased to 3 million, Stanley used a second variation of "The Imp" illustration on the cover in which the sides of the plane are hatched (Figure 24). Also, although

Figure 26 (above, left). The Stanley character changed his ride in the third edition of the 1898 catalog. "The Imp" now rode a Bailey 9½ block plane with Justis A. Traut's 1897 design patent for a "Hand-y," feature which provided a better grip.

Figure 27 (above, right). "The Imp" had his final ride on the cover of the 1902 catalog.

TABLE I		
Number of Planes Sold per Stanley Catalogs		
Catalog Date	No. of Planes Sold	Warehouse
January 1870	NA	55 Chambers Street, New York City
January 1871	6,500	"
September 1871	15,000	"
January 1872	20,000	"
July 1872	30,000	"
October 1872	40,000	"
July 1874	70,000	35 Chambers Street, New York City
April 1875	90,000	"
October 1875	100,000	"
January 1876	100,000	"
July 1876	125,000	"
January 1877	125,000	"
January 1878	150,000	29 Chambers Street, New York City
January 1879	175,000	"
January 1881	250,000	"
September 1881	250,000	"
January 1883	350,000	"
January 1884	450,000	"
January 1885	600,000	"
January 1886	700,000	"
January 1887	800,000	"
1888	900,000	"
1890	1,200,000	"
1892	1,500,000	"
1893	1,800,000	"
1895	2,200,000	"
1897	2,800,000	"
1898	3,000,000	"
1898	3,000,000	107 Chambers Street, New York City
1900	3,000,000	"
1902	Discontinued	"

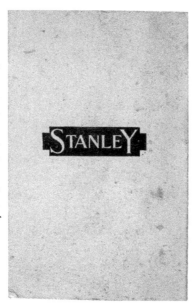

Figures 28, 29, and 30. The 1905 edition (Figure 28, above left) marked a significant change in the pocket catalog. The cover was austere compared to the complex design of the prior years. The 1905 edition had a green cover, and the 1906 (Figure 29, above right) was light brown. The back cover (Figure 30, right) of both was the simple Stanley notched logo with the first and last letters of the company name oversized.

the wording remained the same, the typefaces and layout were changed slightly. The second edition of 1898 catalog is identified by two major changes (Figure 25). The color of the cover was changed to burnt sienna, and the address of Stanley's New York warerooms was new, indicating a move from No. 29 to No. 107 Chambers Street. The third edition of the 1898 catalog (Figure 26) was twenty pages long and had the character riding a Bailey no. 9½ block plane with Justis A. Traut's August 3, 1897, design patent for a "Hand-y" feature on the side of the plane. This feature had indentation on the sides of the plane for a better grip. Shortly after 1900, Stanley eliminated the number of planes sold, probably because it was no longer an effective advertising tool. (Table I summarizes the catalogs from 1870 to 1900.)

Stanley's 1902 pocket catalog (Figure 27) was the last catalog to have "The Imp" featured on the cover. The Bed Rock line of bench planes was introduced for the first time in this catalog.

In 1905, Stanley changed the size of its pocket catalog to 3⅝ x 6 inches. This issue had twenty-four pages, not including the covers. The cover (Figure 28) was simplified, with a greenish color paper with dark blue lettering and Stanley yellow around the notched label in the center. Up to this period, the previous catalogs sold planes only, but the 1905 catalog added miter boxes and braces. It was more diversified, carrying a variety of Stanley's product line.

One year later, in 1906, Stanley issued another catalog (Figure 29) almost identical to the 1905 version except the color of the cover was a light brown instead of green. The rear covers of the 1905 and 1906 catalogs (Figure 30) had Stanley's notched logo with a capital S and Y in the word "Stanley."

The next pocket catalog known to have been published by Stanley was issued four years later in 1910 (Figure 31). This catalog was dated inside the front cover. The center of the cover design was red, fading to pink, 3 1/2 x 6 1/8 inches in size, and twenty-four pages long, not including the covers. The artwork was totally new with the phrase "Standard the World Over" in the center of the front cover. The rear cover shows a red, ten-point star (Figure 32). Each point represented a different type of tool. Inside this catalog, Stanley illustrated a more extensive line of its tools than in earlier catalogs. Air brush illustrations were featured throughout the catalog (Figure 33). Although half of the 1910 catalog was used for planes, other tools were also featured: screwdrivers, miter boxes, levels, braces, squares and bevels, boxwood folding rules, and Zig-Zag rules.

Stanley's 1911 pocket catalog was the same size as the 1910 catalog, but instead of red, the colors were black and white (Figure 34). The content of the twenty-four-page catalog was expanded to include breast drills and vises in addition to the other tools mentioned above. The rear-cover design was also expanded. The back cover featured the addition of a globe behind the ten-point star and tools radiated out from the center of the star (Figure 35). The red covers reappeared in 1912 (Figures 36 and 37). The content of that catalog was identical to the 1911 catalog.

The content of Stanley's 1914 catalog was identical to the 1912, except that breast drills were omitted, replaced by hammers. The 1914 catalog was used until 1918, when a new catalog was issued.

Market conditions were volatile after the United States entered World War I, and Stanley marked the rear cover of the 1914 catalog with a stamp in red ink noting "Owing to the present market conditions, all prices here given are temporarily withdrawn. If you are unable to get a price from your hardware dealer on any article in which you are interested, write us direct" (Figure 38). The 1918 catalog was identical to the 1914 catalog but no prices were listed.

The next pocket catalog that Stanley issued was in 1923. It illustrated its new line of household tools labeled

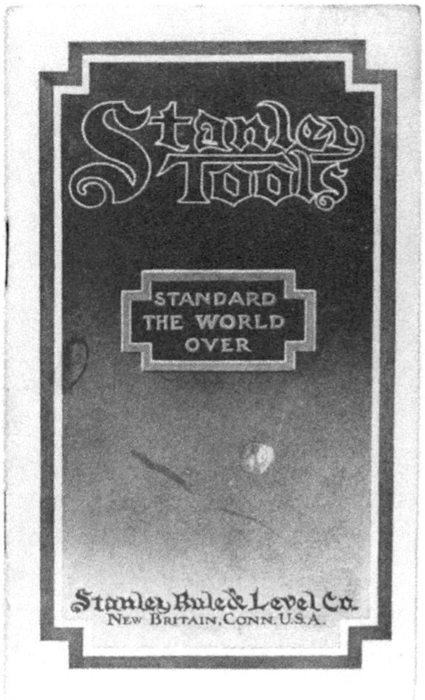

Stanley Tools
STANDARD THE WORLD OVER
Stanley Rule & Level Co.
NEW BRITAIN, CONN. U.S.A.

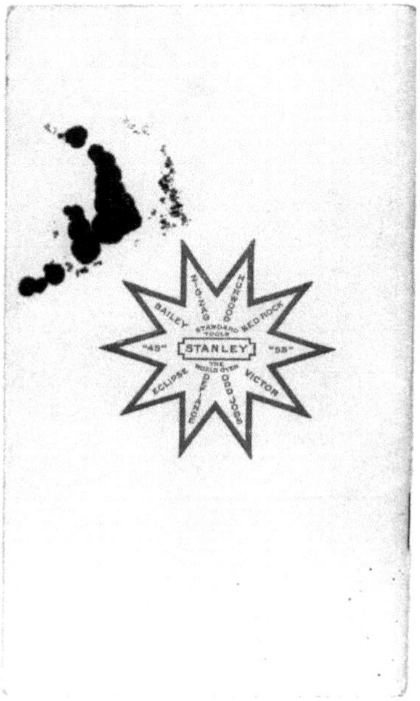

STANLEY

Figures 31 and 32 (above). The front (left) and back (right) covers of the 1910 catalog. There is no evidence that Stanley published any catalogs between 1905 and 1910. The motto "Standard the World Over" was featured on the center of the front cover. The rear cover had a red ten-point star with each point representing a different type of tool.

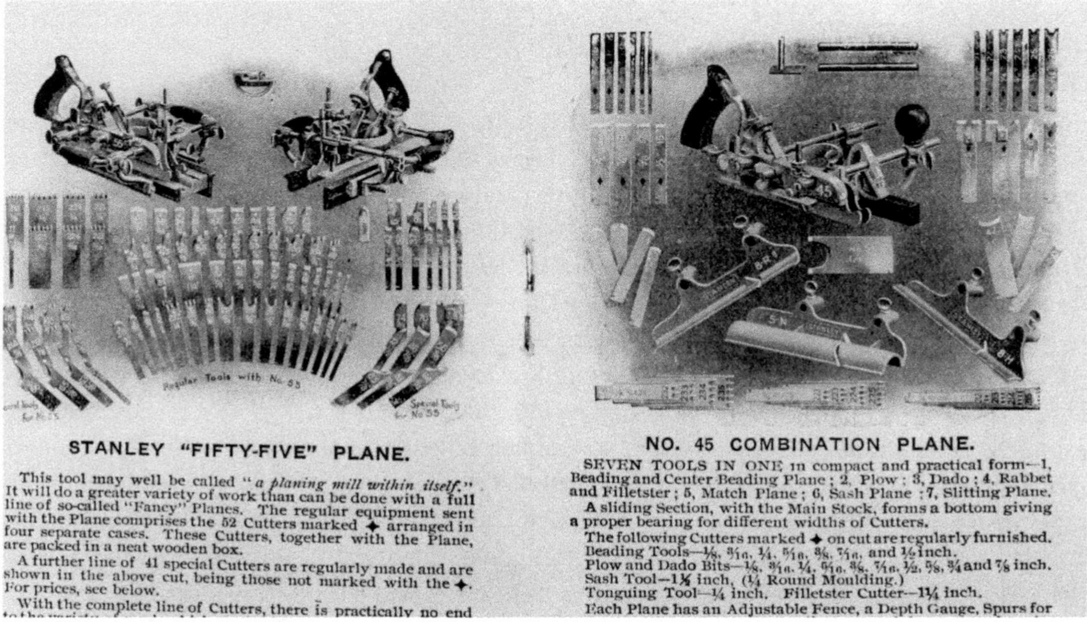

Regular Tools with No. 55
STANLEY "FIFTY-FIVE" PLANE.
This tool may well be called "*a planing mill within itself.*" It will do a greater variety of work than can be done with a full line of so-called "Fancy" Planes. The regular equipment sent with the Plane comprises the 52 Cutters marked ✦ arranged in four separate cases. These Cutters, together with the Plane, are packed in a neat wooden box.
A further line of 41 special Cutters are regularly made and are shown in the above cut, being those not marked with the ✦. For prices, see below.
With the complete line of Cutters, there is practically no end
NO. 45 COMBINATION PLANE.
SEVEN TOOLS IN ONE in compact and practical form—1, Beading and Center Beading Plane; 2, Plow; 3, Dado; 4, Rabbet and Filletster; 5, Match Plane; 6, Sash Plane; 7, Slitting Plane.
A sliding Section, with the Main Stock, forms a bottom giving a proper bearing for different widths of Cutters.
The following Cutters marked ✦ on cut are regularly furnished.
Beading Tools—1/8, 3/16, 1/4, 5/16, 3/8, 7/16, and 1/2 inch.
Plow and Dado Bits—1/8, 3/16, 1/4, 5/16, 3/8, 7/16, 1/2, 5/8, 3/4 and 7/8 inch.
Sash Tool—1 3/8 inch, (1/4 Round Moulding.)
Tonguing Tool—1/4 inch. Filletster Cutter—1 1/4 inch.
Each Plane has an Adjustable Fence, a Depth Gauge, Spurs for

Figure 33 (left). Inside pages of the 1910 catalog. The 1910 catalog had a more extensive line of its tools than its earlier catalogs.

 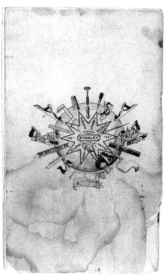

 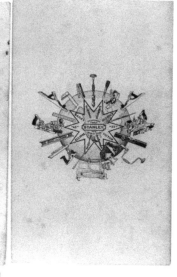

Figures 34 and 35. Front and back covers of the 1911 catalog. This catalog had the same design as the previous year's but was printed in black rather than red.

Four-Square. Figure 39 illustrates the front cover of this twenty-two page, 3½ x 6-inch catalog. Inside was a full page that described each type of tool in the line (Figure 40).

Also in 1923, Stanley printed a four-page catalog (one piece of paper folded in half) on Four-Square tools (Figure 41). This catalog illustrated all thirty-two tools in its line on the inner two pages. It is interesting to note that radios were the "in" thing in the 1920s and were featured on the cover.

The largest catalog to date was Stanley's next pocket catalog, copyrighted in 1926. This catalog (Figure 42) contained forty-eight pages and covered all the major types of tools Stanley made. It did not have, however, every model, only the most sought after tools. Figure 43 shows an example of a typical page from that catalog.

The following year, 1927, the catalog grew again when Stanley issued its largest catalog to date (Figure

Figures 36 and 37 (above). The 1912 catalog had red covers, and the content of that catalog was identical to the 1911 catalog.

Figure 38 (right)The back cover of the 1914 catalog (left) bore a stamp that read, "Owing to the present market conditions, all prices here given are temporarily withdrawn. If you are unable to get a price from your hardware dealer on any article in which you are interested, write us direct."

44). It was fifty-six-pages and was published with two cover variations. On the cover of the first, the lettering "Stanley Tools" was in a light yellow color. In the second

Figures 39 and 40 (far left). Cover and inside page of the 1923 catalog. Stanley did not change the design of the pocket catalog until 1923 when it featured its new line, Four-Square.

Figure 41 (left). In 1923 Stanley also published a four-page catalog focusing on the Four-Square line.

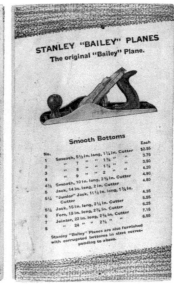

Figures 42 and 43 (above). The 1926 catalog and an inside page.

Figure 44 (below). The fifty-six page 1927 catalog.

Figures 45 and 46. The front cover and inside page of the 1935 catalog. Stanley did not publish a new version of the catalog until the 1960s.

variation it was a deep yellow. These catalogs also advertised some of the Stanley line of hardware that was available at the time.

In 1935, Stanley issued a 10½ x 12½ fold-out catalog (Figure 45), which was placed in the box when a tool was shipped. This informed the buyer that Stanley offered many types of tools, including electric tools and hardware. When folded, the catalog was 3½ x 6¼ inches. Figure 46 shows a page from that catalog that described the original Bailey plane. This was the last pocket catalog Stanley would publish until the 1960s.

Pocket catalogs were an economical way of advertising without the expense of sending out large catalogs. The pocket catalogs were distributed by hardware dealers and by the company itself by packing a copy in the shipping box. Also, dealers could send them out with invoices or could have them available on the store counter. Many were also imprinted with a hardware dealer's name and address.

Pocket catalogs are an interesting journey into the past. They provide a history lesson in the type and styles of printing available over a fifty-year span of Stanley's history and give a graphic lesson in Stanley's tools.

Notes

1. Alvin Sellens, *The Stanley Plane: A History and Descriptive Inventory* (South Dartmouth, Mass.: The Early American Industries Association, 1975), 18.
2. Letter from Carl Stoutenberg, to Walter W. Jacob, October 12, 1993. Stoutenberg attributes Warren Roberts of Maine with describing "Duke."
3. Roger Smith, ed. "The Imp," *British-American Rankological Society Newsletter*, Winter, 1977. Transitional and Metallic Plane information section.
4. *Stanley News 23*, no. 3 (April 1953). Published by Stanley Tools, New Britain, Conn.

Stanley Memorabilia

The word memorabilia is defined as remarkable and worthy things of remembrance. The Stanley Works and The Stanley Rule & Level Co. memorabilia includes employee badges, service awards, and promotional product giveaways. This article will provide a sample of many of the items Stanley issued over the years. It is not, by any means, a complete list.

Figure 1 (above). Glass paperweight (4 inches long) advertising Stanley corrugated hinges, ca. 1892-1893.

One of the earlier known items is the paperweight shown in Figure 1. Made by the Barnes & Abrams Co., of Syracuse, New York, it advertised Stanley corrugated-steel hinges. Distributed to hardware stores around 1892 or 1893, the paperweight boasted that the corrugated-steel hinge was fifty percent stronger than old style hinges.'

In September 1895, the 29th National Encampment of the Grand Army of the Republic (GAR) was held in Louisville, Kentucky. The GAR was comprised of union Civil War Veterans. Some members of GAR, Stanley Post 11, attended this Encampment.[1] Provided with an opportunity for free advertising, the Stanley Works had three ornamental hinges on the delegate's badge (Figure 2). The large hinge, at the top of the badge, was a no. 1430, which had a special nickel

Figure 2 (left). Grand Army of the Republic 1895 badge with Stanley advertising, featuring three Stanley hinges. There is one at the top and two on either side of the date.

Figure 3 (above). Verso of Figure 2 showing the maker's name.

Figure 4 (right). Stanley Works 1917 calendar.

Figure 5 (left). A twenty-five-year recognition Hamilton watch given to Charles Miller, employee of the Stanley Works.

Figure 6 (above). Inside back of the watch showing the engraving.

finish and had "The Stanley Works" stamped into the face in a fancy, scroll design. The badge was manufactured by the Whitehead & Hoag Company of Newark, New Jersey (Figure 3). The acorn on the badge, supported by a lace ribbon, became known as the Acorn Badge of the GAR and represented the 14th U.S. Army Corps.[2]

A calendar issued in 1917 by the Stanley Works advertised hinges and garage hardware (Figure 4). The calendar shows an opulent girl with a bird in hand, suggesting a hope for peace. Unfortunately, the United States had entered The Great War (World War I) in the summer of 1917.[3] The artwork made a very showy calendar in a time of great loss.

Stanley, like a lot of companies, congratulated its employees with awards for years of service. This popular device was, mainly, a mid-twentieth-century concept. But twenty-five years of employment was a milestone, and the Stanley Works gave an employee named Charles Miller a Hamilton watch (Figure 5) for recognition of his twenty-five years of service from 1902 to 1928 (Figure 6). (The honoree of this watch is not the Charles Miller who invented the famous Miller's patent plane.[4]) The watch had a seventeen-jewel movement and was 14K gold-filled.

Stanley awarded 10K gold pins for years of service to the company. These pins were awarded for ten, fifteen, twenty, and twenty-five years of service. Figure 7 shows the ten-year pin

Figure 7 (above, left). Stanley Works gold, ten-year service pin.

Figure 8 (above, right). Stanley Works gold, twenty-five-year service pin.

Figure 9 (above, left). Stanley 1960s twenty-five-year-service award pin.

Figure 10 (above, right). Stanley 1960s twenty-five-year-service award pendant.

Figure 11 (right). This bracelet set with a diamond, was presented to a woman thirty or thirty-five years of service.

with a red background. Each five-year increment-of-service pin had a different colored background and noted the number of years of service. The twenty-five-year was green (Figure 8). The pins were manufactured by Porter & Dyson.

Stanley continued to award service pins for at least the twenty-five-year interval, shown in Figure 9, into the 1960s and beyond. Figure 10 shows a twenty-five-year service award for a female, in pendant form. Along the same lines as the service pin and pendant is the bracelet shown in Figure 11. This award, which is set with a diamond, would have been presented to a woman for thirty or thirty-five years of service. The gunshot-shell penknife award, shown in Figure 12, was definitely for a man. This unique offering was sold by

O.C. Tanner to the Stanley Works.

Two 10K gold lapel emblems, Figures 13 and 14, were also produced for Stanley for use by executive officers. Even today, many companies provide employees with small company emblems. It was inexpensive advertising

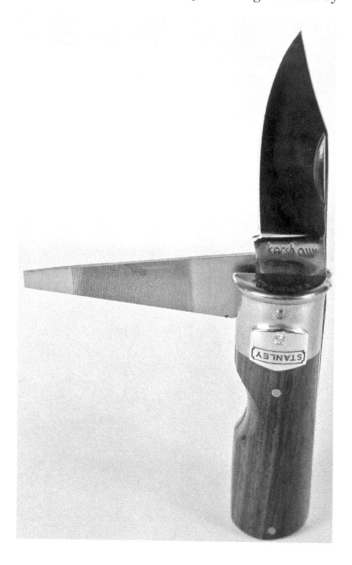

Figure 12 (left). Stanley gunshot-shell penknife with gold emblem set with a diamond.

Figure 13 (top). Stanley 10K gold emblem.

Figure 14 (above). Stanley 10K gold emblem.

Figure 15 (left). Stanley Art Deco lighter with a "Sweet-heart" logo showing its size as compared to a "Walking Liberty" half-dollar.

Figure 16 (below). Stanley Art Deco lighter opened. Note the notched logo on lid.

and provided a physical source of pride.

Around 1935, Stanley gave out small lighters made in the Art Deco style (Figure 15). Manufactured by Weston International Corporation, New York City, the 1½-inch lighter had the red "Sweetheart" design pressed in one end and the new, cut-corner, rectangle logo on the other end (Figure 16).

Stanley produced, in the late 1930s, a novelty watch stand (Figure 17) made from its hinge machines. The stand could be folded up for travel and set up anywhere as a watch stand to hold a pocket watch (Figure 18).

During World War II, Stanley manufactured many military-related items. Each employee was required to wear a badge, for security reasons. Shown in Figure 19

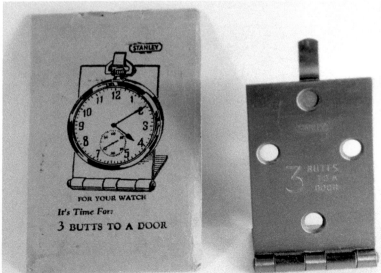

Figure 17. Novelty watch stand made from a hinge with its paper wrapper.

Figure 18. The watch stand shown with a watch.

Figure 19. Stanley Works World War II employment badge.

is badge no. 1317 for a female employee. "The Stanley Works" is against a green background, perhaps denoting her security status.[5]

On March 17, 1943, during Stanley's 100th year, Stanley Tools received the prestigious Army-Navy "E" Production Award (Figure 20),[6] commemorated by a blue ribbon. Each employee, on the day of the award, also received a commemorative pin. Figure 21 illustrates a two-color-enameled, sterling silver "E" award. Another version of the "E" award is shown in Figure 22. This is enameled bronze with the navy shield in the circular field.

During the 1930s and into the 1940s and 1950s, Stanley produced promotional pocket key chain screwdrivers. Shown in Figure 23 is a variety of these promotional screwdrivers. The oldest example shows the "Sweetheart" logo with the other two examples showing the cut-corner logo/trademark.

Around 1939, Stanley gave out pencil clips that advertised "The Tool Box of the World" (Figure 24).[7] These pencil clips were invented by William Halket of Holyoke,

Figure 20 (above). Army-Navy "E" Production Award ribbon.

Figure 21 (above). Army-Navy "E" pin in sterling silver and enamel.

Figure 22 (right). Army-Navy "E" pin in bronze.

Figure 24 (above). Stanley advertising pencil clip.

Figure 25 (below). Stanley advertising ballpoint pens stating that Stanley is "The Toolbox of the World."

Figure 23 (above). Stanley pocket keychain screwdrivers.

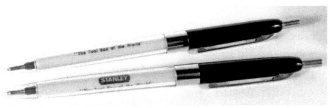

Massachusetts, and patented on August 30, 1927. Apparently, the advertising company that Stanley commissioned was still offering this patented clip in 1939 or later.

In the 1950s and 1960s, Stanley gave out ball point pens advertising "The Tool Box of the World," still capitalizing on the successful late 1930s phrase (Figure 25). [8]

In the last half of the twentieth century, Stanley continued to have various promotional items produced, including mugs, rules, and other tschotskes, all of which are collectible. This article concentrated on the earlier memorabilia.

Notes

1. GAR Stanley Post 11 was named for Lt. Theodore Augustus Stanley, the son of Henry and Eliza North Stanley. Lt. Stanley died in December 1862 of wounds received in the Battle of Fredericksburg.
2. The acorn insignia of the U.S. Regular Army, 14th Corps, was developed after the fall of 1863, when the 14th Corps was encamped around Chattanooga, Tennessee. Very muddy roads and little or no communications, due to the Confederates, made obtaining supplies very difficult. When rations fell short, the corps was reduced to roasting the acorns from the trees under which they were encamped and grinding them up for flour and meal. Ever after, the corps was known as the "Acorn Boys." When, in 1864, a corps badge had to be chosen, it was a no-brainer to use the acorn.
3. America's participation in World War I, began in the summer of 1917, when troops under the command of General John J. "Black Jack" Pershing began to ship into France. Major American troop involvement occurred in 1918. The war ended on November 11, 1918, when a peace treaty was signed at Versailles, France.

4. The question posed by the Charles Miller name is whether or not this gentleman is related to the Charles Miller of Miller Patent fame of the 1870s. Further research may reveal the answer.
5. At the present, all U.S. defense industries have a color-coded badge. Though each company's color coding may be different, the colors usually denote "Company Proprietary" (or "no clearance"), "Secret," and "Top Secret," at the least.
6. "The Army-Navy 'E' Award was granted only to facilities which were particularly outstanding in production for the War and Navy Departments. Excellence in quality and quantity of production were two of the determining factors in granting awards. Others included: (a) overcoming of production obstacles; (b) low rate of absenteeism; (c) avoidance of work stoppages; (d) maintenance of fair labor standards; (e) training of additional labor forces; (f) effective management; (g) record on accidents, health, sanitation, and plant protection; (h) utilization of sub-contracting facilities; (i) cooperation between management and labor as it affected production; and (j) conservation of critical and strategic materials" (found at www.navy.history.mil).
7. Stanley began using the phrase "The Tool Box of the World" in 1939. Therefore, this pencil clip is no earlier than 1939.
8. "The Tool Box of the World" was used until 1968, when Stanley President Don Davis coined the phrase "Stanley Helps You Do Things Right."

Index